Zaner-Bloser

# SPELLING CONNECTIONS

Teacher Resource Book

3

ISBN 0-7367-0056-0

Production Development: Pagination
Spanish Language Consultant: Joan Nieto
New Line Drawings: Diphrent Strokes



Zaner-Bloser, Inc., P.O. Box 16764, Columbus, Ohio 43216-6764 1-800-421-3018

Printed in the United States of America 00 01 02 03 CP 5 4 3 2

# Grade 3 Table of Contents

Name ______________________________

## Short a, Short i

1. land
2. stick
3. plan
4. trip
5. stand
6. act
7. thing
8. last
9. lift
10. band
11. grand
12. swim
13. stamp
14. list
15. sand

1. ______________
2. ______________
3. ______________
4. ______________
5. ______________
6. ______________
7. ______________
8. ______________
9. ______________
10. ______________
11. ______________
12. ______________
13. ______________
14. ______________
15. ______________

## Dear Family,

Good spelling is necessary for effective writing. From the very first unit of Zaner-Bloser's *Spelling Connections,* your child will be encouraged to write his or her thoughts, ideas, and feelings, using the spelling skills learned in previous grade levels in combination with the structured writing skills introduced in the third grade.

The **Home Study Masters** pages suggest activities that you and your child can do together and that will help your child learn spelling and writing skills. These activities will also provide opportunities for you and your child to work together productively and enjoyably.

Name ______________________

# Hoja para estudiar en casa

## Short a, Short i

### Querida familia,

Buenos conocimientos de la ortografía son necesarios para poder escribir de una manera efectiva. Desde la primera unidad de Zaner-Bloser's *Spelling Connections,* animaremos a su hijo o hija a escribir sus pensamientos, ideas y sentimientos. Usará las habilidades de ortografía que aprendió en los grados anteriores, combinadas con las habilidades de escribir de una manera estructurada que se introducen en el tercer grado.

A través del año escolar, recibirán una hoja titulada: **Hoja para estudiar en casa.** Esta hoja sugerirá actividades que ustedes pueden hacer con su hijo o hija para ayudarlo/a a aprender la ortografía y a desarrollar su habilidad de escribir. Estas actividades también les proveerá oportunidades de trabajar con su hijo o hija durante ratos productivos y gratos.

1. *land* tierra; aterrizar
2. *stick* palo
3. *plan* plan; planear
4. *trip* tropezar; viaje
5. *stand* estar de pie; puesto
6. *act* acto; actuar
7. *thing* cosa
8. *last* durar, último
9. *lift* levantar
10. *band* banda
11. *grand* espléndido
12. *swim* nadar
13. *stamp* pisotear; sello
14. *list* lista; hacer una lista
15. *sand* arena

1. ______________________
2. ______________________
3. ______________________
4. ______________________
5. ______________________
6. ______________________
7. ______________________
8. ______________________
9. ______________________
10. ______________________
11. ______________________
12. ______________________
13. ______________________
14. ______________________
15. ______________________

Unit 1

**Practice Master**

Name ______________________

| | | | |
|---|---|---|---|
| 1. act | 3. grand | 5. trip | 7. stick |
| 2. plan | 4. stamp | 6. list | 8. thing |

**A.** Write the spelling words in a-b-c order.

**1.** ______________ **5.** ______________

**2.** ______________ **6.** ______________

**3.** ______________ **7.** ______________

**4.** ______________ **8.** ______________

**B.** Write the spelling word that rhymes with each word below.

**1.** hand ______________ **5.** kick ______________

**2.** sing ______________ **6.** lamp ______________

**3.** fan ______________ **7.** fist ______________

**4.** skip ______________ **8.** fact ______________

Name ____________________

**Unit 1 Practice Master**

| act | grand | trip | stick |
|---|---|---|---|
| plan | stamp | list | thing |

**C.** Choose either vowel **a** or **i** to complete the spelling words. Write the words.

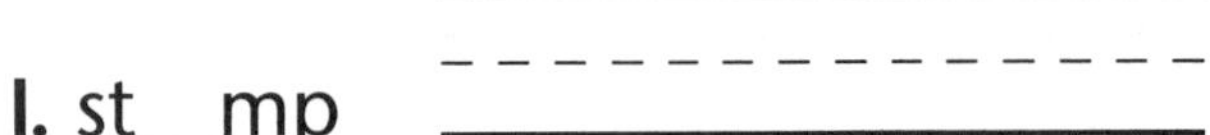

1. st__mp ____________
2. th__ng ____________
3. st__ck ____________
4. gr__nd ____________
5. __ct ____________
6. tr__p ____________
7. pl__n ____________
8. l__st ____________

**D.** Follow the path of each spelling word. Start with the letter in the box. Write the words.

1. 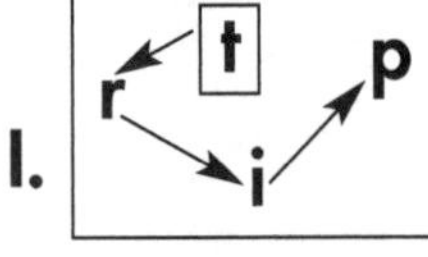

____________

2. 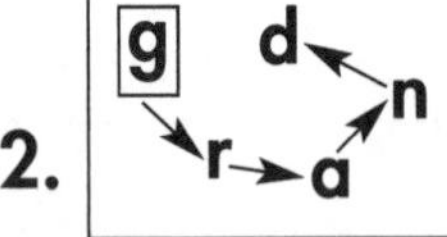

____________

3. 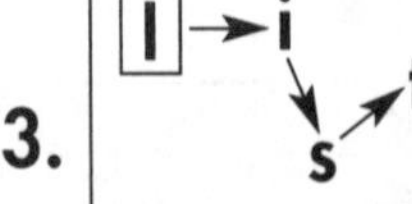

____________

4. 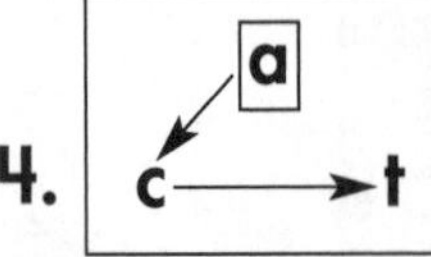

____________

5. 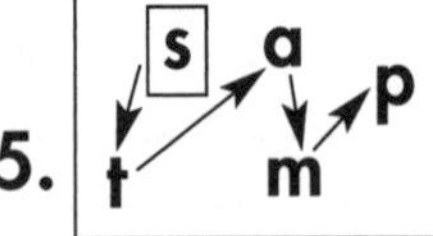

____________

6.  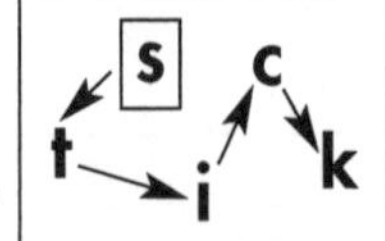

____________

7. 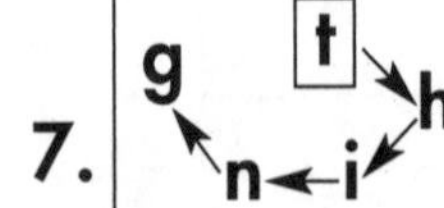

____________

8. 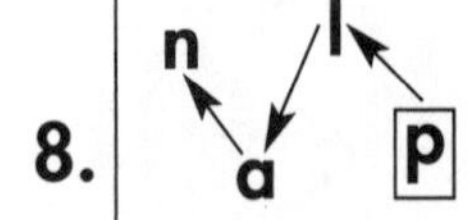

____________

lame ______________________________

ead each sentence. Look at the underlined spelling word. Fill in a ircle. Show if the word is spelled **Right** or **Wrong**.

**Sample**
My dad will dig a hole for a new plant.

| Right | Wrong |
|---|---|
| ● | ○ |

1. The last act in the play was good.
2. My sister plays the drum in the bnad.
3. That is a grand bike you have.
4. We will cut some trees down on that land.
5. I will do my math homework lasd.
6. The big box was hard to lift.
7. I made a list of things to take to camp.
8. To make the toy plane, we had to follow a plann.
9. The little girl liked to play in the sand.
10. You must put a stamp on your letter.
11. To play the game you should stand here.
12. We used a stik for a baseball bat.
13. They went for a swim in the pool.
14. A car is the thing Mother wants most.
15. I am going on a tripp with my family.

**Answer Box**

| | Right | Wrong |
|---|---|---|
| 1. | ○ | ○ |
| 2. | ○ | ○ |
| 3. | ○ | ○ |
| 4. | ○ | ○ |
| 5. | ○ | ○ |
| 6. | ○ | ○ |
| 7. | ○ | ○ |
| 8. | ○ | ○ |
| 9. | ○ | ○ |
| 10. | ○ | ○ |
| 11. | ○ | ○ |
| 12. | ○ | ○ |
| 13. | ○ | ○ |
| 14. | ○ | ○ |
| 15. | ○ | ○ |

Name ____________________

**Homework Master**

Write spelling words that rhyme with the words or picture words below.

1. 

2. kick

3. fast

4. 

5. 

6. him

7. sift

8. 

List these spelling words in a-b-c order.

| grand | sand | act | trip | band | land |
|---|---|---|---|---|---|

1. 
2. 
3. 
4. 
5. 
6. 

One spelling word has not been written yet. Do you know what it is? Unscramble the letters. Write the Mystery Word.

a t d n s

**Mystery Word:** ____________________

Unit 2

Home Study Master

Name ____________________

## Short o, Short e

### Scrambled Words

Write scrambled words on index cards or slips of paper and ask your child to unscramble them and write the words. Then have your child check his or her words against the word list. To provide an extra challenge, use a kitchen timer or a wall clock to record the time it takes your child to unscramble the words. Your child can then repeat the game and try to improve his or her own best time.

1. crop
2. test
3. clock
4. spent
5. drop
6. left
7. sled
8. plot
9. spend
10. west
11. block
12. tent
13. desk
14. flock
15. nest

1. ____________
2. ____________
3. ____________
4. ____________
5. ____________
6. ____________
7. ____________
8. ____________
9. ____________
10. ____________
11. ____________
12. ____________
13. ____________
14. ____________
15. ____________

Name ____________________

# Hoja para estudiar en casa

## Short o, Short e

### Palabras revueltas

Deletreen las palabras en fichas o en cuadros de papel con las letras transpuestas. Díganle a su hijo o hija que arregle las letras y que escriba las palabras correctamente. Luego, díganle que verifique el deletreo de cada palabra usando la lista de palabras. Se puede hacer el ejercicio más interesante con el uso de un minutero o de un reloj de pared para contar cuántos minutos pasó arreglando las letras. Luego su hijo o hija puede repetir el juego y tratar de sobrepasar su mejor tiempo.

1. crop — cosecha
2. test — examen; comprobar
3. clock — reloj
4. spent — pasó; gastó
5. drop — dejar caer; gota
6. left — salió; izquierda
7. sled — luge; trineo
8. plot — trama; conspiración
9. spend — pasar; gastar
10. west — oeste
11. block — cerrar; bloque
12. tent — tienda de campaña
13. desk — escritorio
14. flock — bandada; rebaño; congregarse
15. nest — nido

1. ____________________
2. ____________________
3. ____________________
4. ____________________
5. ____________________
6. ____________________
7. ____________________
8. ____________________
9. ____________________
10. ____________________
11. ____________________
12. ____________________
13. ____________________
14. ____________________
15. ____________________

Name ________________________________

Unit 2 **Practice Master**

| | | | |
|---|---|---|---|
| 1. drop | 3. clock | 5. desk | 7. spent |
| 2. plot | 4. block | 6. nest | 8. spend |

**A.** Write the spelling word that goes with each meaning.

**1.** to pay out money ____________________

**2.** tells time ____________________

**3.** to let fall ____________________

**4.** bird's home ____________________

**B.** Two words are misspelled. Write all the words correctly.

**1.** plote ____________________

**2.** desk ____________________

**3.** spent ____________________

**4.** blok ____________________

Name ____________________

Unit 2 **Practice Master**

| drop | clock | desk | spent |
|---|---|---|---|
| plot | block | nest | spend |

**C.** Write the spelling words that have the **short o** sound.

1. ____________________ 3. ____________________

2. ____________________ 4. ____________________

**D.** Read across and down to find spelling words hidden in the puzzle. Circle and write the words.

| a | d | e | s | k | j | l | b | n | e |
|---|---|---|---|---|---|---|---|---|---|
| b | r | s | p | e | n | d | l | o | s |
| c | o | f | e | h | c | l | o | c | k |
| d | p | g | n | e | s | t | c | p | t |
| p | l | o | t | i | k | m | k | q | u |

1. ____________________ 5. ____________________

2. ____________________ 6. ____________________

3. ____________________ 7. ____________________

4. ____________________ 8. ____________________

Unit 2 **Test Master**

Name ____________________

Read each sentence. Look at the underlined spelling word. Fill in a circle. Show if the word is spelled **Right** or **Wrong**.

**Sample** — Right / Wrong

Put a dat over this letter in the word. ○ ●

**Answer Box**

| | | Right | Wrong |
|---|---|---|---|
| 1. | We will put the red blok on top. | ○ | ○ |
| 2. | The clock was hung on the wall. | ○ | ○ |
| 3. | The farmer had a good croop of corn. | ○ | ○ |
| 4. | My teacher told me to clean my desk. | ○ | ○ |
| 5. | Be careful not to drap your glass. | ○ | ○ |
| 6. | The flock of geese landed on the pond. | ○ | ○ |
| 7. | He holds his pencil in his lef hand. | ○ | ○ |
| 8. | The bird laid three eggs in the nest. | ○ | ○ |
| 9. | We planted beans on that polt of land. | ○ | ○ |
| 10. | We went down the hill on our new sled. | ○ | ○ |
| 11. | Be careful not to spend all your money. | ○ | ○ |
| 12. | My brother spent the summer with our grandmother. | ○ | ○ |
| 13. | It is fun to sleep out in a tennt. | ○ | ○ |
| 14. | I forgot that we had a test today. | ○ | ○ |
| 15. | To get to the park you go west. | ○ | ○ |

Name ______________________________

Make a sentence by putting the words in the correct order. Draw a line under the spelling words in each sentence.

**1.** by tent The nest is the.

**2.** left her just desk She.

**3.** drop the clock Don't.

**4.** I sled your test May?

Look for hidden spelling words.
Read across and down. Circle each word.

| | | | | | | | | | |
|---|---|---|---|---|---|---|---|---|---|
| e | g | h | i | f | a | s | f | d | g |
| c | r | o | p | l | s | p | e | n | t |
| t | a | c | l | o | w | e | s | t | u |
| r | b | l | o | c | k | n | s | u | b |
| s | e | p | t | k | z | d | y | m | o |

Name ______________________________

## Off-We-Go

Have your child write about the most exciting, interesting, or enjoyable trip she or he has ever taken. Some questions you could ask to stimulate your child's recollection of the trip might include:

- Where did you go?
- Who went with you?
- How did you get there?
- What did you see or do?
- What was the best part of the trip?

## Short u

1. lunch
2. until
3. cover
4. buzz
5. become
6. stuff
7. nothing
8. dull
9. month
10. study
11. love
12. uncle
13. cuff
14. none
15. under

1. ______________________
2. ______________________
3. ______________________
4. ______________________
5. ______________________
6. ______________________
7. ______________________
8. ______________________
9. ______________________
10. ______________________
11. ______________________
12. ______________________
13. ______________________
14. ______________________
15. ______________________

Name ______________________________

# Hoja para estudiar en casa

## Short u

1. lunch
almuerzo
2. until
hasta
3. cover
cubrir; tapa
4. buzz
zumbar; zumbido
5. become
hacerse; ponerse
6. stuff
cosas; rellenar
7. nothing
nada
8. dull
embotado; torpe; aburrido
9. month
mes
10. study
estudiar; estudio
11. love
amor; amar
12. uncle
tío
13. cuff
puño
14. none
ninguno
15. under
debajo

1. ______________________
2. ______________________
3. ______________________
4. ______________________
5. ______________________
6. ______________________
7. ______________________
8. ______________________
9. ______________________
10. ______________________
11. ______________________
12. ______________________
13. ______________________
14. ______________________
15. ______________________

### Vámonos

Pídanle a su hijo o hija que escriba sobre el más interesante o el más divertido viaje que haya hecho. Las siguientes son algunas preguntas que pudieran hacerle para ayudarlo/a a recordar el viaje.

- ¿Adónde fuiste?
- ¿Quiénes fueron contigo?
- ¿Cómo viajaron?
- ¿Qué viste y que hiciste?
- ¿Cuál fue la mejor parte del viaje?

Unit 3

**Practice Master**

Name ____________________

| | | | |
|---|---|---|---|
| 1. buzz | 3. under | 5. none | 7. become |
| 2. study | 4. until | 6. love | 8. nothing |

A. Write the spelling word that belongs in each sentence.

1. **Dog** is to **bark** as **bee** is to ____. ____________

2. **Out** is to **in** as **over** is to ____. ____________

3. **Game** is to **practice** as **test** is to ____. ____________

4. **Up** is to **down** as **all** is to ____. ____________

B. Write the spelling word that belongs in each sentence.

1. There was ____ left to do in the barn. ____________

2. We watched the house ____ green as we painted it. ____________

3. Mom said she would ____ to help. ____________

4. We won't start cleaning ____ Ken arrives. ____________

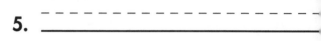

Name ________________________________

Unit 3
**Practice Master**

| buzz | under | none | become |
|---|---|---|---|
| study | until | love | nothing |

**C.** Write the spelling words in a-b-c order.

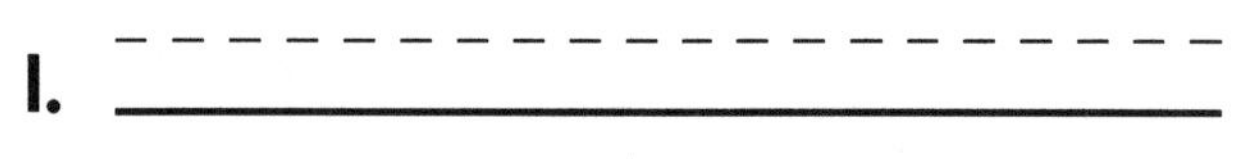

**1.** ____________________ **5.** ____________________

**2.** ____________________ **6.** ____________________

**3.** ____________________ **7.** ____________________

**4.** ____________________ **8.** ____________________

**D.** Use spelling words to complete each puzzle.

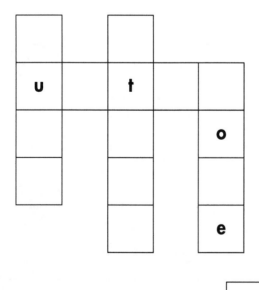

| | | | | |
|---|---|---|---|---|
| u | | t | | |
| | | | | o |
| | | | | |
| | | | | e |

| | | | | | | | | |
|---|---|---|---|---|---|---|---|---|
| | | | b | | | | | |
| | | | | | | | | |
| | | | | | | | | |
| | | n | | | h | | n | |
| | | | m | | | | | |
| | | d | e | | | | | |
| | | | | | | | e | |

Test Master

Name ______________________________

Read each sentence. Look at the underlined spelling word. Fill in a circle. Show if the word is spelled **Right** or **Wrong**.

**Sample**
**I play the durm in the band.** — Right ○ Wrong ●

**Answer Box**

1. I would like to becum a baseball player.
2. The little bee made a very loud buz.
3. I will put a cover on my baby brother.
4. I have a spot on the cuff of my shirt.
5. The point on his pencil was dull.
6. Mom and Dad love each other a lot.
7. I had tomato soup for lunch.
8. I am going away to camp this munth.
9. We wanted some raisins, but there were none.
10. There was nothing in the box.
11. You can't do well on your test unless you stuty.
12. Dad told me to put my stuff away.
13. We took a trip to visit my unkle.
14. She put the shoes under her bed.
15. I will not go home ontil my mom calls.

| | Right | Wrong |
|---|---|---|
| 1. | ○ | ○ |
| 2. | ○ | ○ |
| 3. | ○ | ○ |
| 4. | ○ | ○ |
| 5. | ○ | ○ |
| 6. | ○ | ○ |
| 7. | ○ | ○ |
| 8. | ○ | ○ |
| 9. | ○ | ○ |
| 10. | ○ | ○ |
| 11. | ○ | ○ |
| 12. | ○ | ○ |
| 13. | ○ | ○ |
| 14. | ○ | ○ |
| 15. | ○ | ○ |

Name ______________________________

Finish each puzzle with spelling words.

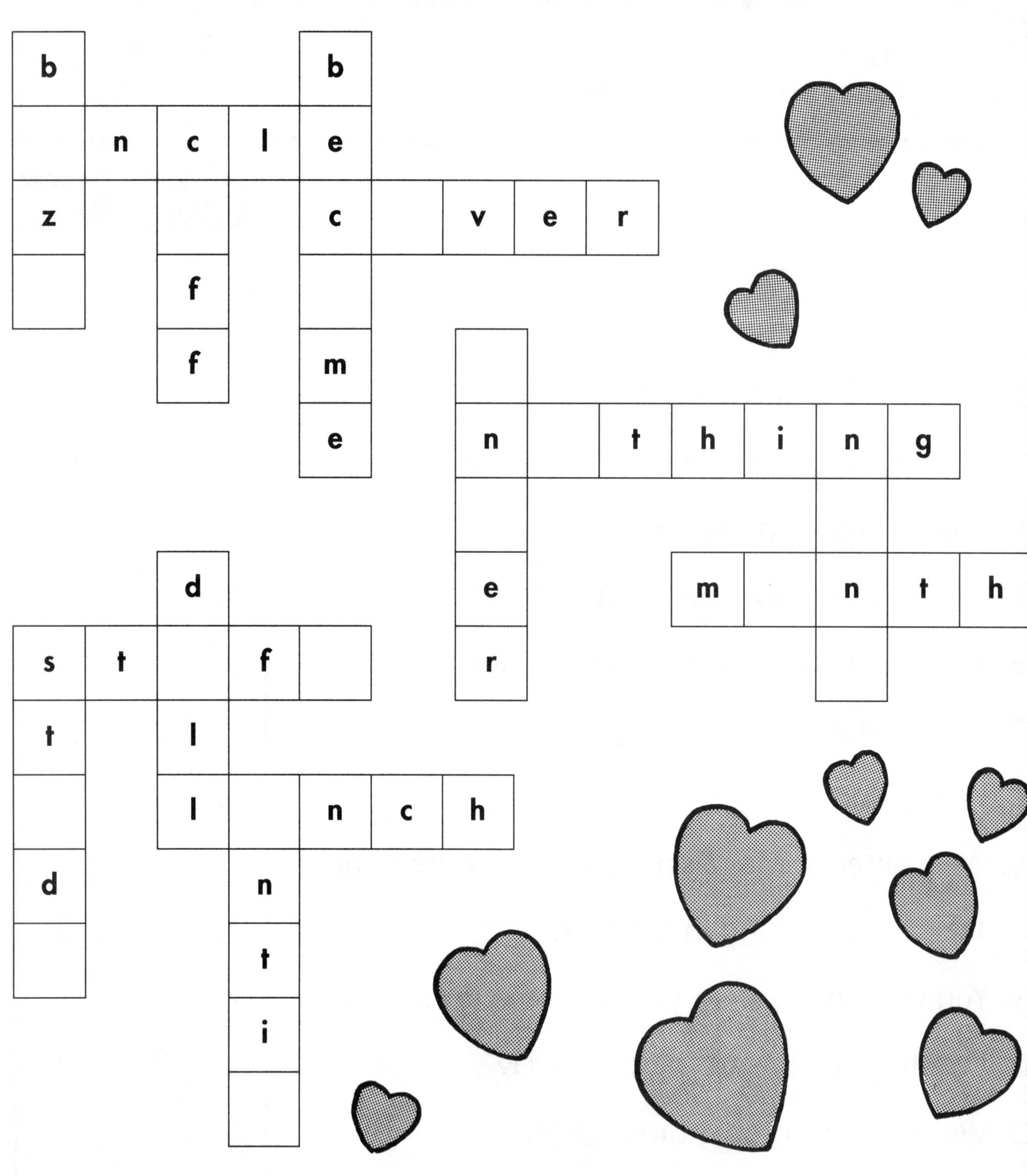


One spelling word is not in any puzzle.
Write that spelling word on the line.

Name ____________________



### Color-a-Vowel

Pronounce each word and have your child write it with a crayon. Then ask your child to use another crayon to draw a ring around the letters that stand for the vowel sound in the word. Be sure that your child understands that in this unit, the vowel sound is spelled with two letters.

**ou, oi**

1. proud
2. boil
3. loud
4. house
5. join
6. cloud
7. sound
8. voice
9. oil
10. round
11. point
12. south
13. found
14. soil
15. ground

1. ____________________
2. ____________________
3. ____________________
4. ____________________
5. ____________________
6. ____________________
7. ____________________
8. ____________________
9. ____________________
10. ____________________
11. ____________________
12. ____________________
13. ____________________
14. ____________________
15. ____________________

Name ______________________

## Hoja para estudiar en casa

### ou, oi

### Colorea vocales

Pronuncien cada palabra y pídanle a su hijo o hija que escriba la palabra con un creyón de pintar. Luego díganle que use un creyón de otro color para circular las letras que indican el sonido vocal en cada palabra. Estén seguros de que su hijo o hija comprende que en la unidad, el sonido vocálico se deletrea con dos letras.

1. *proud* orgulloso — 1. ______
2. *boil* hervir — 2. ______
3. *loud* ruidoso; llamativo — 3. ______
4. *house* casa — 4. ______
5. *join* juntar — 5. ______
6. *cloud* nube — 6. ______
7. *sound* sonido; firme — 7. ______
8. *voice* voz — 8. ______
9. *oil* aceite; petróleo; aceitar — 9. ______
10. *round* redondo — 10. ______
11. *point* puntar; apuntar; punto — 11. ______
12. *south* sur — 12. ______
13. *found* halló — 13. ______
14. *soil* ensuciar; suelo — 14. ______
15. *ground* terreno — 15. ______

Unit 4
**Practice Master**

Name ______________________

| 1. oil | 3. point | 5. loud | 7. south |
|---|---|---|---|
| 2. join | 4. voice | 6. ground | 8. house |

**A.** Replace the underlined part of each sentence with a spelling word.

1. Shall we study at my <u>home</u>? ______________
2. Plant the carrot seeds in the <u>dirt</u>. ______________
3. The birds are flying <u>away from the north</u> for the winter. ______________
4. Let's <u>become members of</u> the math club. ______________
5. He will <u>aim</u> his arrow at the target. ______________
6. You need <u>a greasy liquid</u> for your car. ______________

**B.** Add and subtract letters to make spelling words.

1. proud – pr + l = ______________
2. horse – r + u = ______________
3. coin – c + j = ______________
4. choice – ch + v = ______________
5. mouth – m + s = ______________
6. paint – a + o = ______________

Name ____________________

| oil | point | loud | south |
| --- | --- | --- | --- |
| join | voice | ground | house |

**C.** Write the spelling word that fits each shape.

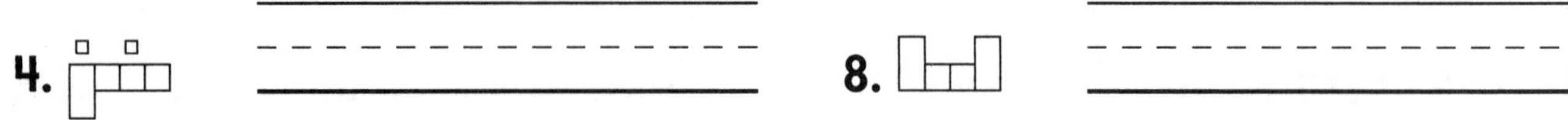

1. ____________________
5. ____________________
2. ____________________
6. ____________________
3. ____________________
7. ____________________
4. ____________________
8. ____________________

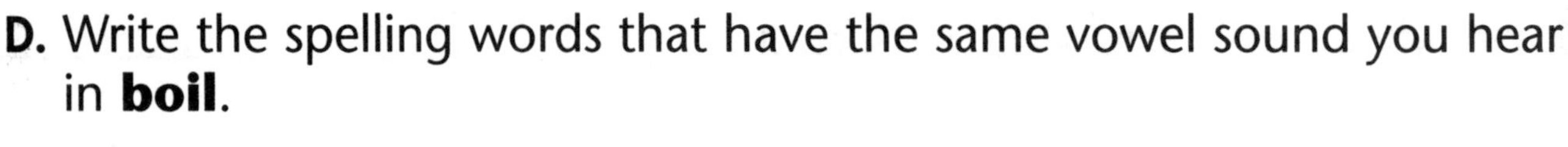

**D.** Write the spelling words that have the same vowel sound you hear in **boil**.

1. ____________________
3. ____________________
2. ____________________
4. ____________________

Name ______________________________

Read each sentence. Look at the underlined spelling word. Fill in a circle. Show if the word is spelled **Right** or **Wrong**.

**Sample** — **It is my job to take the garbage out.** — Right ● Wrong ○

**Answer Box**

| | Sentence | Right | Wrong |
|---|---|---|---|
| 1. | How long should I boil the water? | ○ | ○ |
| 2. | The clowd looked like a ball of cotton. | ○ | ○ |
| 3. | Have you found the ball you lost? | ○ | ○ |
| 4. | There were little bugs all over the ground. | ○ | ○ |
| 5. | You can play at my house today. | ○ | ○ |
| 6. | We would like you to joyn our club. | ○ | ○ |
| 7. | The music from the parade was loud. | ○ | ○ |
| 8. | We changed the oil in our car. | ○ | ○ |
| 9. | Make sure your pencil piont is sharp. | ○ | ○ |
| 10. | We were proud of our school band. | ○ | ○ |
| 11. | The lamp shade was wround. | ○ | ○ |
| 12. | The soil was wet from the rain. | ○ | ○ |
| 13. | The mouse did not make a sound. | ○ | ○ |
| 14. | Many birds fly suoth for the winter. | ○ | ○ |
| 15. | That girl has a pretty singing voice. | ○ | ○ |

Unit 4
Homework Master

Name ______________________________

Draw a ring around the three rhyming words to win each tic-tac-toe game.

| house | cloud | south |
|---|---|---|
| round | proud | found |
| sound | loud | ground |

| ground | point | cloud |
|---|---|---|
| join | south | voice |
| soil | oil | boil |

| proud | loud | found |
|---|---|---|
| point | ground | oil |
| round | join | cloud |

Add and subtract letters to make spelling words.

1. proud – pr + l = ____________
2. horse – r + u = ____________
3. coil – c + b = ____________
4. hound – h + s = ____________
5. coin – c + j = ____________
6. choice – ch + v= ____________
7. bound – b + f = ____________
8. mouth – m + s = ____________
9. paint – a + o = ____________
10. sail – a + o = ____________

Name ______________________________

## Inventions Wanted

To set the stage for this creative writing activity, have your child imagine that he or she can invent something that will improve the lives of people all over the world. Have your child write a paragraph explaining what the invention is, what it looks like, what it does, and how it will make life better. Finally, encourage your child to give the invention a name.

**ew, oo**

1. crew
2. loose
3. news
4. school
5. drew
6. knew
7. smooth
8. pool
9. shoot
10. threw
11. roof
12. fool
13. chew
14. balloon
15. choose

1. ______________
2. ______________
3. ______________
4. ______________
5. ______________
6. ______________
7. ______________
8. ______________
9. ______________
10. ______________
11. ______________
12. ______________
13. ______________
14. ______________
15. ______________

Unit 5

Name ____________________

## Hoja para estudiar en casa

**ew, oo**

### Invenciones

Para comenzar esta actividad de escritos creadores, pídanle a su hijo o hija que imagine que puede inventar algo que va a mejorar las vidas de personas que viven en todas partes del mundo. Díganle que escriba un párrafo explicando qué es la invención, cómo es, qué hace, y cómo va a mejorar el nivel de la vida. Finalmente, anímenlo(a) a nombrar la invención.

1. crew — tripulación
2. loose — flojo; suelto
3. news — noticias
4. school — escuela
5. drew — dibujó
6. knew — sabía; conocía
7. smooth — liso; suave
8. pool — piscina; trucos
9. shoot — disparar
10. threw — tiró
11. roof — techo
12. fool — bobo; tonto
13. chew — mascar
14. balloon — globo
15. choose — escoger

1. ____________________
2. ____________________
3. ____________________
4. ____________________
5. ____________________
6. ____________________
7. ____________________
8. ____________________
9. ____________________
10. ____________________
11. ____________________
12. ____________________
13. ____________________
14. ____________________
15. ____________________

Name ______________________



| | | | |
|---|---|---|---|
| 1. new | 3. threw | 5. roof | 7. school |
| 2. knew | 4. pool | 6. choose | 8. balloon |

**A.** A dictionary has three parts.

| Front | Middle | Back |
|---|---|---|
| a–g | h–p | q–z |

school choose news

1. Which word is found in the front? ______________________

2. Which word is found in the middle? ______________________

3. Which word is found in the back? ______________________

**B.** Write the spelling word that belongs in each sentence.

1. Sam blew air into the ____. ______________________

2. I ____ the ball to Ellen. ______________________

3. We went for a swim in the ____. ______________________

4. Birds like to sit on our ____. ______________________

Name ______________________________

| | | | |
|---|---|---|---|
| news | threw | roof | school |
| knew | pool | choose | balloon |

**C.** Which spelling word begins with a silent letter? Write the word. ______________________

**D.** Use spelling words to complete the puzzle.

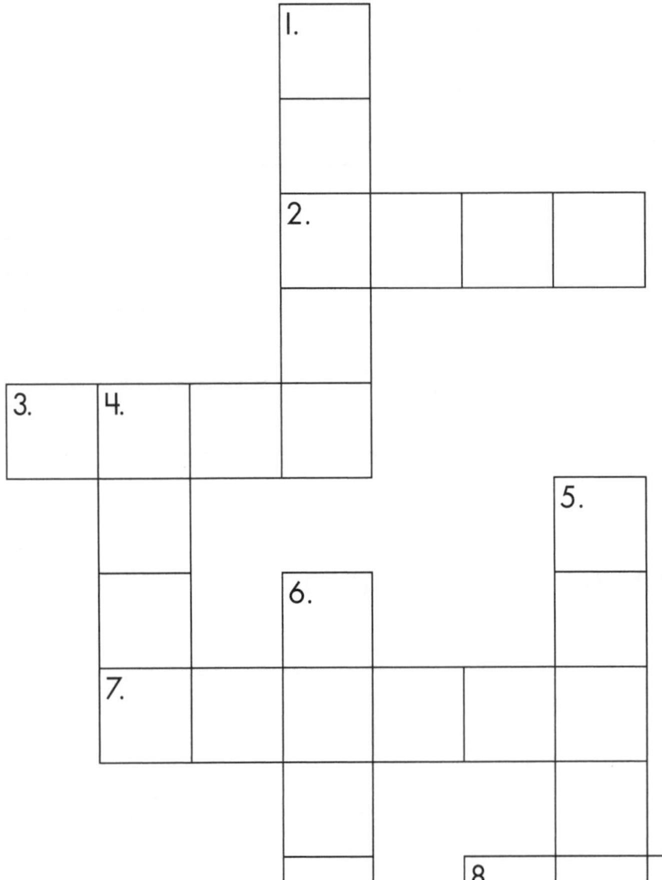


**Across**

**2.** the top of a house
**3.** did know
**7.** a place where you learn things
**8.** a small body of water

**Down**

**1.** did throw
**4.** recent happenings reported over television and radio
**5.** brightly colored toy
**6.** to pick out

Name ____________________

Read each sentence. Look at the underlined spelling word. Fill in a circle. Show if the word is spelled **Right** or **Wrong**.

**Sample**
**The plane flue high in the sky.** — Right ○ Wrong ●

**Answer Box**

1. The big red baloon was full of air.
2. Make sure you chew your food well.
3. Did she chewse a dog for a pet?
4. The captain of the ship had a good krew.
5. My teacher liked the picture that I drew.
6. It can be fun to fool your friends.
7. The teacher new her students well.
8. The laces on your shoe are loose.
9. My mom and dad told me the good newz.
10. We went swimming in the cool pool.
11. The heavy rain caused a leak in our ruf.
12. We had fun at the school picnic.
13. I saw a star shoot across the sky.
14. Beth found a stone that was very smooth.
15. Scott thew the ball to the catcher.

| | Right | Wrong |
|---|---|---|
| 1. | ○ | ○ |
| 2. | ○ | ○ |
| 3. | ○ | ○ |
| 4. | ○ | ○ |
| 5. | ○ | ○ |
| 6. | ○ | ○ |
| 7. | ○ | ○ |
| 8. | ○ | ○ |
| 9. | ○ | ○ |
| 10. | ○ | ○ |
| 11. | ○ | ○ |
| 12. | ○ | ○ |
| 13. | ○ | ○ |
| 14. | ○ | ○ |
| 15. | ○ | ○ |

Name ______________________________

Use spelling words to complete the puzzle.

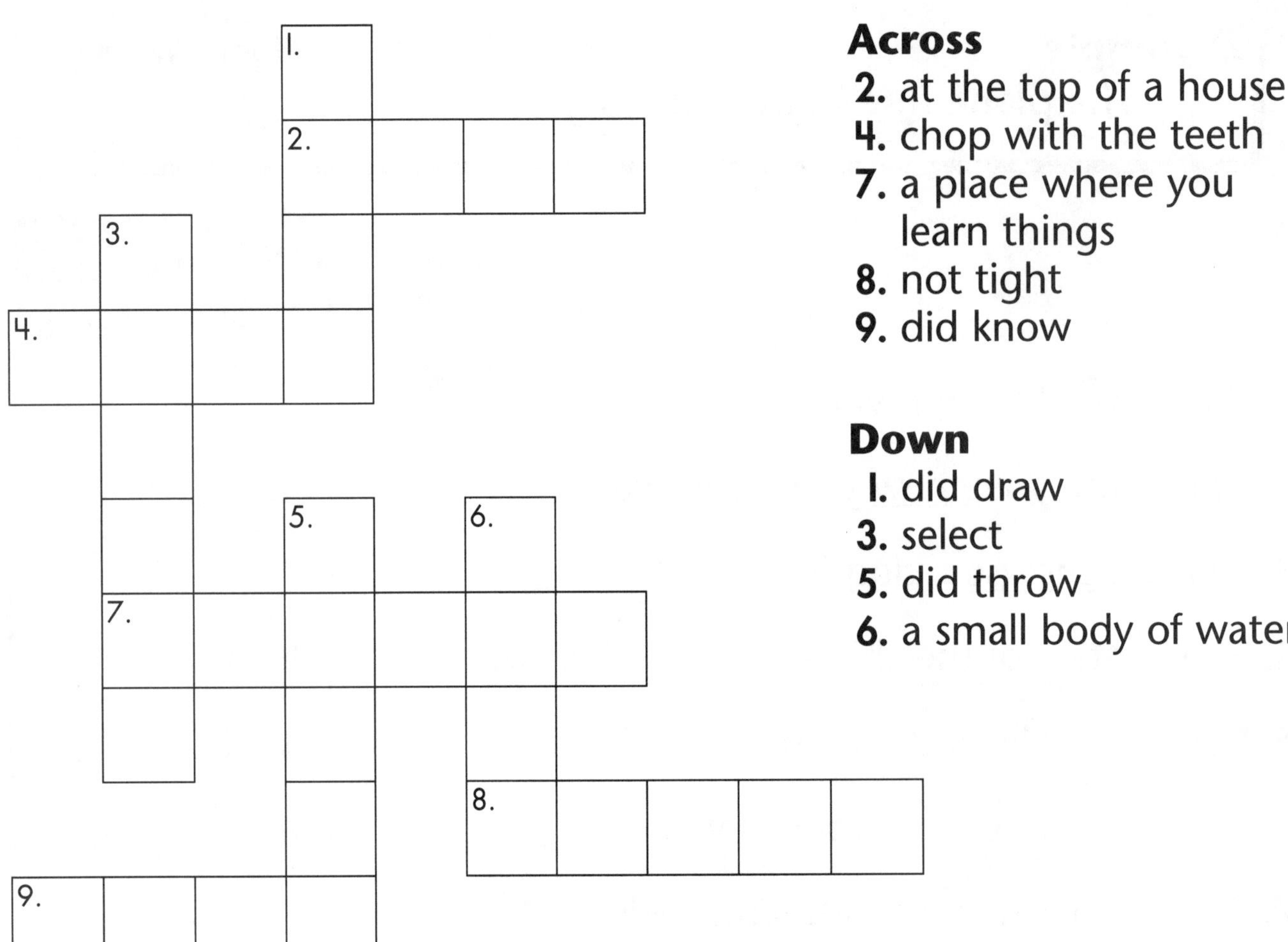

**Across**

**2.** at the top of a house
**4.** chop with the teeth
**7.** a place where you learn things
**8.** not tight
**9.** did know

**Down**

**1.** did draw
**3.** select
**5.** did throw
**6.** a small body of water

Write each group of words in a-b-c order.

| news<br>shoot<br>balloon | 1. ______<br>2. ______<br>3. ______ | smooth<br>crew<br>fool | 1. ______<br>2. ______<br>3. ______ |
|---|---|---|---|

Name ____________________

## Home Study Master

### Assessment and Review

1. plan
2. stick
3. grand
4. stamp
5. drop
6. spend
7. clock
8. spent
9. none
10. until
11. love
12. nothing
13. point
14. house
15. voice
16. ground
17. threw
18. school
19. knew
20. choose

### Use Your Imagination

Ask your child to write sentences using two words from the spelling list in each. Continue until he or she has written ten sentences. None of the words should be used more than once. Check the sentences for correct spelling and understanding of the meaning of the words.

1. ____________________
2. ____________________
3. ____________________
4. ____________________
5. ____________________
6. ____________________
7. ____________________
8. ____________________
9. ____________________
10. ____________________
11. ____________________
12. ____________________
13. ____________________
14. ____________________
15. ____________________
16. ____________________
17. ____________________
18. ____________________
19. ____________________
20. ____________________

Name ______________________

Unit 6

# Hoja para estudiar en casa

## Assessment and Review

1. plan — plan; planear
2. stick — palo
3. grand — espléndido
4. stamp — pisotear; sello
5. drop — dejar caer; gota
6. spend — pasar; gastar
7. clock — reloj
8. spent — pasó; gastó
9. none — ninguno
10. until — hasta
11. love — amor; amar
12. nothing — nada
13. point — puntar; apuntar; punto
14. house — casa
15. voice — voz
16. ground — terreno
17. threw — tiró
18. school — escuela
19. knew — sabía; conocía
20. choose — escoger

## Usa tu imaginación

Pidan a su hijo o hija que escriba algunas oraciones que contengan cada una dos palabras de la lista de palabras para deletrear de esta unidad. Sigan hasta que él o ella haya escrito diez oraciones. Cada palabra debe usarse solamente una vez. Comprueben la ortografía y la comprensión de los significados de las palabras en las oraciones de su hijo o hija.

1. ______
2. ______
3. ______
4. ______
5. ______
6. ______
7. ______
8. ______
9. ______
10. ______
11. ______
12. ______
13. ______
14. ______
15. ______
16. ______
17. ______
18. ______
19. ______
20. ______

Name ______________________________

Unit 6 **Test Master**

**A.** One word is misspelled in each group. Write the letter of the misspelled word.

| | a. | b. | c. | |
|---|---|---|---|---|
| 1. | **a.** fool | **b.** stick | **c.** throo | ☐ |
| 2. | **a.** grownd | **b.** point | **c.** knew | ☐ |
| 3. | **a.** left | **b.** howse | **c.** cover | ☐ |
| 4. | **a.** choose | **b.** voice | **c.** untel | ☐ |
| 5. | **a.** nuthing | **b.** south | **c.** plan | ☐ |
| 6. | **a.** found | **b.** clok | **c.** month | ☐ |
| 7. | **a.** grand | **b.** luve | **c.** block | ☐ |
| 8. | **a.** sand | **b.** nune | **c.** plan | ☐ |

**B.** Read each sentence. If a word is misspelled, write **X**. If each word is spelled correctly, write **C**.

1. I felt a dop of rain. ☐
2. We spent one dollar today. ☐
3. Hurry, the shool bus is here! ☐
4. Would you like this stamp for your collection? ☐

Name ______________________



## Vowel-Consonant-e

### Concentration

Write the spelling words on index cards or slips of paper with blank spaces in place of the letters that spell the long vowel sounds. (Note that in the case of vowel-consonant-**e** pattern words, such as **face**, the letters that spell the long vowel sound are separated by another letter.) Write the letters that are missing from each word on separate cards. Place each set of cards face-down in two stacks. Have your child draw one card from each stack and try to make a spelling word from the two parts. If a spelling word can be made, have your child read the word and then write it. If no spelling word can be made, have him or her return the cards to the stacks, shuffle the cards, and continue until all the cards have been used.

1. state
2. close
3. slide
4. face
5. globe
6. pave
7. size
8. smoke
9. flame
10. broke
11. prize
12. skate
13. smile
14. plane
15. stone

1. ______
2. ______
3. ______
4. ______
5. ______
6. ______
7. ______
8. ______
9. ______
10. ______
11. ______
12. ______
13. ______
14. ______
15. ______

Name ______________________

# Hoja para estudiar en casa

## Concentración

Deletreen las palabras en fichas o en cuadros de papel dejando en blanco las letras para los sonidos largos de las vocales. (Noten que en las palabras con el modelo de **vocal-consonante-e**, tales como **face** [cara], las letras para el sondio largo de la vocal están separadas por otra letra.) Escriban las letras que faltan en otras fichas. Pongan cada serie de fichas boca abajo en dos montones. Díganle a su hijo o hija que tome una ficha de cada montón y que trate de componer una palabra usando las dos fichas. Si es posible componer una palabra, díganle a su hijo o hija que lea la palabra y luego que la escriba. Si es imposible componer una palabra, déjenle poner las dos fichas en los dos montones, barajar las fichas de cada montón, y continuar el juego hasta que no queden fichas.

## Vowel-Consonant-e

1. state — estado — 1. ______
2. close — cerca; cerrar — 2. ______
3. slide — deslizar; resbalón — 3. ______
4. face — cara; enfrentarse — 4. ______
5. globe — globo — 5. ______
6. pave — pavimentar — 6. ______
7. size — tamaño — 7. ______
8. smoke — humo; fumar — 8. ______
9. flame — llama; quemar — 9. ______
10. broke — rompió — 10. ______
11. prize — premio — 11. ______
12. skate — patinar; patín — 12. ______
13. smile — sonreir(se) — 13. ______
14. plane — avión — 14. ______
15. stone — piedra — 15. ______

Name ____________________

**Unit 7**
**Practice Master**

| | | | |
|---|---|---|---|
| 1. face | 3. plane | 5. smile | 7. close |
| 2. state | 4. size | 6. broke | 8. stone |

**A.** Write a spelling word for each clue.

1. I am found on the front of your head. ____________________
2. I fly through the air. ____________________
3. I am something your face does. ____________________
4. I can also be called a rock. ____________________

**B.** Write the spelling word that belongs in each sentence.

1. The fans all wanted to be ____ to the star player. ____________________
2. What ____ sneaker do you wear? ____________________
3. The runner just ____ the world record time! ____________________
4. I'll show you on the ____ map where our team will travel. ____________________

Unit 7
**Practice Master**

Name ______________________

| face | plane | smile | close |
|---|---|---|---|
| state | size | broke | stone |

**C.** Circle the misspelled word in each sentence. Write each word correctly.

1. It's nice to see a smil on your face. ______________
2. The ston in that necklace is beautiful. ______________
3. What stat do you live in? ______________

**D.** Circle every other letter. These letters form spelling words. Write each word. The first letter is circled to get you started.

1. (f) r a n c l e ______________
2. (s) n i c z b e ______________
3. (c) z l a o p s t e ______________
4. (b) a r k o h k z e ______________
5. (p) q l c a v n d e ______________

Unit 7

Test Master

Name ____________________

Read each sentence. Look at the underlined spelling word. Fill in a circle. Show if the word is spelled **Right** or **Wrong**.

**Sample**

A nickel is equal to five pennies. — Right ● Wrong ○

1. My brother brok our best vase.
2. The score was klose near the end of the game.
3. The clown had a funny fase.
4. The campfire had a warm orange flame.
5. A model of the earth is called a globe.
6. This jet was much larger than that palne.
7. Chris won a prize for wearing the best costume.
8. Mom wants to know what size dress you wear.
9. In the winter I like to skate with my friends.
10. It is fun to slidd on the smooth ice.
11. You have a friendly smile.
12. The heavy gray smoke filled the sky.
13. The trees in our state are beautiful.
14. The little boy threw a stoan into the pond.
15. The crew will pave Bank Street next week.

**Answer Box**

| | Right | Wrong |
|---|---|---|
| 1. | ○ | ○ |
| 2. | ○ | ○ |
| 3. | ○ | ○ |
| 4. | ○ | ○ |
| 5. | ○ | ○ |
| 6. | ○ | ○ |
| 7. | ○ | ○ |
| 8. | ○ | ○ |
| 9. | ○ | ○ |
| 10. | ○ | ○ |
| 11. | ○ | ○ |
| 12. | ○ | ○ |
| 13. | ○ | ○ |
| 14. | ○ | ○ |
| 15. | ○ | ○ |

Name ______________________________

**A.** Circle every other letter on the stone wall. These letters form spelling words. Write each word. The first one is done as an example.

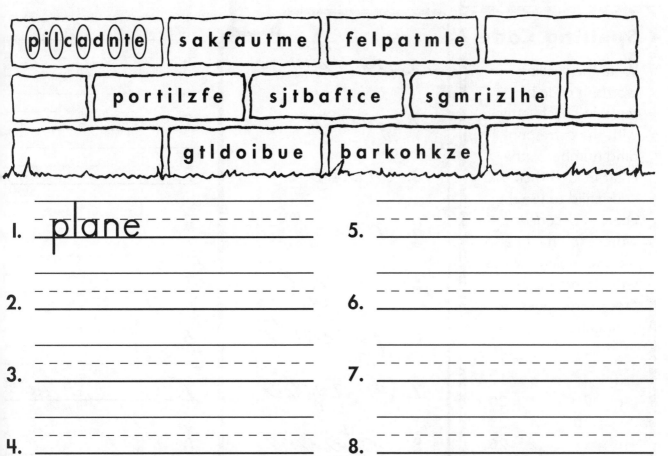

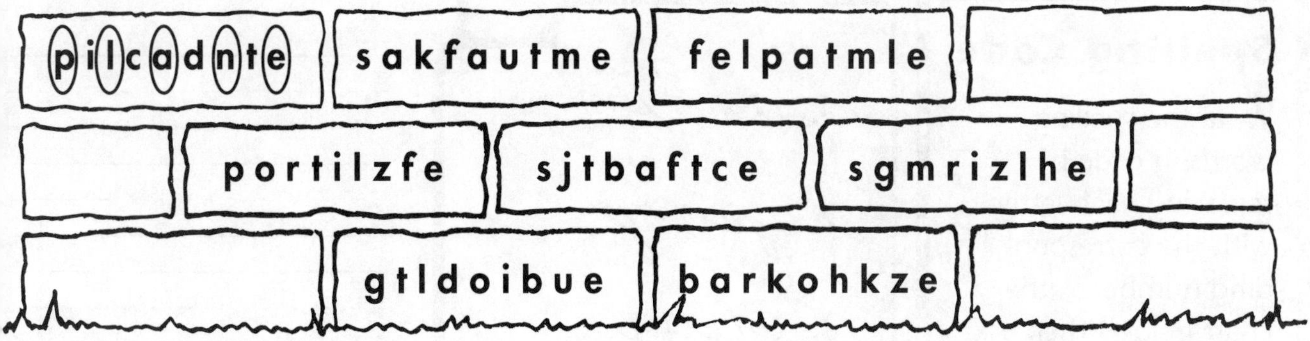

pilcadnte
sakfautme
felpatmle
portilzfe
sjtbaftce
sgmrizlhe
gtldoibue
barkohkze

1. plane ____________
2. ____________
3. ____________
4. ____________
5. ____________
6. ____________
7. ____________
8. ____________

**B.** Use the code to complete each spelling word.

| ▲ = a | ■ = e | ● = i | ❤ = o |
|---|---|---|---|

1. s l ___ d ___ ● ■
2. s m ___ k ___ ❤ ■
3. p l ___ n ___ ▲ ■
4. f ___ c ___ ▲ ■
5. s ___ z ___ ● ■
6. p ___ v ___ ▲ ■
7. c l ___ s ___ ❤ ■
8. s t ___ n ___ ❤ ■

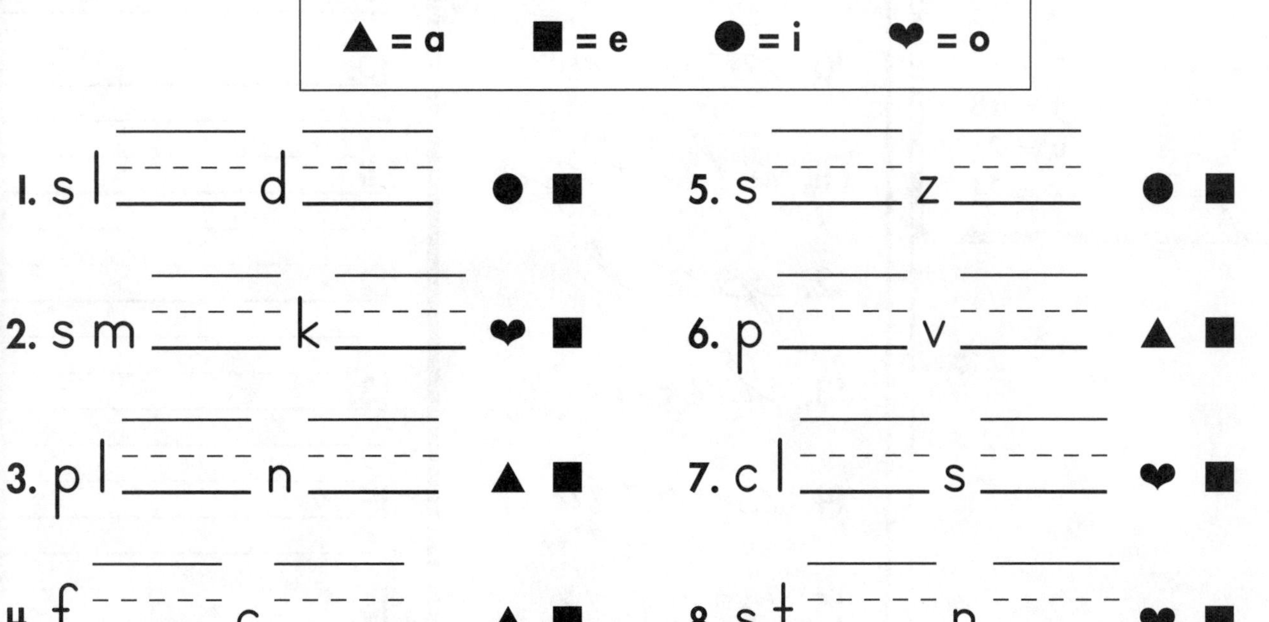

Name ______________________

Unit 8

**Home Study Master**

## Long a: ai, ay

1. aid
2. pay
3. chain
4. mail
5. tray
6. paint
7. maybe
8. plain
9. lay
10. main
11. always
12. pail
13. laid
14. away
15. paid

### Spelling Code

Write the spelling words in code by replacing each letter with the correspon-ding number in the chart below. Then ask your child to use the chart to decode the words. You might also include spelling words written in code in "secret messages" to your child.

| | |
|---|---|
| a = 1 | n = 14 |
| d = 4 | q = 17 |
| g = 7 | t = 20 |
| j = 10 | w = 23 |
| m = 13 | z = 26 |
| p = 16 | c = 3 |
| s = 19 | f = 6 |
| v = 22 | i = 9 |
| y = 25 | l = 12 |
| b = 2 | o = 15 |
| e = 5 | r = 18 |
| h = 8 | u = 21 |
| k = 11 | x = 24 |

1. ______
2. ______
3. ______
4. ______
5. ______
6. ______
7. ______
8. ______
9. ______
10. ______
11. ______
12. ______
13. ______
14. ______
15. ______

Name ______________________

## Hoja para estudiar en casa

### Deletrear en claves

Deletreen las palabras en clave usando el número que corresponde a cada letra en el cuadro siguiente. Luego pídanle a su hjio o hija que use el cuadro para descifrar las palabras. Con su hijo o hija pueden usar también palabras escritas en claves en "mensajes secretos".

| | |
|---|---|
| a = 1 | n = 14 |
| d = 4 | q = 17 |
| g = 7 | t = 20 |
| j = 10 | w = 23 |
| m = 13 | z = 26 |
| p = 16 | c = 3 |
| s = 19 | f = 6 |
| v = 22 | i = 9 |
| y = 25 | l = 12 |
| b = 2 | o = 15 |
| e = 5 | r = 18 |
| h = 8 | u = 21 |
| k = 11 | x = 24 |

### Long a: ai, ay

1. aid — ayudar; ayuda
2. pay — pagar; sueldo
3. chain — cadena; encadenar
4. mail — enviar; correo
5. tray — bandeja
6. paint — pintar; pintura
7. maybe — quizás
8. plain — llano; evidente
9. lay — poner; reposar
10. main — principal
11. always — siempre
12. pail — balde
13. laid — puso
14. away — ausente; lejos
15. paid — pagó

1. ______________________
2. ______________________
3. ______________________
4. ______________________
5. ______________________
6. ______________________
7. ______________________
8. ______________________
9. ______________________
10. ______________________
11. ______________________
12. ______________________
13. ______________________
14. ______________________
15. ______________________

Name ______________________

| | | | |
|---|---|---|---|
| 1. pay | 3. away | 5. laid | 7. main |
| 2. maybe | 4. always | 6. mail | 8. chain |

**A.** Unscramble the underlined words in the sentences. Write the words.

1. This is the <u>niam</u> road to town. ______________

2. I will <u>pya</u> your way. ______________

3. Is your bicycle <u>hinac</u> broken? ______________

4. I delivered the <u>mial</u> today. ______________

**B.** Circle the misspelled word in each sentence. Write each word correctly.

1. It's time to put everything awey. ______________

2. I will pai you tomorrow. ______________

3. Alway make sure the cap is on tight. ______________

4. Maibe we should use a larger paintbrush. ______________

Name ______________________________



| pay | away | laid | main |
| --- | --- | --- | --- |
| maybe | always | mail | chain |

**C.** Write the spelling word that belongs in each sentence.

**1.** Someone ____ a book on my chair. ______________________

**2.** Our projects will be shown in the ____ hallway. ______________________

**3.** My mobile is the one hanging from a ____. ______________________

**4.** I will ____ the letter. ______________________

**D.** Use the letters in the box to write five spelling words. You can use a letter more than once.

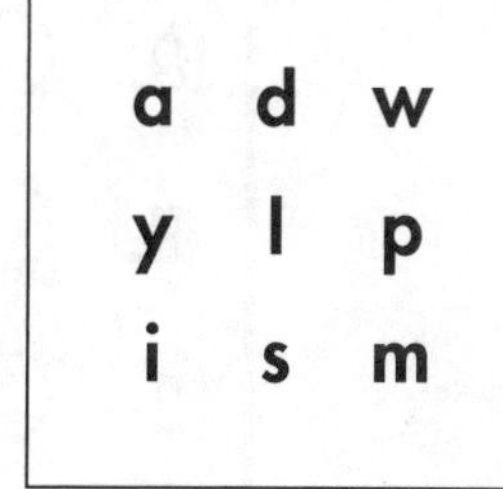


**1.** ______________________

**2.** ______________________

**3.** ______________________

**4.** ______________________

**5.** ______________________

Unit 8

**Test Master**

Name ______________________________

Read each sentence. Look at the underlined spelling word. Fill in a circle. Show if the word is spelled **Right** or **Wrong**.

**Sample**

| | Right | Wrong |
|---|---|---|
| **My big brother played a game with me.** | ● | ○ |

1. We will give aid to help needy people.
2. My sister always wins in tennis.
3. I went away to camp for the summer.
4. He lade his school books on the table.
5. Where did you lay your homework?
6. Did you check for mayl yet?
7. The tent is held up by one mane pole.
8. Mom said that maybee we could go swimming.
9. I paid for the book myself.
10. Ted put sand in his pael.
11. I will paint my wagon red.
12. My dad will paye the clerk for the food.
13. We ordered a tray of plain pizza.
14. The gate was kept closed with a chain.
15. She put her plate on a tray.

**Answer Box**

| | Right | Wrong |
|---|---|---|
| 1. | ○ | ○ |
| 2. | ○ | ○ |
| 3. | ○ | ○ |
| 4. | ○ | ○ |
| 5. | ○ | ○ |
| 6. | ○ | ○ |
| 7. | ○ | ○ |
| 8. | ○ | ○ |
| 9. | ○ | ○ |
| 10. | ○ | ○ |
| 11. | ○ | ○ |
| 12. | ○ | ○ |
| 13. | ○ | ○ |
| 14. | ○ | ○ |
| 15. | ○ | ○ |

Name ________________________

Unit 8 **Homework Master**

Unscramble the underlined word in the sentence.
Write the spelling word.

1. Can you carry this rtya?

2. Why are you laywas smiling?

3. This is the niam road to town.

4. Please don't spill the iptna.

5. Have you diap for this milk?

6. The kitten ran ywaa from home.

7. Mybae it will rain tonight.

8. We got lots of mial today.

9. I will pya your way.

10. Jill wanted to carry water in a lipa.

Use the letters in the box to write five other spelling words. You can use a letter more than once.

| a | c | d |
|---|---|---|
| h | i | l |
| n | p | y |

11. ________

12. ________

13. ________

14. ________

15. ________

Unit 9

Name ______________________________

**Home Study Master**

## Long e: ee, ea

### Record-a-Word

Encourage your child to say and spell each of the spelling words into a tape recorder. Replay the tape so that you and your child can check the spelling against the word list.

1. sheep
2. dream
3. street
4. east
5. treat
6. mean
7. wheels
8. peace
9. real
10. cheese
11. leave
12. stream
13. sweet
14. teacher
15. heat

1. ______
2. ______
3. ______
4. ______
5. ______
6. ______
7. ______
8. ______
9. ______
10. ______
11. ______
12. ______
13. ______
14. ______
15. ______

Name ______________________

Unit 9

## Hoja para estudiar en casa

### Grabar una palabra

Animen a su hijo o hija a que diga y a que deletree cada una de las palabras usando una grabadora. Luego pongan la cinta y escuchen las palabras para averiguar el deletreo de las palabras usadas con la grabadora con la lista de las palabras de la lección.

### Long e: ee, ea

1. *sheep* oveja
2. *dream* soñar; sueño
3. *street* calle
4. *east* este
5. *treat* tratar; convite
6. *mean* significar; antipático
7. *wheels* ruedas
8. *peace* paz
9. *real* real; verdadero
10. *cheese* queso
11. *leave* salir; dejar
12. *stream* arroyo
13. *sweet* dulce
14. *teacher* maestro
15. *heat* calentar; calor

1. ______________________
2. ______________________
3. ______________________
4. ______________________
5. ______________________
6. ______________________
7. ______________________
8. ______________________
9. ______________________
10. ______________________
11. ______________________
12. ______________________
13. ______________________
14. ______________________
15. ______________________

Name ______________________

1. east 3. stream 5. teacher 7. wheels
2. real 4. heat 6. sheep 8. street

**A.** Write the spelling words with the **long e** sound spelled **ea**.

1. ______________ 4. ______________

2. ______________ 5. ______________

3. ______________

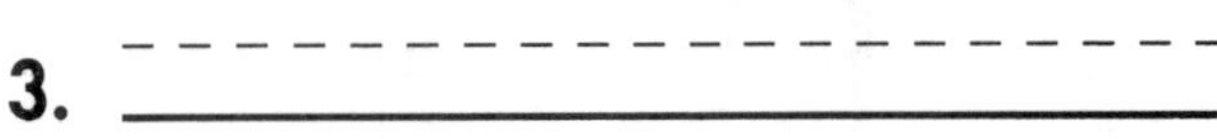

**B.** Write a spelling word to answer each question.

1. What word names a farm animal? ______________

2. What part of a bicycle is round? ______________

3. What is the opposite of pretend? ______________

4. What is the direction opposite of west? ______________

Unit 9
Practice Master

Name ____________________

| east | stream | teacher | wheels |
| --- | --- | --- | --- |
| real | heat | sheep | street |

**C.** Make the spelling words by using the letters in the soup bowl. You may use some letters more than once. Write the words.

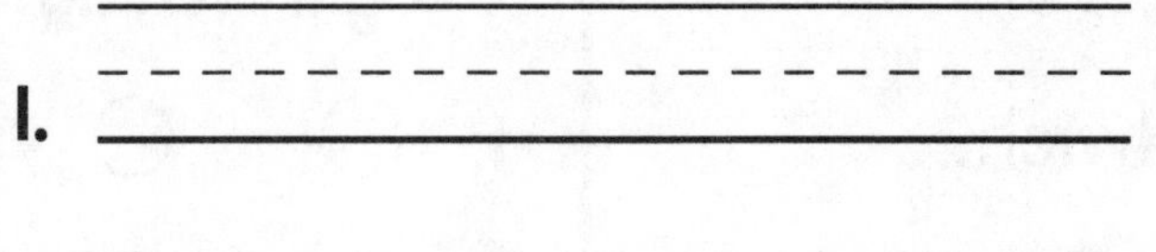

1. ____________________

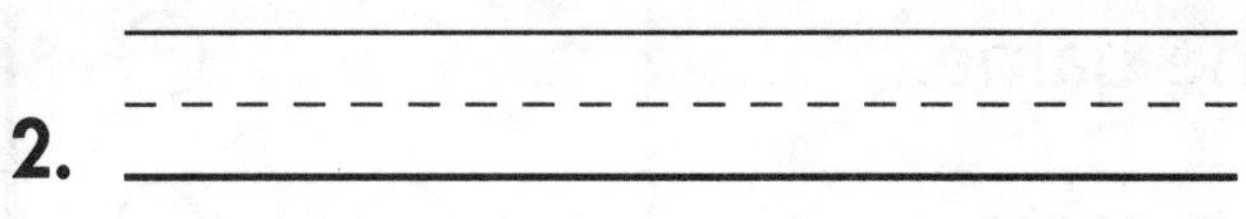

2. ____________________

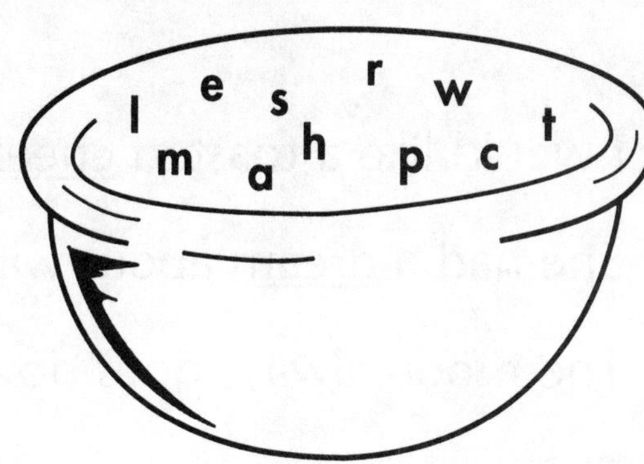


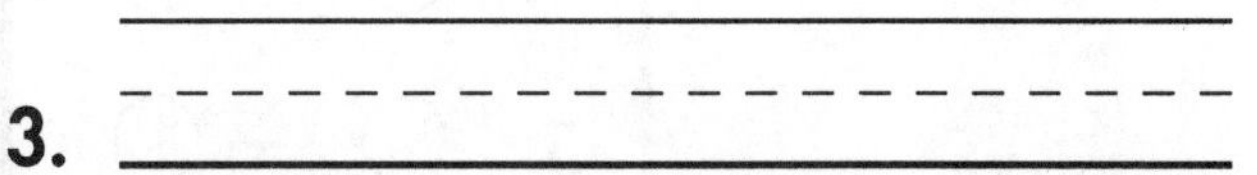

3. ____________________

6. ____________________

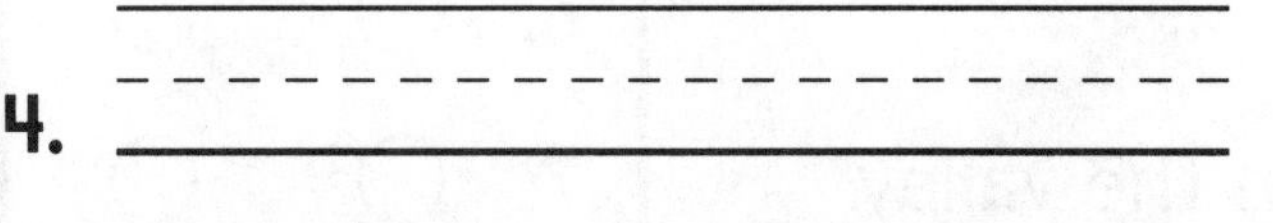

4. ____________________

7. ____________________

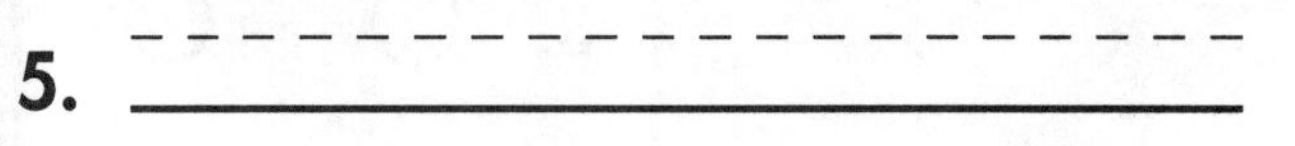

5. ____________________

8. ____________________

**D.** Words that have almost the same meanings are called **synonyms**. Write the spelling word that is a synonym for each word.

1. creek ____________________

2. road ____________________

3. true ____________________

**Test** **Master**

Name ____________________

Read each sentence. Look at the underlined spelling word. Fill in a circle. Show if the word is spelled **Right** or **Wrong**.

**Sample**

| | Right | Wrong |
|---|---|---|
| It is polite to say pleaze and thank you. | ○ | ● |

1. I would like a toasted cheeze sandwich.
2. She had a dream about winning the game.
3. The moon always goes down in the easte.
4. The heat of the sun kept us warm.
5. Tell me when it is time to leave.
6. Please tell me what you meen.
7. After the storm there was pease in the valley.
8. That doll looks almost rael.
9. There were many sheep in the field.
10. We floated our boats on the streem.
11. We will turn left at the next street.
12. Kim gave me an apple that was very sweet.
13. I gave my homework to my teacher.
14. Mom took us to a movie as a treat.
15. That dump truck has ten wheeles.

**Answer Box**

| | Right | Wrong |
|---|---|---|
| 1. | ○ | ○ |
| 2. | ○ | ○ |
| 3. | ○ | ○ |
| 4. | ○ | ○ |
| 5. | ○ | ○ |
| 6. | ○ | ○ |
| 7. | ○ | ○ |
| 8. | ○ | ○ |
| 9. | ○ | ○ |
| 10. | ○ | ○ |
| 11. | ○ | ○ |
| 12. | ○ | ○ |
| 13. | ○ | ○ |
| 14. | ○ | ○ |
| 15. | ○ | ○ |

Name ______________________ **Homework Master**

Make ten spelling words by using the letters in the soup bowl. You may use some letters more than once. Write the words on the lines.

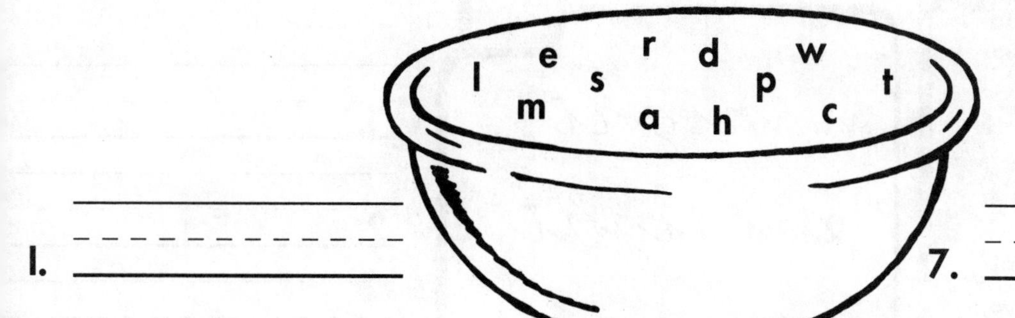


1. ______________
2. ______________
3. ______________
4. ______________
5. ______________
6. ______________
7. ______________
8. ______________
9. ______________
10. ______________

Unscramble the letters to make spelling words. Write them on the lines.

1. v e a l e ______________
2. n a m e ______________
3. h a t e ______________
4. s t e w e ______________

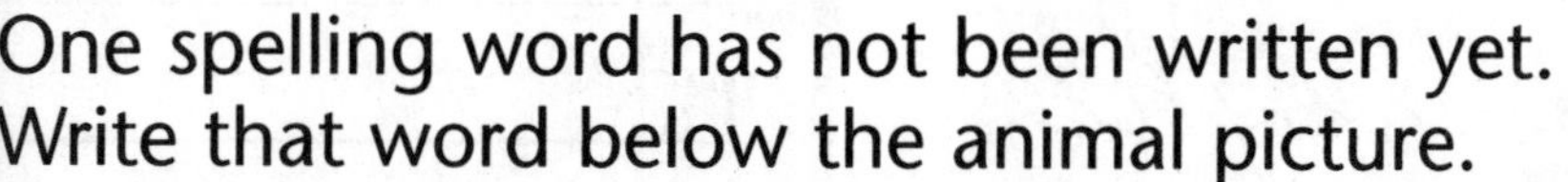

One spelling word has not been written yet.
Write that word below the animal picture. ______________

Unit 10

Home Study Master

Name ______________________

Long i: i, igh

1. night
2. bright
3. find
4. light
5. wild
6. high
7. blind
8. fight
9. sight
10. kind
11. sign
12. knight
13. mild
14. right
15. sigh

1. ______
2. ______
3. ______
4. ______
5. ______
6. ______
7. ______
8. ______
9. ______
10. ______
11. ______
12. ______
13. ______
14. ______
15. ______

## And That's How It Happened

To introduce this creative writing activity, you might want to read some of Rudyard Kipling's *Just So Stories* to your child. These stories are whimsical explanations of how some things came to be, such as why the elephant has a long trunk. Help your child think of something about the world that he or she would like to explain. If necessary, you might suggest one of the following topics:

- Why rabbits have cottontails
- Why the seasons change
- What causes the wind to blow

Name ______________________

# Hoja para estudiar en casa

## Long i: i, igh

1. *night* noche
2. *bright* brillante; inteligente
3. *find* hallar
4. *light* luz; ligero
5. *wild* salvaje
6. *high* alto
7. *blind* ciego
8. *fight* pelear; peleo
9. *sight* vista
10. *kind* amable; especie
11. *sign* letrero; señal
12. *knight* caballero (de la edad media)
13. *mild* manso
14. *right* derecha; correcto
15. *sigh* suspirar; suspiro

1. ______
2. ______
3. ______
4. ______
5. ______
6. ______
7. ______
8. ______
9. ______
10. ______
11. ______
12. ______
13. ______
14. ______
15. ______

### Y así fue cómo pasó

Para comenzar esta actividad de escritura creadora, podrían leer a su hijo o hija algunos de los cuentos de *Just So Stories* de Rudyard Kipling. Estos cuentos son explicaciones divertidas de acontecimientos naturales; por ejemplo: Por qué tiene el elefante una trompa larga. Ayuden a su hijo o hija a pensar en algo natural que quiere explicar. Puedan sugerir unos de los tópicos siguientes:

- Por qué los conejos tienen colas de algodón
- Por qué cambian las estaciones
- Qué hace soplar el viento

Name ____________________

**Unit 10**
**Practice Master**

| | | | |
|---|---|---|---|
| 1. kind | 3. sign | 5. night | 7. light |
| 2. mild | 4. high | 6. right | 8. bright |

**A.** Words that are opposites are called **antonyms**. Write the spelling word that is an antonym for each word.

**1.** day ____________________

**2.** mean ____________________

**3.** left ____________________

**4.** low ____________________

**5.** heavy ____________________

**6.** dim ____________________

**B.** Write the spelling words in a-b-c order.

**1.** ____________________

**2.** ____________________

**3.** ____________________

**4.** ____________________

**5.** ____________________

**6.** ____________________

**7.** ____________________

**8.** ____________________

Name ______________________________

| | | | |
|---|---|---|---|
| kind | sign | night | light |
| mild | high | right | bright |

**C.** Write the spelling word to solve each riddle.

**1.** I give useful information. What am I? ______________

**2.** I'm not left or wrong. What am I? ______________

**3.** I come after day. What am I? ______________

**D.** Use this code to find spelling words. Write the words.

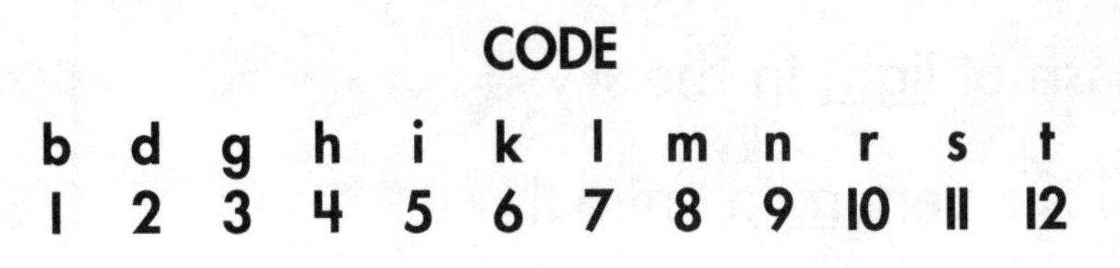

**CODE**

| b | d | g | h | i | k | l | m | n | r | s | t |
|---|---|---|---|---|---|---|---|---|---|---|---|
| 1 | 2 | 3 | 4 | 5 | 6 | 7 | 8 | 9 | 10 | 11 | 12 |

**1.** 11-5-3-9 ______________

**2.** 1-10-5-3-4-12 ______________

**3.** 6-5-9-2 ______________

**4.** 4-5-3-4 ______________

**5.** 7-5-3-4-12 ______________

**6.** 8-5-7-2 ______________

**7.** 10-5-3-4-12 ______________

**8.** 9-5-3-4-12 ______________

Unit 10

Name ____________________ **Test Master**

Read each sentence. Look at the underlined spelling word. Fill in a circle. Show if the word is spelled **Right** or **Wrong**.

**Sample**

The falling snow was a beautiful sight. — Right ● Wrong ○

**Answer Box**

| | | | Right | Wrong |
|---|---|---|---|---|
| 1. | Do you know a song about three blind mice? | 1. | ○ | ○ |
| 2. | The sun is very bright today. | 2. | ○ | ○ |
| 3. | Most rabbits don't like to figth. | 3. | ○ | ○ |
| 4. | I can't find my glasses. | 4. | ○ | ○ |
| 5. | Those clouds are hy in the sky. | 5. | ○ | ○ |
| 6. | Do you know what kind of fruit this is? | 6. | ○ | ○ |
| 7. | We saw a flash of light in the sky. | 7. | ○ | ○ |
| 8. | A little lamb is a very mild animal. | 8. | ○ | ○ |
| 9. | Did the knite in the story ride on a horse? | 9. | ○ | ○ |
| 10. | The stars and moon can be seen at night. | 10. | ○ | ○ |
| 11. | The turn you want is on the right. | 11. | ○ | ○ |
| 12. | He gave a sigh when he finally finished. | 12. | ○ | ○ |
| 13. | Leaves changing color is a siet you should see. | 13. | ○ | ○ |
| 14. | We didn't see the sighn at the corner. | 14. | ○ | ○ |
| 15. | A bear is a wilde animal. | 15. | ○ | ○ |

Unit **10** **Homework Master**

Name ______________________________

Use the letters on the leaves to make spelling words. Write one spelling on each petal.

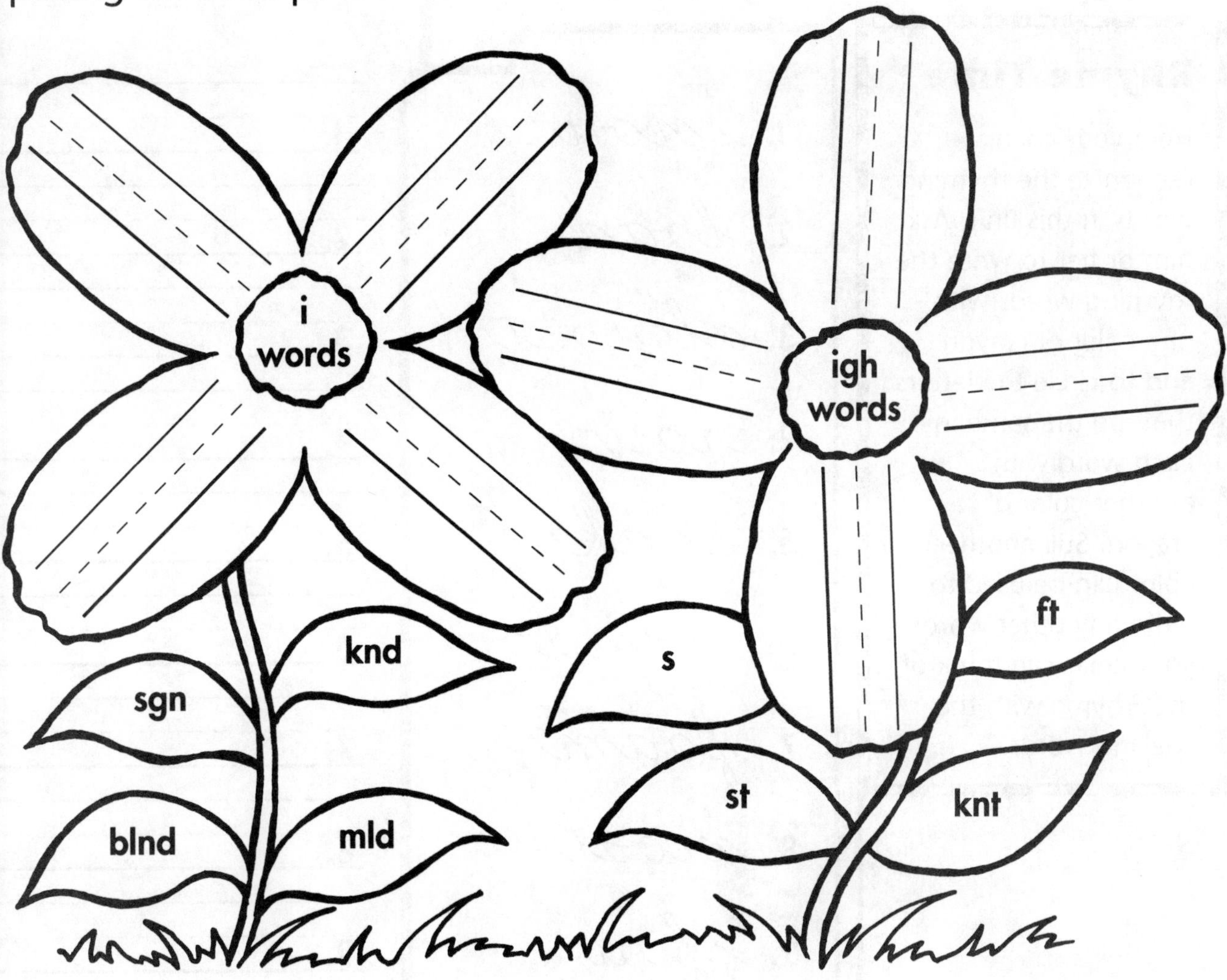


Finish the sentences. Use antonyms for the words in dark print. The first one is done as an example.

1. The opposite of **day** is night.
2. The opposite of **dim** is ____________.
3. The opposite of **tame** is ____________.
4. The opposite of **left** is ____________.
5. The opposite of **lose** is ____________.
6. The opposite of **low** is ____________.
7. The opposite of **dark** is ____________.

Name ________________________

Unit 11
**Home Study Master**

## Long o: ow, oa, o

### Rhyme Time

Help your child recognize the rhyming words in this unit. Ask him or her to write the rhyming words with one color of crayon and to circle the letters that are the same in each word with another color of crayon. Still another color can be used to write any other words your child can think of that rhyme with the spelling words.

1. snow
2. load
3. almost
4. row
5. soak
6. window
7. foam
8. most
9. flow
10. goat
11. throw
12. float
13. blow
14. below
15. soap

1. ______
2. ______
3. ______
4. ______
5. ______
6. ______
7. ______
8. ______
9. ______
10. ______
11. ______
12. ______
13. ______
14. ______
15. ______

Name ____________________

# Hoja para estudiar en casa

## Long o: ow, oa, o

### La hora de rimas

Ayuden a su hijo o hija a reconocer las palabras que riman en esta unidad. Pídanle que deletree las palabras que riman con un creyón de un color y que circule las letras que son iguales con un creyón de otro color. Su hijo o hija debe pensar en otras palabras que riman con las palabras de la lección y puede escribirlas con un creyón de diferente color.

1. snow — nevar; nieve
2. load — cargar; carga
3. almost — casi
4. row — fila; remar
5. soak — remojar
6. window — ventana
7. foam — espuma
8. most — la mayoría
9. flow — fluir; flujo
10. goat — cabra
11. throw — tirar
12. float — flotar
13. blow — soplar; golpe
14. below — debajo
15. soap — jabón

1. ____________________
2. ____________________
3. ____________________
4. ____________________
5. ____________________
6. ____________________
7. ____________________
8. ____________________
9. ____________________
10. ____________________
11. ____________________
12. ____________________
13. ____________________
14. ____________________
15. ____________________

Name ______________________

Unit 11 **Practice Master**

| | | | |
|---|---|---|---|
| 1. row | 3. below | 5. soap | 7. float |
| 2. snow | 4. window | 6. goat | 8. almost |

**A.** Write the spelling word in each group that has the **long o** sound.

**1.** soup, soap, still ______

**2.** goat, give, got ______

**3.** run, rock, row ______

**4.** sniff, snow, snap ______

**B.** Unscramble the letters to make spelling words. Write the words. The first letter of each word is in dark print to get you started.

**1.** don**w**iw ______

**2.** l**a**msot ______

**3.** **b**oelw ______

**4.** ta**f**lo ______

**C.** Replace the underlined part of each sentence with a spelling word.

**1.** We are <u>just about</u> ready to start. ______

**2.** Please put these desks in a <u>straight line</u>. ______

Name ______________________________

| | | | |
|---|---|---|---|
| row | below | soap | float |
| snow | window | goat | almost |

**D.** Write the spelling words on the kite tails. Write each group in a-b-c order. Each word must have the spelling pattern shown on the kite.

Name ____________________

Read each sentence. Look at the underlined spelling word. Fill in a circle. Show if the word is spelled **Right** or **Wrong**.

**Sample**

| | Right | Wrong |
|---|---|---|
| The bridge was too low for the large truck. | ● | ○ |

1. By noon, Phil was allmost done with his work.
2. He planted flowers beelow his window.
3. The wind began to blow very hard.
4. It is easy to flot in the pool.
5. Honey will flow slowly if it is cold.
6. There was a lot of foam on top of his soda.
7. A baby gote is called a kid.
8. The mule can carry a heavy load.
9. Of all my friends, I like Jill the mowst.
10. The houses were in a long row.
11. We rode our sled in the snow.
12. Sandra had to saok her sore thumb.
13. Use soap and water to get clean.
14. She can thro a ball a long way.
15. I opened my window to get fresh air.

**Answer Box**

| | Right | Wrong |
|---|---|---|
| 1. | ○ | ○ |
| 2. | ○ | ○ |
| 3. | ○ | ○ |
| 4. | ○ | ○ |
| 5. | ○ | ○ |
| 6. | ○ | ○ |
| 7. | ○ | ○ |
| 8. | ○ | ○ |
| 9. | ○ | ○ |
| 10. | ○ | ○ |
| 11. | ○ | ○ |
| 12. | ○ | ○ |
| 13. | ○ | ○ |
| 14. | ○ | ○ |
| 15. | ○ | ○ |

Name ____________________

Write the spelling words on the kite tails. Write each group in a-b-c order. Each word must have the spelling pattern shown on the kite.

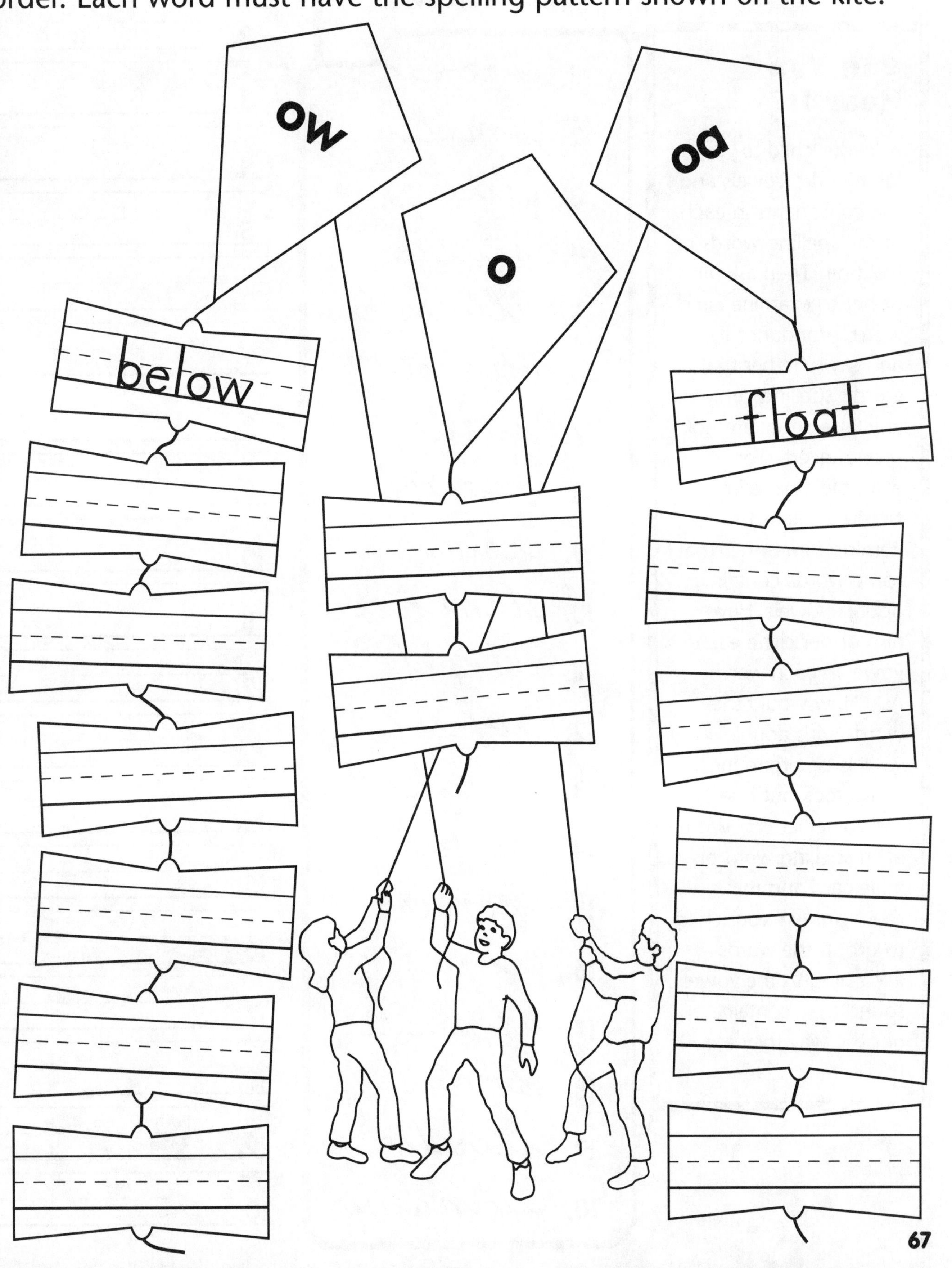

Name ______________________

Unit 12

**Home Study Master**

## Can You Hear It?

Ask your child to identify the vowels and the consonants in each of the spelling words in this unit. Then ask him or her to examine each word, pronounce it, and say whether that word's spelling contains any letters that are not pronounced. (For example, final **e** in **broke** is silent.) Remind him or her that some words contain double vowels. Have him or her circle each vowel in each word. Ask: How would the words with double vowels be pronounced if you took out one of the vowel letters? Write each spelling word on a file card and mix them up. Ask your child to group the words according to the vowel sound they contain, not the way they are spelled.

## Assessment and Review

1. broke
2. smile
3. close
4. state
5. always
6. chain
7. laid
8. maybe
9. real
10. teacher
11. street
12. wheels
13. bright
14. mild
15. kind
16. right
17. almost
18. snow
19. float
20. window

1. ______
2. ______
3. ______
4. ______
5. ______
6. ______
7. ______
8. ______
9. ______
10. ______
11. ______
12. ______
13. ______
14. ______
15. ______
16. ______
17. ______
18. ______
19. ______
20. ______

Unit 12

Name ______________________

## Hoja para estudiar en casa

## Assessment and Review

1. broke
rompió
2. smile
sonreir(se)
3. close
cerca; cerra
4. state
estado
5. always
siempre
6. chain
cadena
7. laid
puso
8. maybe
quizás
9. real
real; verdadero
10. teacher
maestro
11. street
calle
12. wheels
ruedas
13. bright
brillante; inteligente
14. mild
manso
15. kind
amable; especie
16. right
derecha; correcto
17. almost
casi
18. snow
nevar; nieve
19. float
flotar
20. window
ventana

### ¿Lo puedes oír?

Indiquen a su hijo o hija que identifique las vocales y consonantes en cada palabra de la lista de palabras de esta unidad. Pidan que observe cada palabra para deletrear, que la pronuncie, y que diga si esa palabra contiene algunas letras que no se pronuncian. Recuérdenle que algunas palabras contienen vocales dobles. Pidan que encierre en un círculo cada vocal en cada palabra. Pregunten: ¿Qué sonido tendrían las palabras con vocales dobles si quitaras una de las letras de las vocales? Escriban cada palabra de la lista en una ficha y mézclenlas. Luego pidan a see hijo o hija que agrupe las palabras según el sonido vocálico que contengan, no según la forma en que se deletrean.

1. ______
2. ______
3. ______
4. ______
5. ______
6. ______
7. ______
8. ______
9. ______
10. ______
11. ______
12. ______
13. ______
14. ______
15. ______
16. ______
17. ______
18. ______
19. ______
20. ______

Unit 12

Test Master

Name ____________________

**A.** Look at these spelling words. Write **C** for each word that is spelled correctly. Write **NC** for each word that is not spelled correctly.

1. chain ☐
2. flot ☐
3. allways ☐
4. real ☐
5. smile ☐
6. laid ☐
7. snow ☐
8. brite ☐
9. broke ☐
10. allmost ☐
11. stat ☐
12. ryte ☐
13. techer ☐
14. window ☐
15. close ☐

**B.** Write the letter of the correct spelling that matches the dictionary respelling.

1. /mīld/ ☐
   - **a.** mild
   - **b.** milde
   - **c.** miled
2. /strēt/ ☐
   - **a.** steet
   - **b.** stret
   - **c.** street
3. /kīnd/ ☐
   - **a.** cind
   - **b.** kind
   - **c.** kinde
4. /hwēlz/ ☐
   - **a.** weels
   - **b.** wheels
   - **c.** weals
5. /**mā**′bē/ ☐
   - **a.** maybe
   - **b.** mabe
   - **c.** maby

Name ______________________

**Home Study Master** Unit 13

## sh, ch, tch, th, wr, ck

### Describe It

Describing things in detail makes it easier for listeners or readers to "see" what we are talking or writing about. Use this game to help your child practice describing.

Choose any object (or person) in the house and, without naming it, describe it for your child. Have your child listen carefully to the description and try to guess what or who you are describing. Then have your child write descriptions of three other things or people in your house and read the descriptions to you so that you can guess their identities.

1. *shape* 1. ______
2. *church* 2. ______
3. *watch* 3. ______
4. *father* 4. ______
5. *wrap* 5. ______
6. *check* 6. ______
7. *finish* 7. ______
8. *sharp* 8. ______
9. *mother* 9. ______
10. *write* 10. ______
11. *catch* 11. ______
12. *chase* 12. ______
13. *shall* 13. ______
14. *thick* 14. ______
15. *wrote* 15. ______

Name ____________________

Unit 13

## Hoja para estudiar en casa

### sh, ch, tch, th, wr, ck

### Descríbelo

Una descripción detallada facilita la comprensión porque el oyente o el lector puede "ver" la cosa de la que hablamos o de la que escribimos. Usen este juego para ayudar a su hijo o hija a practicar la descripción.

Escojan cualquier objeto (o persona) en la casa y, sin nombrarlo, descríbanlo a su hijo o hija. Pídanle que escuche la descripción con cuidado y que luego advine lo que o a quién describe. Entonces díganle que escriba descripciones de tres cosas o personas más que están en su casa y que les lea sus descripciones. Ahora les toca a Uds. adivinar sus identidades.

1. shape — forma; amoldar
2. church — iglesia
3. watch — mirar; reloj
4. father — padre
5. wrap — envolver; enroparse
6. check — cheque; verificar
7. finish — terminar
8. sharp — agudo
9. mother — madre
10. write — escribir
11. catch — agarrar; coger
12. chase — correr tras
13. shall — va a ... (indica el futuro)
14. thick — grueso
15. wrote — escribió

1. ____________________
2. ____________________
3. ____________________
4. ____________________
5. ____________________
6. ____________________
7. ____________________
8. ____________________
9. ____________________
10. ____________________
11. ____________________
12. ____________________
13. ____________________
14. ____________________
15. ____________________

Name ________________________

Unit 13 **Practice Master**

| | | | |
|---|---|---|---|
| 1. write | 3. check | 5. watch | 7. father |
| 2. shall | 4. church | 6. mother | 8. finish |

**A.** Write the spelling words in a-b-c order.

1. ________________ 5. ________________

2. ________________ 6. ________________

3. ________________ 7. ________________

4. ________________ 8. ________________

**B.** Add **sh**, **th**, or **ch** to make spelling words. Write the words.

1. __ __ a l l

4. __ __ u r __ __

2. f i n i __ __

5. f a __ __ e r

3. __ __ e c k

6. m o __ __ e r

Unit **13**

Name ______________________ **Practice Master**

| | | | |
|---|---|---|---|
| write | check | watch | father |
| shall | church | mother | finish |

**C.** Change one letter in the word to make a spelling word. Use the letters in the Lost Letter Box. Use each letter only once.

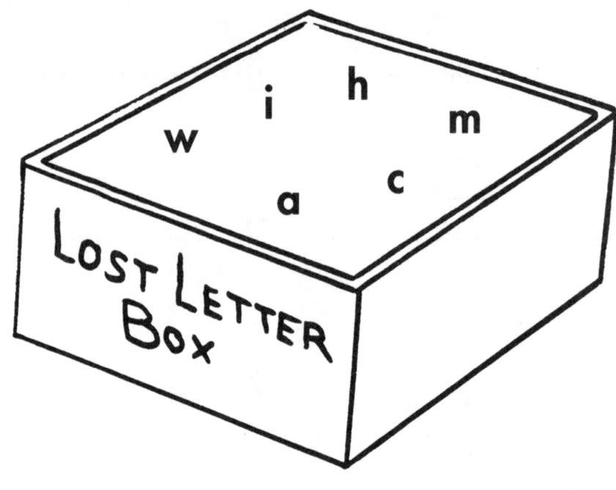


**1.** wrote ______________

**2.** shell ______________

**3.** cheek ______________

**4.** bother ______________

**5.** fatter ______________

**6.** catch ______________

**D.** Follow the path of each spelling word. Start with the letter in the box. Write the words.

**1.** 

______________

**2.** 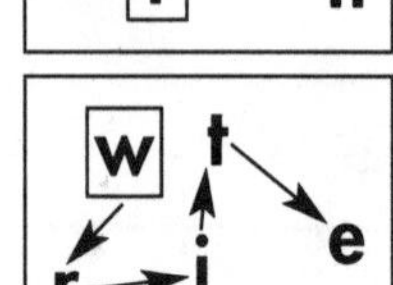

______________

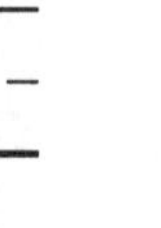

**3.** 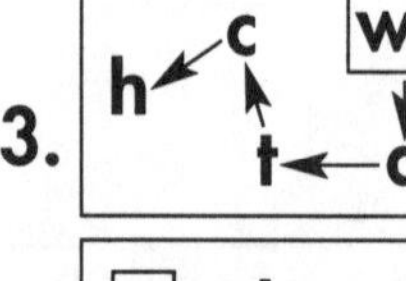

______________

**4.** s → h → a
l ← l
______________

Name ____________________

Read each sentence. Look at the underlined spelling word. Fill in a circle. Show if the word is spelled **Right** or **Wrong**.

**Sample** | Right | Wrong
**It is not polite to showt out loud.** | ○ | ●

**Answer Box**

| | Right | Wrong |
|---|---|---|
| 1. I like to play cach with my baseball. | ○ | ○ |
| 2. Little children like to chase fireflies. | ○ | ○ |
| 3. Mom had to chek the oil in the car. | ○ | ○ |
| 4. There is a bell near the top of the chirch. | ○ | ○ |
| 5. I like to help my father work on the car. | ○ | ○ |
| 6. He will soon finish his homework. | ○ | ○ |
| 7. You look a lot like your mother. | ○ | ○ |
| 8. I think that I shal fly my kite. | ○ | ○ |
| 9. The balloon was in the shap of an animal. | ○ | ○ |
| 10. The point on the pencil is very sharp. | ○ | ○ |
| 11. The branch on the tree was thik. | ○ | ○ |
| 12. I like to watch my baby sister play. | ○ | ○ |
| 13. It is fun to wrapp the gifts. | ○ | ○ |
| 14. Will you writ to me soon? | ○ | ○ |
| 15. I rote a letter to you yesterday. | ○ | ○ |

Name ______________________

Change one letter in the word to make a spelling word. Use the letters in the Lost Letter Box. Use each letter only once.

1. cheek 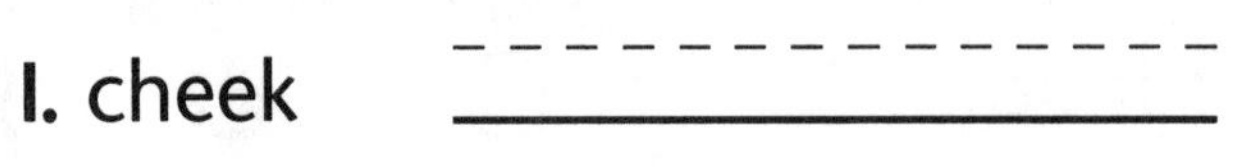

2. chose 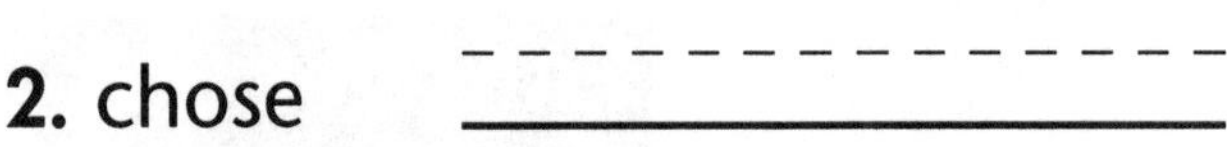

3. share 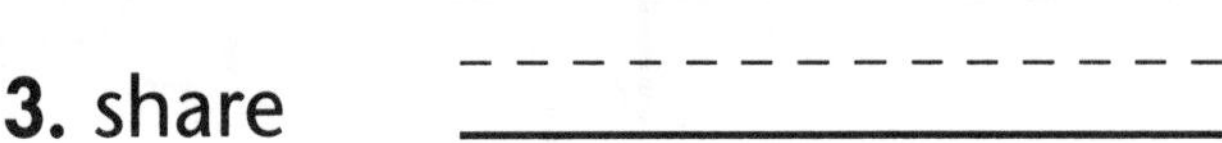

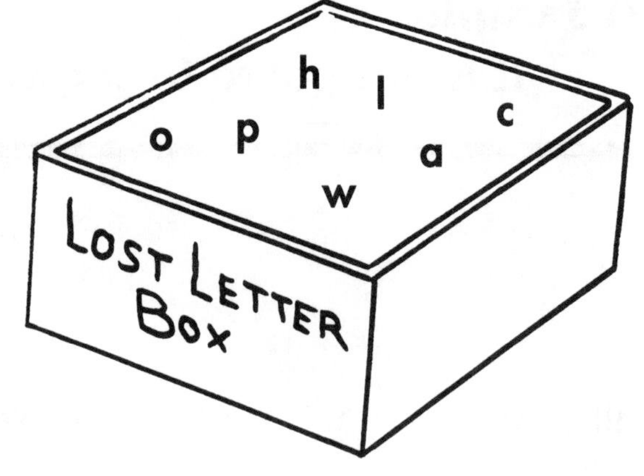


4. shawl ______________________

5. hatch ______________________

6. fatter ______________________

7. write ______________________

Write the missing letters to complete each spelling word.

1. ___ ___ i t e

2. ___ ___ u r ___ ___

3. ___ ___ i ___ ___

4. c a ___ ___ ___

5. ___ ___ a p e

6. w r ___ ___

7. f i n i ___ ___

8. m o ___ ___ e r

Name ______________________

Unit 14

**Home Study Master**

## Super Sleuth

Play a game with the spelling words by having your child name and spell a word from the clues you provide. Possible clues would be definitions, synonyms, antonyms, rhyming words, or hints to spelling patterns. Example: This word names a kind of wooden wall. (**fence**)

## Consonants: /j/, /s/

1. change
2. fence
3. space
4. age
5. center
6. large
7. since
8. price
9. page
10. ice
11. dance
12. pencil
13. slice
14. place
15. city

1. ______
2. ______
3. ______
4. ______
5. ______
6. ______
7. ______
8. ______
9. ______
10. ______
11. ______
12. ______
13. ______
14. ______
15. ______

Name ____________________

**Hoja para estudiar en casa**

## Consonants: /j/, /s/

### Super detective

En este juego su hijo o hija tiene que adivinar una palabra usando las pistas que Uds. le dan. Luego tiene que nombrar la palabra y deletrearla. Unas pistas posibles serían: (1) definiciones de palabras, (2) sinónimos, (3) antónimos, (4) palabras que riman, y (5) indicaciones de los modelos ortográficos. Por ejemplo: Esta palabra significa una clase de pared de madera. (**fence**)

1. *change* cambiar; cambio
2. *fence* cercado
3. *space* espacio
4. *age* edad; envejecer
5. *center* centro
6. *large* grande
7. *since* desde
8. *price* precio
9. *page* página
10. *ice* hielo
11. *dance* bailar; baile
12. *pencil* lápiz
13. *slice* tajada; troncha
14. *place* lugar; poner
15. *city* ciudad

1. ____________________
2. ____________________
3. ____________________
4. ____________________
5. ____________________
6. ____________________
7. ____________________
8. ____________________
9. ____________________
10. ____________________
11. ____________________
12. ____________________
13. ____________________
14. ____________________
15. ____________________

Name ______________________

Unit 14 **Practice Master**

| | | | |
|---|---|---|---|
| 1. age | 3. change | 5. since | 7. dance |
| 2. large | 4. ice | 6. place | 8. city |

**A.** Write the spelling word to answer each question.

1. What do you do when you listen to music? ______________
2. What is another name for a very large town? ______________
3. What word rhymes with **prince**? ______________
4. What do you put into a drink to make it very cold? ______________
5. What word rhymes with **race**? ______________

**B.** Write the spelling words in which the **j** sound is spelled **g**.

______________

______________

______________

Name ______________________

| age | change | since | dance |
|---|---|---|---|
| large | ice | place | city |

**C.** Write the spelling word to solve each riddle.

**1.** What goes up and never comes down? ______________

**2.** What is the hardest thing about learning to skate? ______________

**3.** Why did the woman have her pocketbook open? (She was expecting some ____ in the weather.) ______________

**D.** Use spelling words to complete the puzzles.

_ _ a _ _ e

i

_ e

y

p _ a _ e

_ i _ _ e

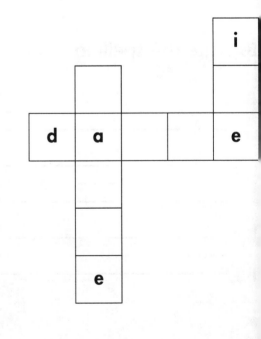

i

d a _ _ e

_ e

Unit **14**

**Test Master**

Name ______________________________

Read each sentence. Look at the underlined spelling word. Fill in a circle. Show if the word is spelled **Right** or **Wrong**.

**Sample**
She had a pleasant smile on her <u>fase</u>. Right ○ Wrong ●

1. Do you know the <u>age</u> of that house?
2. Put a dot in the <u>sentre</u> of the circle.
3. I got wet in the pool, so I must <u>change</u> clothes.
4. We shop for groceries in the <u>city</u>.
5. The school <u>danse</u> will be tomorrow night.
6. My brother and I painted the <u>fence</u> white.
7. Would you like some <u>ice</u> for your juice?
8. The new pants were too <u>larje</u> for him.
9. Which <u>page</u> tells about pet care?
10. Make sure you have a sharp <u>pensil</u>.
11. Do you know which <u>place</u> has the best books?
12. I will buy that bike if the <u>price</u> is right.
13. How long has it been <u>cince</u> you have eaten?
14. I would like a large <u>slice</u> of watermelon.
15. The strange ship came from outer <u>space</u>.

**Answer Box**

| | Right | Wrong |
|---|---|---|
| 1. | ○ | ○ |
| 2. | ○ | ○ |
| 3. | ○ | ○ |
| 4. | ○ | ○ |
| 5. | ○ | ○ |
| 6. | ○ | ○ |
| 7. | ○ | ○ |
| 8. | ○ | ○ |
| 9. | ○ | ○ |
| 10. | ○ | ○ |
| 11. | ○ | ○ |
| 12. | ○ | ○ |
| 13. | ○ | ○ |
| 14. | ○ | ○ |
| 15. | ○ | ○ |

Name ______________________________

Finish each puzzle. Use spelling words.

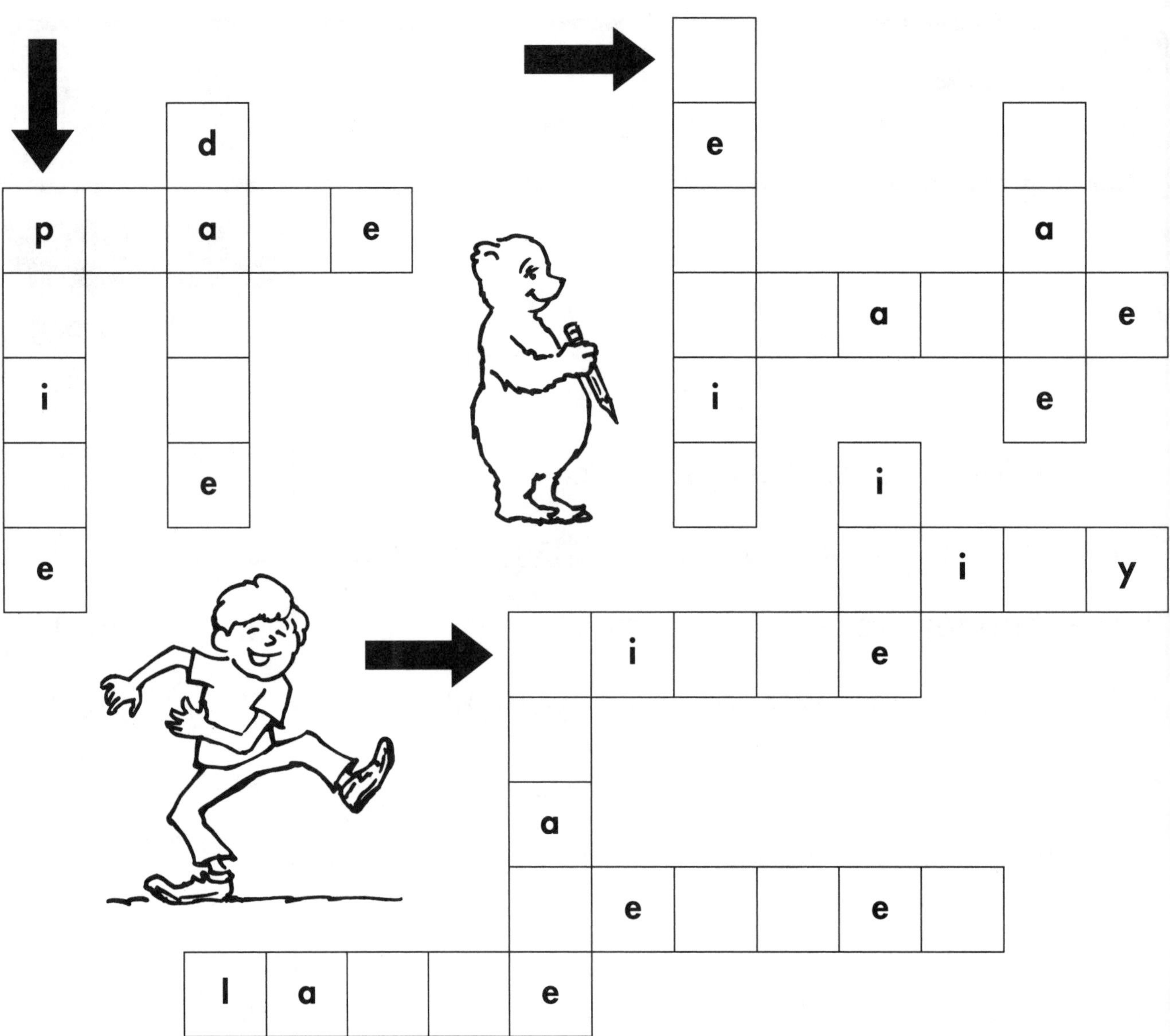


Complete the sentences. Use spelling words.

**1.** I would like a ____ of bread. ______________

**2.** Roses are in front of the wooden ____. ______________

**3.** Please tell me your birthday and your ____. ______________

Name ____________________

## Digraphs, Clusters

### Treasure Hunt

Have your child pretend that he or she is a pirate and has hidden a treasure somewhere in or near your house.

Ask your child to write directions to find the treasure. Tell him or her to list all of the directions in the proper order so that you will be able to find it. Your child may also include a map.

1. *shook* 
2. *flash*
3. *speech*
4. *think*
5. *strong*
6. *cloth*
7. *brook*
8. *stitch*
9. *string*
10. *scratch*
11. *fresh*
12. *spring*
13. *switch*
14. *stretch*
15. *splash*

1. ____________________
2. ____________________
3. ____________________
4. ____________________
5. ____________________
6. ____________________
7. ____________________
8. ____________________
9. ____________________
10. ____________________
11. ____________________
12. ____________________
13. ____________________
14. ____________________
15. ____________________

Name ______________________

**Hoja para estudiar en casa** Unit 15

## Búsqueda de tesoro

Pídanle a su hijo o hija que pretenda que es pirata y que ha escondido un tesoro en un lugar dentro o cerca de su casa.

Díganle que escriba instrucciones para llegar al tesoro. Pídanle que haga una lista de todas las instrucciones en orden lógico para que Uds. puedan hallar el tesoro. También puede incluir un mapa.

## Digraphs, Clusters

1. *shook* sacudió; tembló
2. *flash* rayo
3. *speech* discurso
4. *think* pensar
5. *strong* fuerte
6. *cloth* tela
7. *brook* arroyo
8. *stitch* coser
9. *string* cuerdecilla
10. *scratch* rasguñar; rasguño
11. *fresh* fresco
12. *spring* primavera; saltar
13. *switch* cambiar
14. *stretch* estirar(se)
15. *splash* chapoteo; chapotear

1. ______________________
2. ______________________
3. ______________________
4. ______________________
5. ______________________
6. ______________________
7. ______________________
8. ______________________
9. ______________________
10. ______________________
11. ______________________
12. ______________________
13. ______________________
14. ______________________
15. ______________________

Unit 15

Practice Master

Name ______________________________

| | | | |
|---|---|---|---|
| 1. shook | 3. splash | 5. stretch | 7. strong |
| 2. fresh | 4. speech | 6. think | 8. cloth |

**A.** Write the spelling words in a-b-c order.

**1.** ____________________ **5.** ____________________

**2.** ____________________ **6.** ____________________

**3.** ____________________ **7.** ____________________

**4.** ____________________ **8.** ____________________

**B.** Write the spelling word that belongs in each sentence.

**1.** Mom ____ the rug. ____________________

**2.** I had to ____ about the answer. ____________________

**3.** Use this ____ to wash the windows. ____________________

**4.** The heavy rope was very ____. ____________________

Name ______________________

| | | | |
|---|---|---|---|
| shook | splash | stretch | strong |
| fresh | speech | think | cloth |

**C.** Write the spelling words that end with **ch** or **sh** digraphs. Circle the consonant cluster in each of the words.

1. ______________________ 3. ______________________

2. ______________________ 4. ______________________

**D.** Use spelling words to complete the puzzle.

s
_ t _ o _ g
s o
_ _ i n _
r
s p _ e _ _
t l
o
h

Unit 15
Test Master

Name ______________________________

Read each sentence. Look at the underlined spelling word. Fill in a circle. Show if the word is spelled **Right** or **Wrong**.

**Sample**
**Let's count the stripes on the flag.**

| | Right | Wrong |
|---|---|---|
| Sample | ● | ○ |

1. A rubber band can stritch very far.
2. He waxed his car with a clean cloth.
3. We saw a bright flash of light in the sky.
4. Nothing tastes better than fresh fruit.
5. A cat can scrach with its hind leg.
6. We shook the paint can before we opened it.
7. The mayor gave a speach.
8. The dog went into the pool with a splash.
9. Many pretty flowers bloom in the spring.
10. My dad can stich the cuff of my pants.
11. We built a bridge across the bruk.
12. My cat likes to play with a ball of string.
13. A steel beam is very stronge.
14. We can switch seats at the next stop.
15. Do you think that we'll be done on time?

**Answer Box**

| | Right | Wrong |
|---|---|---|
| 1. | ○ | ○ |
| 2. | ○ | ○ |
| 3. | ○ | ○ |
| 4. | ○ | ○ |
| 5. | ○ | ○ |
| 6. | ○ | ○ |
| 7. | ○ | ○ |
| 8. | ○ | ○ |
| 9. | ○ | ○ |
| 10. | ○ | ○ |
| 11. | ○ | ○ |
| 12. | ○ | ○ |
| 13. | ○ | ○ |
| 14. | ○ | ○ |
| 15. | ○ | ○ |

Name ________________________________

Look for hidden spelling words. Read across and down. Circle each word.

| | | | | | | | | | | | |
|---|---|---|---|---|---|---|---|---|---|---|---|
| s | p | l | a | s | h | k | l | s | a | s | m |
| t | o | t | c | h | s | i | m | p | c | o | o |
| r | s | o | i | s | w | n | o | r | t | m | t |
| e | p | s | h | c | i | s | t | i | t | c | h |
| t | e | a | c | r | t | h | i | n | k | t | s |
| c | e | d | s | a | c | o | s | g | r | h | p |
| h | c | l | o | t | h | f | l | a | s | h | l |
| i | h | e | a | c | n | o | n | f | c | n | a |
| l | o | n | p | h | t | c | h | o | l | k | s |

Underline the five spelling words in the tongue twisters. Then try to say the tongue twisters.

1. Sharon shook seven sore hands.
2. Fred will fry fresh fish for free.
3. By the brook, Brenda broke a bright blue balloon.
4. This thick string is strong.

Name ______________________

Unit 16

**Home Study Master**

## Spelling Banner

Help your child make a spelling banner. Have him or her write each spelling word on an index card and punch a hole in the top of the card. Provide shoelaces or yarn so that he or she can lace the cards together in groups according to the spellings of the long vowel sounds. Help your child hang the banner and encourage him or her to read and spell from it frequently. Occasionally you might also suggest that your child write the groups of words.

## The Schwa Sound

1. afraid
2. around
3. upon
4. never
5. open
6. animal
7. ever
8. about
9. again
10. another
11. couple
12. awake
13. over
14. asleep
15. above

1. ______
2. ______
3. ______
4. ______
5. ______
6. ______
7. ______
8. ______
9. ______
10. ______
11. ______
12. ______
13. ______
14. ______
15. ______

Name ______________________

Unit 16

**Hoja para estudiar en casa**

## Una banderola

Ayuden a su hijo o hija a hacer una banderola. Pídanle que escriba cada palabra en una ficha y perforen las fichas. Dénle lazos de zapato o hilado para atar las fichas en grupos según el deletreo de los sonidos largos de las vocales. Ayúdenlo/a a colgar la banderola y anímenlo/a a que lea y deletree las palabras en la banderola a menudo. A veces pueden sugerir que su hijo o hija escriba los grupos de palabras.

## The Schwa Sound

1. *afraid* — asustado; (tiene) miedo
2. *around* — alrededor
3. *upon* — en; sobre
4. *never* — nunca
5. *open* — abierto
6. *animal* — animal
7. *ever* — jamás; siempre
8. *about* — sobre; de
9. *again* — otra vez
10. *another* — otro
11. *couple* — pareja
12. *awake* — despertado
13. *over* — acabado; por encima de
14. *asleep* — dormido
15. *above* — encima

1. ______________________
2. ______________________
3. ______________________
4. ______________________
5. ______________________
6. ______________________
7. ______________________
8. ______________________
9. ______________________
10. ______________________
11. ______________________
12. ______________________
13. ______________________
14. ______________________
15. ______________________

Unit 16

Practice Master

Name ______________________

| | | | |
|---|---|---|---|
| 1. about | 3. around | 5. never | 7. open |
| 2. again | 4. another | 6. over | 8. animal |

**A.** Write the spelling words in a-b-c order.

1. ______________________
2. ______________________
3. ______________________
4. ______________________
5. ______________________
6. ______________________
7. ______________________
8. ______________________

**B.** Write the spelling word that goes with each meaning.

1. once more ______________________
2. in a circular path ______________________
3. a different one ______________________
4. a dog or cat ______________________

Name ____________________

Unit 16 Practice Master

| about | around | never | open |
| --- | --- | --- | --- |
| again | another | over | animal |

**C.** Write the spelling word that is an antonym for each word.

**1.** close ____________________

**2.** under ____________________

**3.** always ____________________

**D.** Read across and down to find spelling words hidden in the puzzle. Circle and write the words.

| b | a | n | i | m | a | l | a | p | r | e |
| --- | --- | --- | --- | --- | --- | --- | --- | --- | --- | --- |
| o | i | e | k | h | g | w | b | c | m | l |
| p | o | v | e | r | a | r | o | u | n | d |
| w | p | e | t | a | i | d | u | x | o | z |
| q | e | r | l | w | n | t | t | j | g | f |
| a | n | o | t | h | e | r | s | s | i | t |

**1.** ____________________

**2.** ____________________

**3.** ____________________

**4.** ____________________

**5.** ____________________

**6.** ____________________

**7.** ____________________

**8.** ____________________

Unit **16**

**Test Master**

Name ____________________

Read each sentence. Look at the underlined spelling word. Fill in a circle. Show if the word is spelled **Right** or **Wrong**.

**Sample**

Is there <u>eny</u> more soup left? — Right ○ Wrong ●

**Answer Box**

1. I am not <u>afraid</u> of dogs.
2. The young man was <u>about</u> six feet tall.
3. A horse is my favorite <u>animel</u>.
4. The clown did the trick <u>agian</u>.
5. A small clock hung <u>above</u> the fireplace.
6. Jan would like <u>another</u> apple.
7. We will get there <u>arownd</u> eight o'clock.
8. It is about time for the baby to fall <u>asleep</u>.
9. What time will you be <u>awake</u> tomorrow?
10. The young <u>cuple</u> went roller-skating.
11. Did you <u>evre</u> tell a tall tale?
12. The ocean will <u>never</u> run out of salt.
13. Please do not leave the door <u>open</u>.
14. He hit the baseball <u>over</u> the fence.
15. The kitten slept <u>upun</u> my bed.

| | Right | Wrong |
|---|---|---|
| 1. | ○ | ○ |
| 2. | ○ | ○ |
| 3. | ○ | ○ |
| 4. | ○ | ○ |
| 5. | ○ | ○ |
| 6. | ○ | ○ |
| 7. | ○ | ○ |
| 8. | ○ | ○ |
| 9. | ○ | ○ |
| 10. | ○ | ○ |
| 11. | ○ | ○ |
| 12. | ○ | ○ |
| 13. | ○ | ○ |
| 14. | ○ | ○ |
| 15. | ○ | ○ |

Unit **16**

Name ____________________ **Homework Master**

Complete each sentence. Use a spelling word.

1. **Awake** means the opposite of ____________
2. **Close** means the opposite of ____________
3. **Under** means the opposite of ____________
4. **Brave** means the opposite of ____________
5. **Below** means the opposite of ____________
6. **Always** means the opposite of ____________

Follow the lines from one egg to another. Try to find nine spelling words. Write each word. You may use each letter many times.

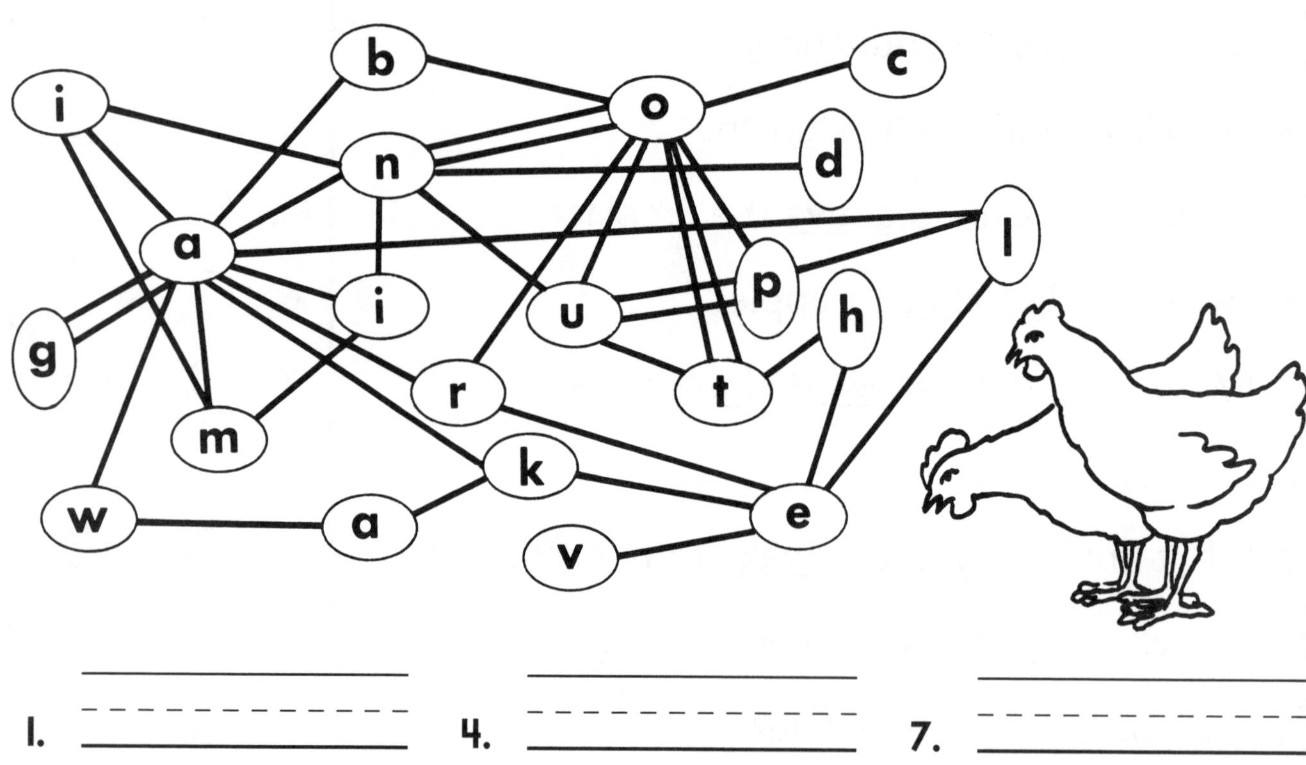


1. ____________
2. ____________
3. ____________
4. ____________
5. ____________
6. ____________
7. ____________
8. ____________
9. ____________

Name ____________________

## Home Study Master

### Use Spelling Clues

Using clues to spell words is not only stimulating for your child, it is also more effective than memorizing them. You might want to encourage your child to invent her or his own activity in which spelling clues are used.

### Words Writers Use

1. friend
2. very
3. people
4. your
5. after
6. busy
7. other
8. were
9. should
10. once
11. would
12. sure
13. little
14. every
15. could

1. ____________________
2. ____________________
3. ____________________
4. ____________________
5. ____________________
6. ____________________
7. ____________________
8. ____________________
9. ____________________
10. ____________________
11. ____________________
12. ____________________
13. ____________________
14. ____________________
15. ____________________

Name ____________________

**Hoja para estudiar en casa** Unit 17

## Words Writers Use

1. friend — amigo
2. very — muy
3. people — gente; personas
4. your — tu; su
5. after — después
6. busy — ocupado
7. other — otro
8. were — fueron; eran; estuvieron
9. should — debe
10. once — una vez
11. would — expresa el condicional
12. sure — seguro
13. little — pequeño; poco
14. every — cada
15. could — podía

1. ____________________
2. ____________________
3. ____________________
4. ____________________
5. ____________________
6. ____________________
7. ____________________
8. ____________________
9. ____________________
10. ____________________
11. ____________________
12. ____________________
13. ____________________
14. ____________________
15. ____________________

### El uso de pistas

El uso de pistas no es sólo más interesante para su hijo o hija; es también más eficaz que el uso de la memoria. Quizás quisieran animar a su hijo o hija a que invente una actividad en la cual usa pistas para deletrear.

Name ______________________

| | | | |
|---|---|---|---|
| 1. other | 3. once | 5. friend | 7. could |
| 2. were | 4. little | 6. would | 8. people |

**A.** Letters are missing from these spelling words. Write the words.

**1.** w __ r __ ______________ **5.** p __ __ ple ______________

**2.** fr __ __ nd ______________ **6.** __ ther ______________

**3.** on __ e ______________ **7.** w __ __ ld ______________

**4.** c __ __ ld ______________ **8.** li __ __ le ______________

**B.** Circle the misspelled word in each sentence. Write each word correctly.

**1.** My best freind lives next door.

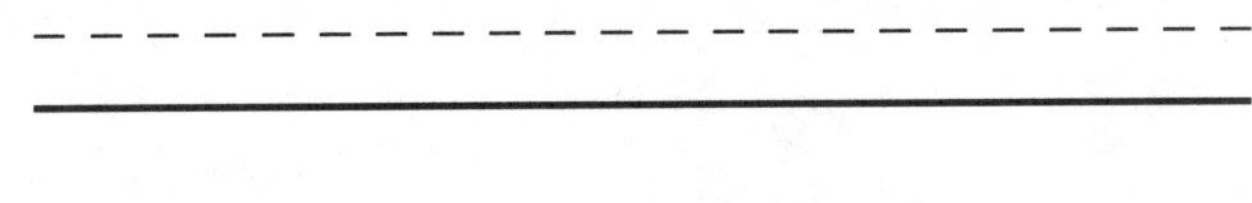

**2.** Many peple work in a city.

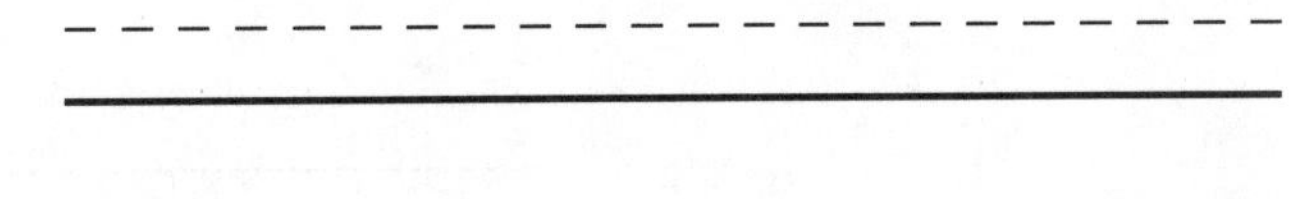

**3.** Wer you afraid of my cat? ______________

**4.** This bike is too littel for me. ______________

Name ______________________

Unit 17 **Practice Master**

| other | once | friend | could |
|---|---|---|---|
| were | little | would | people |

**C.** Write the spelling words that rhyme.

**1.** ______________________ **2.** ______________________

**D.** Use spelling words to complete each puzzle.

l
f r _ _ _ d
t
t
e

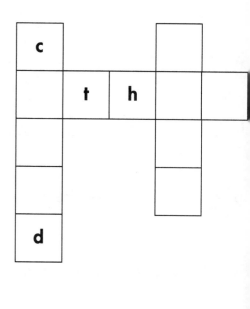

c
_ t h _ _
d

p _ _ p _ _
n

Unit **17**

**Test Master**

Name ______________________________

Read each sentence. Look at the underlined spelling word. Fill in a circle. Show if the word is spelled **Right** or **Wrong**.

**Sample** — Right / Wrong

The student <u>askt</u> her teacher a question. ○ ●

**Answer Box**

| Sentence | | Right | Wrong |
|---|---|---|---|
| 1. We went to the store <u>after</u> dinner. | 1. | ○ | ○ |
| 2. I will make a cake if I'm not too <u>bisy</u>. | 2. | ○ | ○ |
| 3. I wish that I <u>cud</u> have more carrots. | 3. | ○ | ○ |
| 4. He brushes his teeth after <u>evry</u> meal. | 4. | ○ | ○ |
| 5. We played football with our new <u>freind</u>. | 5. | ○ | ○ |
| 6. I went swimming with the <u>litle</u> children. | 6. | ○ | ○ |
| 7. We went horseback riding <u>once</u>. | 7. | ○ | ○ |
| 8. They took a bus to the <u>other</u> side of town. | 8. | ○ | ○ |
| 9. Many <u>peopel</u> went to the beach. | 9. | ○ | ○ |
| 10. I know that I <u>should</u> rest for a while. | 10. | ○ | ○ |
| 11. That soup is <u>veri</u> hot. | 11. | ○ | ○ |
| 12. Make <u>sure</u> that you lock the back door. | 12. | ○ | ○ |
| 13. The students <u>were</u> ready to go home. | 13. | ○ | ○ |
| 14. My teacher said that he <u>wood</u> help me. | 14. | ○ | ○ |
| 15. Remember to take <u>your</u> toys home. | 15. | ○ | ○ |

Unit 17

**Homework Master**

Name ______________________

Circle the misspelled word in each sentence. Write each word correctly on the line.

1. We will paint aftr we clean the walls.
2. Today is a viry hot day.
3. Evre spring we go on a class trip.
4. My best freind lives next door.
5. Many peple work in a city.
6. Wer you afraid of my cat?
7. Is this yuor desk?
8. Wons I saw a fawn in the woods.
9. I woud like you to play with me.
10. This bike is too littel for me.

Find the hidden spelling words. Circle each word.

| | | | | | | | | | |
|---|---|---|---|---|---|---|---|---|---|
| c | a | s | g | o | c | h | a | n | m |
| w | h | y | i | z | o | t | h | e | r |
| a | s | k | v | b | u | s | y | a | s |
| s | o | m | e | p | l | u | t | d | e |
| s | h | o | u | l | d | r | e | a | d |
| a | t | o | h | a | v | e | n | o | f |

Unit 18

Name ________________________

**Home Study Master**

## Assessment and Review

1. father
2. finish
3. mother
4. write
5. change
6. place
7. large
8. since
9. splash
10. strong
11. stretch
12. think
13. again
14. another
15. animal
16. around
17. friend
18. people
19. once
20. would

### Scrambled Words

Write each word on the spelling list of this unit backwards. Give your child the list and ask him or her to rewrite each word correctly. He or she may refer to the spelling list for help. If he or she does this easily, rewrite the list but mix up the letters in each word. Have your child unscramble the letters and write the words correctly.

1. ____
2. ____
3. ____
4. ____
5. ____
6. ____
7. ____
8. ____
9. ____
10. ____
11. ____
12. ____
13. ____
14. ____
15. ____
16. ____
17. ____
18. ____
19. ____
20. ____

Name ____________________

Unit 18

**Hoja para estudiar en casa**

## Palabras revueltas

Escriban al revés cada palabra de la lista de palabras para deletrear de esta unidad. Den la lista a su hijo o hija y pídanle que escriba cada palabra correctamente. Puede usar la lista de palabras de esta unidad como ayuda. Si él o ella hace esto fácilmente, escriban la lista de palabras otra vez, mezclando las letras en cada palabra. Indiquen a su hijo o hija que ponga las letras en el orden correcto.

## Assessment and Review

1. father — padre
2. finish — terminar
3. mother — madre
4. write — escribir
5. change — cambiar; cambio
6. place — lugar; poner
7. large — grande
8. since — desde
9. splash — chapoteo; chapotear
10. strong — fuerte
11. stretch — estirar(se)
12. think — pensar
13. again — otra vez
14. another — otro
15. animal — animal
16. around — alrededor
17. friend — amigo
18. people — gente; personas
19. once — una vez
20. would — expresa el condicional

1. ____________________
2. ____________________
3. ____________________
4. ____________________
5. ____________________
6. ____________________
7. ____________________
8. ____________________
9. ____________________
10. ____________________
11. ____________________
12. ____________________
13. ____________________
14. ____________________
15. ____________________
16. ____________________
17. ____________________
18. ____________________
19. ____________________
20. ____________________

Unit **18** Test Master

Name ______________________________

**A.** Write the letter of the misspelled word in each group. If no word is misspelled, write the letter **d** for none.

1. **a.** place **b.** splash **c.** larj **d.** none ☐
2. **a.** father **b.** since **c.** strong **d.** none ☐
3. **a.** stretch **b.** frend **c.** mother **d.** none ☐
4. **a.** aminal **b.** change **c.** another **d.** none ☐
5. **a.** every **b.** peeple **c.** cloth **d.** none ☐
6. **a.** could **b.** wonce **c.** would **d.** none ☐

**B.** Read each sentence. If an underlined word is misspelled, write the letter that is under the word. If no underlined words are misspelled, write the letter **d** for none.

1. I <u>think</u> (**a**) that I will <u>finich</u> (**b**) my chores and <u>write</u> (**c**) a letter. <u>none</u> (**d**) ☐

2. Let's walk <u>arownd</u> (**a**) on the <u>ice</u> (**b**) <u>again</u> (**c**). <u>none</u> (**d**) ☐

Name ____________________



## Silly Sentences

Have your child use the spelling words in silly sentences or tongue twisters in which as many of the words as possible contain the same vowel sound. Example: The **cross boss** was **lost** in the **soft straw**.

### Vowel: /ô/

1. draw
2. cost
3. dawn
4. across
5. belong
6. cross
7. soft
8. crawl
9. song
10. boss
11. straw
12. lawn
13. raw
14. lost
15. law

1. ____________________
2. ____________________
3. ____________________
4. ____________________
5. ____________________
6. ____________________
7. ____________________
8. ____________________
9. ____________________
10. ____________________
11. ____________________
12. ____________________
13. ____________________
14. ____________________
15. ____________________

Name ____________________



## Hoja para estudiar en casa

### Frases tontas

Pídanle a su hijo o hija que use las palabras de la lección en frases tontas o en trabalenguas que contienen tantas palabras como sea posible con el mismo sonido vocal. Por ejemplo: The **cross boss** was **lost** in the **soft straw**. (El amo enojado se perdió en la paja floja.)

### Vowel: /ô/

1. *draw* dibujar
2. *cost* precio; valor; cuesta
3. *dawn* amanecer
4. *across* al otro lado de
5. *belong* pertenecer a
6. *cross* cruz; cruzar; enojado
7. *soft* suave
8. *crawl* gatear
9. *song* canción
10. *boss* jefe; amo
11. *straw* paja; pajita
12. *lawn* césped
13. *raw* crudo
14. *lost* perdido; perdió
15. *law* ley

1. ____________________
2. ____________________
3. ____________________
4. ____________________
5. ____________________
6. ____________________
7. ____________________
8. ____________________
9. ____________________
10. ____________________
11. ____________________
12. ____________________
13. ____________________
14. ____________________
15. ____________________

Unit 19

Practice Master

Name ____________________

| | | | |
|---|---|---|---|
| 1. soft | 3. across | 5. belong | 7. law |
| 2. lost | 4. song | 6. draw | 8. straw |

**A.** Write the spelling word that belongs in each sentence.

1. **Find** is to **found** as **lose** is to ____. ____________

2. **Rough** is to **smooth** as **hard** is to ____. ____________

3. **Read** is to **story** as **sing** is to ____. ____________

4. **Follow** is to **rule** as **obey** is to ____. ____________

**B.** Write the spelling words that rhyme with **wrong**.

1. ____________

2. ____________

Write the spelling word that rhymes with **cost**.

3. ____________

Write the spelling words that rhyme with **raw**.

4. ____________

5. ____________

6. ____________

Name ____________________

Unit 19 **Practice Master**

| soft | across | belong | law |
|---|---|---|---|
| lost | song | draw | straw |

**C.** Write the spelling words that end with the vowel sound you hear in **saw**. Circle the letters that make that sound.

1. ____________________
2. ____________________
3. ____________________

**D.** Read each question. Unscramble the letters in dark print to make spelling words. Write the words, then answer each question. Circle **Yes** or **No**.

1. Is a cat's fur **fsto**? ____________ **Yes** **No**
2. Should you obey the **wal**? ____________ **Yes** **No**
3. Do cars go **socars** bridges? ____________ **Yes** **No**
4. Do little animals sometimes get **stlo**? ____________ **Yes** **No**
5. Do you know where the erasers **longbe**? ____________ **Yes** **No**
6. Can you be quiet and sing a **ongs**? ____________ **Yes** **No**

Unit 19

Test Master

Name ______________________

Read each sentence. Look at the underlined spelling word. Fill in a circle. Show if the word is spelled **Right** or **Wrong**.

**Sample**

I thought I saw a small bird.

| | Right | Wrong |
|---|---|---|
| Sample | ● | ○ |

1. Step on the stone to get across this brook.
2. The office workers had a meeting with their boss.
3. Where do these dishes beelong?
4. How much will my lunch cost?
5. Soon the baby began to crall.
6. Where should we cros the brook?
7. We left to go fishing just before dawn.
8. I can drau funny pictures.
9. We must always obey the law.
10. It's fun to help mow the lawn.
11. When we went on a trip, we got lost.
12. Wild animals eat their meat raw.
13. My new pillow is very sof.
14. The lady sang a beautiful song.
15. Mom and Dad put strawe in the basket.

**Answer Box**

| | Right | Wrong |
|---|---|---|
| 1. | ○ | ○ |
| 2. | ○ | ○ |
| 3. | ○ | ○ |
| 4. | ○ | ○ |
| 5. | ○ | ○ |
| 6. | ○ | ○ |
| 7. | ○ | ○ |
| 8. | ○ | ○ |
| 9. | ○ | ○ |
| 10. | ○ | ○ |
| 11. | ○ | ○ |
| 12. | ○ | ○ |
| 13. | ○ | ○ |
| 14. | ○ | ○ |
| 15. | ○ | ○ |

Unit 19

Name ______________________ **Homework Master**

Read each question. Unscramble the letters in dark print to make spelling words. Write the words. Then answer each question. Circle **Yes** or **No**.

1. Is a cat's fur **fsto**?
   ______________ **Yes** **No**
2. Should you obey the **wal**?
   ______________ **Yes** **No**
3. Does a **waln** turn green in summer?
   ______________ **Yes** **No**
4. Do babies learn to **rlawc**?
   ______________ **Yes** **No**
5. Do you use a fork to **rawd** pictures?
   ______________ **Yes** **No**
6. Do cars go **socars** bridges?
   ______________ **Yes** **No**
7. Does everyone know how much pianos **stoc**?
   ______________ **Yes** **No**
8. Do little animals sometimes get **stlo**?
   ______________ **Yes** **No**
9. Would you ever eat a **war** lobster?
   ______________ **Yes** **No**
10. Does the moon come up at **awdn**?
    ______________ **Yes** **No**
11. Do horses sleep on **swart** sometimes?
    ______________ **Yes** **No**
12. Is a leader sometimes called a **sbos**?
    ______________ **Yes** **No**
13. Do you know where the erasers **longbe**?
    ______________ **Yes** **No**
14. Can you sit and **ssroc** your legs?
    ______________ **Yes** **No**
15. Can you be quiet and sing a **ongs**?
    ______________ **Yes** **No**

Name ____________________

**Unit 20**

**Home Study Master**

## r-Controlled Vowel: /ôr/

### Chance of a Lifetime

Announce to your child that he or she has just won a dream vacation to anywhere in or out of the world. You are travel agents, and you are going to help plan his or her dream vacation.

Help your child write up a travel itinerary listing the places he or she would like to go and the things he or she would like to do and see.

1. story
2. wore
3. north
4. board
5. form
6. corner
7. warm
8. score
9. morning
10. forget
11. before
12. storm
13. tore
14. order
15. war

1. ____________________
2. ____________________
3. ____________________
4. ____________________
5. ____________________
6. ____________________
7. ____________________
8. ____________________
9. ____________________
10. ____________________
11. ____________________
12. ____________________
13. ____________________
14. ____________________
15. ____________________

Name ____________________

## Hoja para estudiar en casa

### r-Controlled Vowel: /ôr/

### ¡Qué suerte!

Anuncien a su hijo o hija que acaba de ganar unas vacaciones fantásticas a cualquier sitio en este mundo o fuera de él. Uds. son agentes de viajes y van a ayudarlo/a a planear sus vacaciones.

Ayuden a su hijo o hija a escribir un itinerario con una lista de los lugares que quisiera visitar y las cosas que quisiera hacer y ver.

1. story
cuento
2. wore
llevó (ropa)
3. north
norte
4. board
tabla
5. form
forma; formar
6. corner
rincón; esquina
7. warm
caliente; calentar
8. score
cuenta; tantos
9. morning
(por la) mañana
10. forget
olvidar
11. before
antes
12. storm
tormenta
13. tore
rompió
14. order
orden; mandar
15. war
guerra

1. ____________________
2. ____________________
3. ____________________
4. ____________________
5. ____________________
6. ____________________
7. ____________________
8. ____________________
9. ____________________
10. ____________________
11. ____________________
12. ____________________
13. ____________________
14. ____________________
15. ____________________

Name ____________________



| | | | |
|---|---|---|---|
| 1. form | 3. forget | 5. morning | 7. board |
| 2. order | 4. story | 6. before | 8. warm |

**A.** Write the spelling words in a-b-c order.

1. ____________________ 5. ____________________

2. ____________________ 6. ____________________

3. ____________________ 7. ____________________

4. ____________________ 8. ____________________

**B.** Write the base word for each of the following words.

1. warmest ____________________ 4. forming ____________________

2. boarded ____________________ 5. ordered ____________________

3. stories ____________________ 6. forgetful ____________________

Unit 20

**Practice Master**

Name ______________________

| | | | |
|---|---|---|---|
| form | forget | morning | board |
| order | story | before | warm |

**C.** Replace the underlined word in each sentence with an antonym. Use spelling words.

**1.** We will leave early in the <u>night</u>. ______________

**2.** Mary arrived <u>after</u> everyone else. ______________

**3.** Did you <u>remember</u> the map? ______________

**4.** There was a <u>cool</u> breeze blowing across the lake. ______________

**D.** Use the code to complete the puzzle.

| | | | | | | |
|---|---|---|---|---|---|---|
| 14 | 1 | 11 | 8 | | | |
| 5 | 10 | 11 | 8 | | | |
| 12 | 13 | 10 | 11 | 15 | | |
| 2 b | 10 o | 1 a | 11 r | 3 d | | |
| 10 | 11 | 3 | 4 | 11 | | |
| 2 | 4 | 5 | 10 | 11 | 4 | |
| 5 | 10 | 11 | 6 | 4 | 13 | |
| 8 | 10 | 11 | 9 | 7 | 9 | 6 |

**CODE**

| | |
|---|---|
| 1 = a | 9 = n |
| 2 = b | 10 = o |
| 3 = d | 11 = r |
| 4 = e | 12 = s |
| 5 = f | 13 = t |
| 6 = g | 14 = w |
| 7 = i | 15 = y |
| 8 = m | |

Name ____________________

Read each sentence. Look at the underlined spelling word. Fill in a circle. Show if the word is spelled **Right** or **Wrong**.

**Sample**

**He knew <u>mor</u> songs than I did.**

| Right | Wrong |
|---|---|
| ○ | ● |

1. She took a bath <u>befour</u> she went to bed.
2. He cut the <u>boared</u> in half.
3. We put the lamp in the <u>corner</u>.
4. Please don't <u>forgit</u> your ball and bat.
5. We used the blocks to <u>from</u> a wall.
6. He got up very late this <u>mornin</u>.
7. The closest star is there in the <u>north</u>.
8. I would like to <u>order</u> a new desk.
9. Do you know what the final <u>scor</u> was?
10. We closed the windows before the <u>storm</u>.
11. My favorite <u>storie</u> is about wild animals.
12. He <u>tore</u> his shirt on a rock.
13. Our President spoke out against <u>war</u>.
14. I think that it will be <u>warm</u> today.
15. That was a pretty dress she <u>wore</u> to the party.

**Answer Box**

| | Right | Wrong |
|---|---|---|
| 1. | ○ | ○ |
| 2. | ○ | ○ |
| 3. | ○ | ○ |
| 4. | ○ | ○ |
| 5. | ○ | ○ |
| 6. | ○ | ○ |
| 7. | ○ | ○ |
| 8. | ○ | ○ |
| 9. | ○ | ○ |
| 10. | ○ | ○ |
| 11. | ○ | ○ |
| 12. | ○ | ○ |
| 13. | ○ | ○ |
| 14. | ○ | ○ |
| 15. | ○ | ○ |

Name ________________________________

Use the code. Fill in the skyscraper with the spelling words.

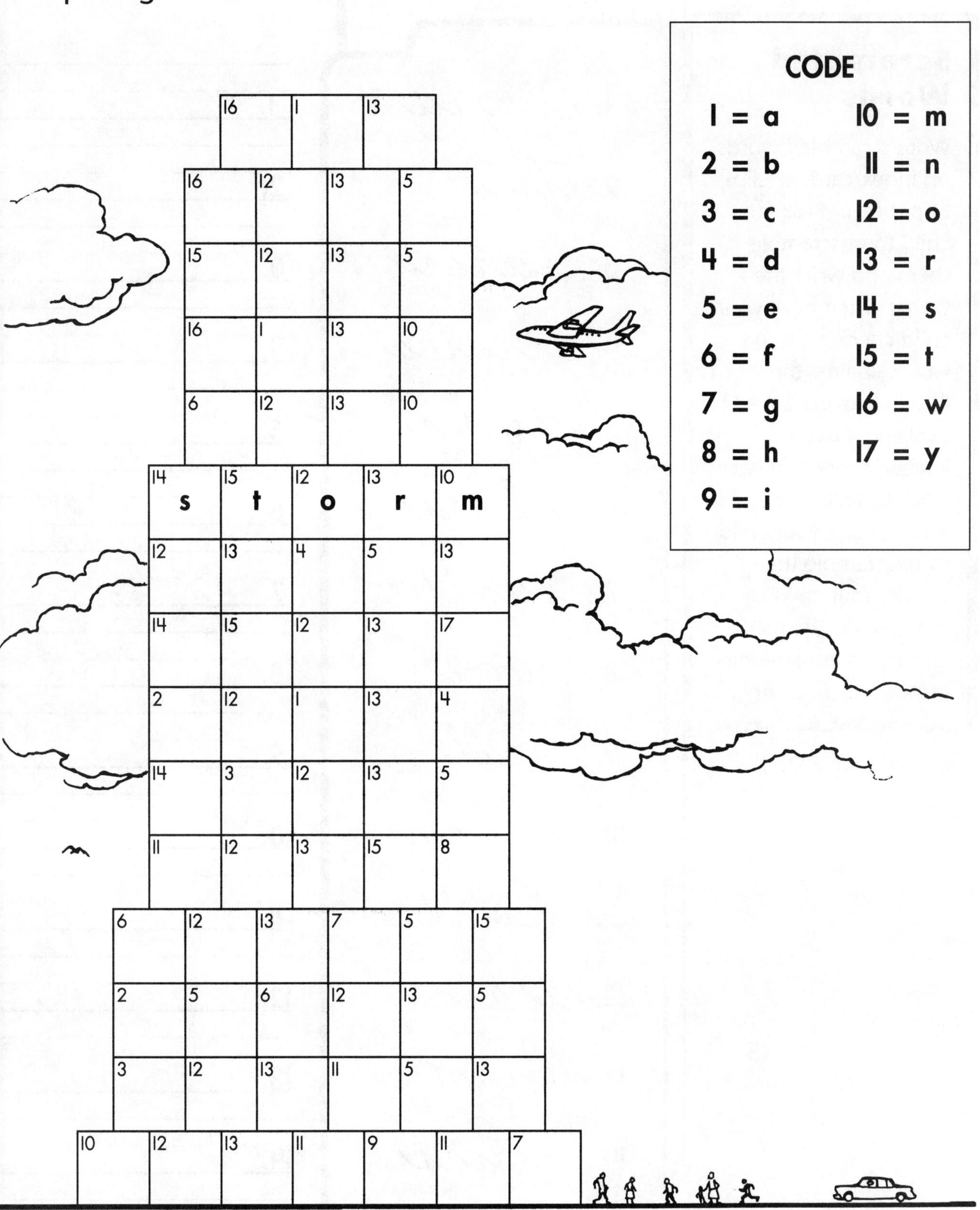

Name ______________________

Unit 21

**Home Study Master**

## Scrambled Words

Write scrambled words on index cards or slips of paper and ask your child to unscramble them and write the words. Then have your child check his or her words against the word list. To provide an extra challenge, use a kitchen timer or a wall clock to record the time it takes your child to unscramble the words. Your child can then repeat the game and try to improve his or her own best time.

## r-Controlled Vowel: /ûr/

1. word
2. fur
3. early
4. circus
5. turn
6. skirt
7. earth
8. work
9. curl
10. learn
11. hurt
12. dirt
13. earn
14. shirt
15. heard

1. ______________
2. ______________
3. ______________
4. ______________
5. ______________
6. ______________
7. ______________
8. ______________
9. ______________
10. ______________
11. ______________
12. ______________
13. ______________
14. ______________
15. ______________

Name ____________________

Unit 21

**Hoja para estudiar en casa**

## r-Controlled Vowel: /ûr/

### Palabras revueltas

Deletreen las palabras en fichas o en cuadros de papel con las letras transpuestas. Díganle a su hijo o hija que arregle las letras y que escriba las palabras correctamente. Luego, díganle que verifique el deletreo de cada palabra usando la lista de palabras. Se puede hacer el ejercicio más interesante con el uso de un minutero o de un reloj de pared para contar cuántos minutos pasó arreglando las letras. Entonces su hijo o hija puede repetir el juego y tratar de sobrepasar su mejor tiempo.

1. word — palabra
2. fur — piel (animal)
3. early — temprano
4. circus — circo
5. turn — dar una vuelta
6. skirt — falda
7. earth — tierra
8. work — trabajo; obra; trabajar
9. curl — bucle; rizar
10. learn — aprender
11. hurt — herido; lastimar
12. dirt — suelo
13. earn — ganar
14. shirt — camisa
15. heard — oído; oyó

1. ____________________
2. ____________________
3. ____________________
4. ____________________
5. ____________________
6. ____________________
7. ____________________
8. ____________________
9. ____________________
10. ____________________
11. ____________________
12. ____________________
13. ____________________
14. ____________________
15. ____________________

Unit 21
Practice Master

Name ______________________________

| | | | |
|---|---|---|---|
| 1. turn | 3. early | 5. word | 7. dirt |
| 2. hurt | 4. heard | 6. work | 8. circus |

**A.** Write the spelling word that belongs in each sentence.

1. Soon it will be the lion's ____ to perform. ______________
2. It takes practice and hard ____ to be a lion tamer. ______________
3. Nets help to keep trapeze artists from getting ____. ______________
4. The performers get up ____ to begin their chores. ______________
5. I thought I ____ a lion roar. ______________
6. The trained horses kicked up ____ as they pranced. ______________

**B.** These words are all smaller parts of something. Write the spelling word that names that thing.

1. clowns, elephants, acrobats, ____ ______________
2. consonants, vowels, ____ ______________

Name ______________________________

Unit **21**

**Practice Master**

| turn | early | word | dirt |
|---|---|---|---|
| hurt | heard | work | circus |

**C.** Write the spelling words in a-b-c order.

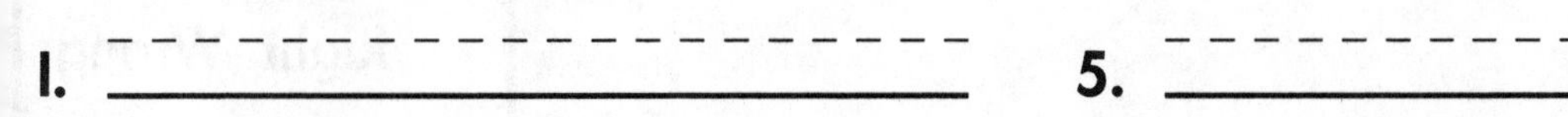

1. ______________________ 5. ______________________

2. ______________________ 6. ______________________

3. ______________________ 7. ______________________

4. ______________________ 8. ______________________

**D.** Write the spelling words that these letters and symbols spell.

▲ = ear ❍ = or ■ = ir ✲ = ur

1. w ❍ k ______________ 5. d ■ t ______________

2. ▲ l y ______________ 6. t ✲ n ______________

3. c ■ c u s ______________ 7. h ▲ d ______________

4. h ✲ t ______________ 8. w ❍ d ______________

Name ____________________

Read each sentence. Look at the underlined spelling word. Fill in a circle. Show if the word is spelled **Right** or **Wrong**.

**Sample**

**We gave some bread to the brids.** — Right ○ Wrong ●

## Answer Box

| | Right | Wrong |
|---|---|---|
| 1. We saw a funny clown at the cirkus. | ○ | ○ |
| 2. She made a pretty curl. | ○ | ○ |
| 3. We planted some seeds in the dirt. | ○ | ○ |
| 4. They went to the park early in the morning. | ○ | ○ |
| 5. He wanted to ern money for a new bike. | ○ | ○ |
| 6. Worms live in the earth. | ○ | ○ |
| 7. A rabbit has a warm pher coat. | ○ | ○ |
| 8. We herd a loud noise outside. | ○ | ○ |
| 9. I hope that you didn't hirt yourself. | ○ | ○ |
| 10. You must lern your new spelling words. | ○ | ○ |
| 11. Usually Jonathan wears a shirt with short sleeves. | ○ | ○ |
| 12. The girl wore a warm red skurt. | ○ | ○ |
| 13. After Karen bats, it will be your tern. | ○ | ○ |
| 14. She did not miss one word on her test. | ○ | ○ |
| 15. Cutting wood is hard werk. | ○ | ○ |

Name ____________________

Add an **s** to each verb. Put the new words in the puzzle.

**Across**
3. curl
5. work
6. turn

**Down**
1. earn
2. hurt
4. learn

Write each group of words in a-b-c order.

1. heard, earth, circus ________ ________ ________

2. fur, word, skirt ________ ________ ________

3. early, dirt, shirt ________ ________ ________

Name ______________________

Unit 22

**Home Study Master**

## r-Controlled Vowel: /âr/

1. bear
2. air
3. fare
4. pear
5. care
6. their
7. hair
8. bare
9. fair
10. there
11. pair
12. wear
13. chair
14. where
15. hare

1. ______
2. ______
3. ______
4. ______
5. ______
6. ______
7. ______
8. ______
9. ______
10. ______
11. ______
12. ______
13. ______
14. ______
15. ______

Unit 22

Name ____________________

**Hoja para estudiar en casa**

## r-Controlled Vowel: /âr/

### Vámonos

Pídanle a su hijo o hija que escriba sobre el más interesante o el más divertido viaje que haya hecho. Las siguientes son algunas preguntas que pudieran hacerle para ayudarlo/a a recordar el viaje.

- ¿Adónde fuiste?
- ¿Quiénes fueron contigo?
- ¿Cómo viajaron?
- ¿Qué viste y que hiciste?
- ¿Cuál fue la mejor parte del viaje?

1. *bear* oso; aguantar
2. *air* aire
3. *fare* pasaje
4. *pear* pera
5. *care* cuidado; importarle
6. *their* su (de ellos)
7. *hair* pelo; cabellos
8. *bare* desnudo
9. *fair* feria; justo
10. *there* allí
11. *pair* par; emparejar
12. *wear* llevar (ropa)
13. *chair* silla
14. *where* donde; ¿dónde?
15. *hare* liebre

1. ____________________
2. ____________________
3. ____________________
4. ____________________
5. ____________________
6. ____________________
7. ____________________
8. ____________________
9. ____________________
10. ____________________
11. ____________________
12. ____________________
13. ____________________
14. ____________________
15. ____________________

Name ______________________

Unit 22 **Practice Master**

| | | | |
|---|---|---|---|
| 1. air | 3. bear | 5. care | 7. there |
| 2. chair | 4. wear | 6. where | 8. their |

**A.** Write the spelling word that belongs in each sentence.

**1.** We breathe ____. ______________

**2.** I ____ about you. ______________

**3.** They took ____ toys home with them. ______________

**4.** I will go ____ you tell me to. ______________

**B.** Write the spelling word to solve each riddle.

**1.** What is a feeling of worry or concern? ______________

**2.** What do we call the mixture of gases that we breathe? ______________

**3.** What word means "to put on"? ______________

**4.** What is a piece of furniture that you sit on? ______________

Unit 22

Practice Master

Name ______________________

| air | bear | care | there |
|---|---|---|---|
| chair | wear | where | their |

**C.** Write the spelling word that is a homophone for each word.

1. bare ______________

2. where ______________

3. their ______________

**D.** Use spelling words to complete the puzzle.

**Across**

1. to what place
2. to have feelings
3. you breathe it
4. a large animal
5. in that place

**Down**

1. to have on (clothes)
2. you sit on it
5. belonging to them

Unit 22

Name ______________________________ **Test Master**

Read each sentence. Look at the underlined spelling word. Fill in a circle. Show if the word is spelled **Right** or **Wrong**.

**Sample**

One leg of the chair was broken.

| | Right | Wrong |
|---|---|---|
| Sample | ● | ○ |

1. The spring air was fresh and clean.
2. I came downstairs with bare feet.
3. The big black bair slept in its cave.
4. My mother takes kare of my baby sister.
5. I sat on a chare in the front row.
6. The captain was very fair to his crew.
7. We paid a fare to go across the bridge.
8. She wore her hiar in curls.
9. I know a story about a fox and a lazy hare.
10. He wore a paire of black shoes.
11. Every pear on the tree was ripe.
12. They were told to make their beds.
13. Please put your toys over ther.
14. What will you wear to the party?
15. He doesn't know whair he left his glasses.

**Answer Box**

| | Right | Wrong |
|---|---|---|
| 1. | ○ | ○ |
| 2. | ○ | ○ |
| 3. | ○ | ○ |
| 4. | ○ | ○ |
| 5. | ○ | ○ |
| 6. | ○ | ○ |
| 7. | ○ | ○ |
| 8. | ○ | ○ |
| 9. | ○ | ○ |
| 10. | ○ | ○ |
| 11. | ○ | ○ |
| 12. | ○ | ○ |
| 13. | ○ | ○ |
| 14. | ○ | ○ |
| 15. | ○ | ○ |

Name ______________________

Change the letters around to make spelling words. The clues will help you. Write each spelling word.

**Clues**

1. 

a fruit ______

2. 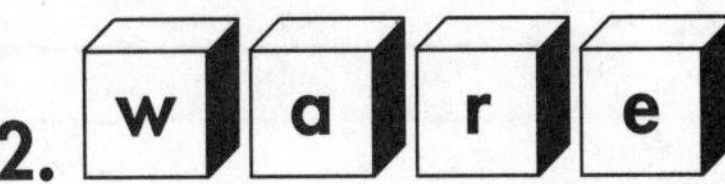

to put on ______

3. 

like a rabbit ______

4. 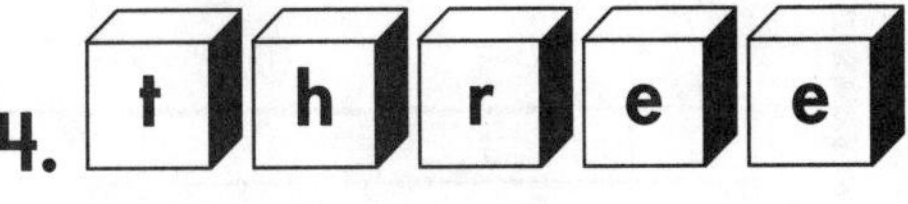

at or in that place ______

5. 

the price of a bus ride ______

Finish each rhyme by writing two spelling words.

1. Sniff the ______ at the ______.

2. Sit in the ______ and comb your ______.

3. I do not know ______ the zoo keeps the ______.

4. If for shoes I wear this ______, will you ______?

5. ______ feathers are not there, so baby birds look ______!

Name ____________________

Unit 23 **Home Study Master**

## Homophones

1. way
2. its
3. owe
4. sell
5. great
6. sail
7. cell
8. scent
9. oh
10. cent
11. it's
12. grate
13. weigh
14. sale
15. sent

### Working With Homophones

Say the spelling words and encourage your child to listen carefully to the vowel sound in each. This will help her or him associate the spelling patterns with the sounds they stand for. Since word meaning is important in the study of homophones, it is helpful for students to hear the words in sentences.

1. ____________
2. ____________
3. ____________
4. ____________
5. ____________
6. ____________
7. ____________
8. ____________
9. ____________
10. ____________
11. ____________
12. ____________
13. ____________
14. ____________
15. ____________

Name ____________________

# Hoja para estudiar en casa

## Homophones

### Trabajar con los homófonos

Pronuncien las palabras y díganle a su hijo o hija que se fije en el sonido vocal en cada palabra. De esta manera puede ver y oír la correspondencia entre los modelos ortográficos y los sonidos que representan. En el estudio de los homófonos hay que aprender el deletreo según el significado de la palabra. Por lo tanto, si los estudiantes oyen las palabras en frases, podrán ayudarlos mejor.

1. way — manera; camino
2. its — su
3. owe — deber
4. sell — vender
5. great — gran; fantástico
6. sail — vela; navegar
7. cell — célula; celda
8. scent — olor; perfume
9. oh — ay
10. cent — centavo
11. it's — es
12. grate — rallar
13. weigh — pesar
14. sale — venta
15. sent — envió

1. ____________________
2. ____________________
3. ____________________
4. ____________________
5. ____________________
6. ____________________
7. ____________________
8. ____________________
9. ____________________
10. ____________________
11. ____________________
12. ____________________
13. ____________________
14. ____________________
15. ____________________

Name ____________________

Unit 23 **Practice Master**

| | | | |
|---|---|---|---|
| 1. oh | 3. its | 5. sent | 7. way |
| 2. sell | 4. it's | 6. great | 8. weigh |

**A.** Write the spelling word that is a homophone for each word.

1. cent ____________
2. grate ____________
3. owe ____________
4. cell ____________
5. weigh ____________
6. it's ____________

**B.** One wrong word is used in each of the following sentences. Circle that word and write the correct word.

1. Do you want to cell this old lamp? ____________
2. The kitten can't find it's toy. ____________
3. George Washington was a grate man. ____________
4. Mother scent the package on Friday. ____________
5. Use that scale to way yourself. ____________

Unit 23

**Practice Master**

Name ______________________________

| oh | its | sent | way |
|---|---|---|---|
| sell | it's | great | weigh |

**C.** Write the homophone that belongs in each sentence.

1. Do you think (its, it's) raining? ______________
2. How much does that (way, weigh)? ______________
3. That puppy seems to have hurt (its, it's) paw. ______________
4. I think this is the correct (way, weigh) to solve the puzzle. ______________

**D.** Read across and down to find spelling words hidden in the puzzle. Circle and write the words.

| | | | | | |
|---|---|---|---|---|---|
| w | e | i | g | h | d |
| a | b | t | r | c | e |
| y | f | s | e | l | l |
| a | g | h | a | i | o |
| s | e | n | t | j | r |

1. ______________ 4. ______________
2. ______________ 5. ______________
3. ______________ 6. ______________

Name ____________________ **Test Master**

Read each sentence. Look at the underlined spelling word. Fill in a circle. Show if the word is spelled **Right** or **Wrong**.

**Sample**

Our flag is <u>read</u>, white, and blue. Right ○ Wrong ●

1. Each <u>cell</u> of the plant stores water.
2. This pencil will cost only one <u>cent</u>.
3. <u>It's</u> a long way to go from here.
4. The kitten stayed close to <u>its</u> mother.
5. When she heard the crash, Mom said, "<u>Oh</u>, no!"
6. I <u>owe</u> my friend some baseball cards.
7. The main <u>saile</u> was torn.
8. Beth and Tom went to a garage <u>sale</u>.
9. These roses have a nice <u>scent</u>.
10. We went to the market to <u>sel</u> our cow.
11. My dad <u>sent</u> my mother flowers.
12. Carl said that the movie was <u>great</u>.
13. Jean will <u>grate</u> the carrots for the salad.
14. We didn't know which <u>way</u> to turn.
15. The clerk had to <u>wiegh</u> the seeds on a scale.

**Answer Box**

| | Right | Wrong |
|---|---|---|
| 1. | ○ | ○ |
| 2. | ○ | ○ |
| 3. | ○ | ○ |
| 4. | ○ | ○ |
| 5. | ○ | ○ |
| 6. | ○ | ○ |
| 7. | ○ | ○ |
| 8. | ○ | ○ |
| 9. | ○ | ○ |
| 10. | ○ | ○ |
| 11. | ○ | ○ |
| 12. | ○ | ○ |
| 13. | ○ | ○ |
| 14. | ○ | ○ |
| 15. | ○ | ○ |

Name ____________________

One wrong word is used in each of the following sentences. Circle that word. Write the correct word on the line.

1. Do you want to cell this old lamp?

2. It is fun to sale on a hot summer day.

3. Its your turn to go first.

4. The police officer will lock the door to the sell.

5. The kitten can't find it's toy.

6. The fall day was breezy but owe so nice.

7. My brother does not oh any money on his new bike.

8. The sent of the roses made me sneeze.

9. George Washington was a grate man.

10. A penny is only worth one scent.

11. Which weigh should we turn at the stop sign?

12. Mother scent the package on Friday.

13. I helped great the carrots.

14. Use that scale to way yourself.

15. Our neighbors had a big sail on Saturday.

Name ______________________________



## Assessment and Review

1. across
2. draw
3. belong
4. straw
5. before
6. forget
7. warm
8. morning
9. circus
10. heard
11. early
12. work
13. their
14. wear
15. there
16. where
17. great
18. sent
19. it's
20. weigh

1. ______
2. ______
3. ______
4. ______
5. ______
6. ______
7. ______
8. ______
9. ______
10. ______
11. ______
12. ______
13. ______
14. ______
15. ______
16. ______
17. ______
18. ______
19. ______
20. ______

### Now I Am an Author

Ask your child to write a very short one paragraph story, using as many of the words from the list in this unit as possible. The story can be real or imaginary. If he or she wishes, your child may draw an illustration for the story. Check for the correct spelling and meaning of the words. Share these compositions with the rest of the family.

Name ____________________



# Hoja para estudiar en casa

## Assessment and Review

### Ahora soy autor

Pidan a su hijo o hija que escriba un cuento muy corto de un párrafo, usando tantas palabras de la lista de esta unidad como puede. El cuento puede ser verdadero o fantástico. Si él o ella desea, puede dibujar una ilustración para el cuento. Comprueben que haya deletreado bien las palabras y que entienda sus significados. Compartan estas composiciones con otros miembros de la familia.

1. *across* — al otro lado de
2. *draw* — dibujar
3. *belong* — pertenecer a
4. *straw* — paja; pajita
5. *before* — antes
6. *forget* — olvidar
7. *warm* — caliente; calentar
8. *morning* — (por la) mañana
9. *circus* — circo
10. *heard* — oído; oyó
11. *early* — temprano
12. *work* — trabajo; obra; trabajar
13. *their* — su (de ellos)
14. *wear* — llevar (ropa)
15. *there* — allí
16. *where* — donde
17. *great* — gran; fantástico
18. *sent* — envió
19. *it's* — es
20. *weigh* — pesar

1. ____________________
2. ____________________
3. ____________________
4. ____________________
5. ____________________
6. ____________________
7. ____________________
8. ____________________
9. ____________________
10. ____________________
11. ____________________
12. ____________________
13. ____________________
14. ____________________
15. ____________________
16. ____________________
17. ____________________
18. ____________________
19. ____________________
20. ____________________

Name ______________________________

**Test Master** Unit **24**

**A.** Read each of these phrases. Write the letter of the phrase that contains a misspelled word.

**1. a.** Befor I leave
**b.** A warm day
**c.** An early bus
☐

**2. a.** That sercus clown
**b.** Before the dawn
**c.** As we work
☐

**3. a.** Weigh the peanuts
**b.** Heard a noise
**c.** Belawng to me
☐

**4. a.** Chose ther books
**b.** Will not forget
**c.** Tore his shirt
☐

**5. a.** The scent of roses
**b.** Acros the bridge
**c.** Pay the fare
☐

**6. a.** Knows it's mine
**b.** In the morning
**c.** A greate game
☐

**B.** Write the letter of the word that is spelled correctly and fits the sentence.

**1.** She ____ me a letter.
**a.** cent
**b.** scent
**c.** sent
☐

**2.** ____ does this road lead?
**a.** War
**b.** Whar
**c.** Where
☐

**3.** Make a bed of ____.
**a.** straugh
**b.** staw
**c.** straw
☐

**4.** When will we be ____?
**a.** there
**b.** thare
**c.** their
☐

**5.** Shall I ____ a coat?
**a.** ware
**b.** wear
**c.** where
☐

**6.** Please ____ me a map.
**a.** drau
**b.** draw
**c.** drawe
☐

Unit 25

## Home Study Master

Name ______________________

### Double Consonants

1. supper
2. happen
3. pepper
4. kitten
5. sudden
6. letter
7. dinner
8. cotton
9. lesson
10. mitten
11. bottom
12. summer
13. better
14. ladder
15. ribbon

### Context Clues

Have your child listen while you say sentences from which a spelling word is missing. Encourage your child to use the "clues" in the incomplete sentence to help him or her decide which of the spelling words best fits the sentence. You might prefer to write each sentence, leaving a blank space in which your child can write the missing word. Example: A baby cat is called a _____. (**kitten**)

1. ______________________
2. ______________________
3. ______________________
4. ______________________
5. ______________________
6. ______________________
7. ______________________
8. ______________________
9. ______________________
10. ______________________
11. ______________________
12. ______________________
13. ______________________
14. ______________________
15. ______________________

Name ______________________

# Hoja para estudiar en casa

## Pistas en el contexto

Díganle a su hijo o hija que escuche mientras Uds. dicen una frase en que falta una palabra de la lección. Animen a su hijo o hija a que use las "pistas" en la frase incompleta para ayudarlo/a a decidir cual de las palabras sería mejor en la frase. Si prefieren, escriban cada frase, dejando un espacio, y su hijo o hija puede escribir la palabra que falta en el espacio. Por ejemplo: A small cat is called a _____. (**kitten**). [Un gato pequeño se llama un _____. (**gatito**)].

## Double Consonants

1. *supper* — cena
2. *happen* — ocurrir
3. *pepper* — pimienta
4. *kitten* — gatito
5. *sudden* — repentino
6. *letter* — letra; carta
7. *dinner* — comida
8. *cotton* — algodón
9. *lesson* — lección
10. *mitten* — mitón
11. *bottom* — fondo
12. *summer* — verano
13. *better* — mejor
14. *ladder* — escalera; escala
15. *ribbon* — cinta

1. ______________________
2. ______________________
3. ______________________
4. ______________________
5. ______________________
6. ______________________
7. ______________________
8. ______________________
9. ______________________
10. ______________________
11. ______________________
12. ______________________
13. ______________________
14. ______________________
15. ______________________

Unit 25

**Practice Master**

Name ____________________

| 1. sudden | 3. cotton | 5. summer | 7. dinner |
|---|---|---|---|
| 2. happen | 4. lesson | 6. better | 8. letter |

**A.** Write the spelling words in a-b-c order.

1. ____________________
2. ____________________
3. ____________________
4. ____________________
5. ____________________
6. ____________________
7. ____________________
8. ____________________

**B.** Write the spelling word that belongs in each group.

1. silk, wool, ____ ____________________
2. occur, take place, ____ ____________________
3. lunch, breakfast, ____ ____________________
4. winter, spring, fall, ____ ____________________

Unit 25 Practice Master

Name ____________________

| sudden | cotton | summer | dinner |
| --- | --- | --- | --- |
| happen | lesson | better | letter |

**C.** Unscramble the letters. Use them to complete the spelling words. Write the words.

**1.** n o l e ___ ___ s s ___ ___ ____________________

**2.** r e e l ___ ___ t t ___ ___ ____________________

**3.** u s e n ___ ___ d d ___ ___ ____________________

**4.** r e e b ___ ___ t t ___ ___ ____________________

**D.** Write spelling words to complete the puzzle.

**1.** something to be learned

**2.** to take place

**3.** good, ____, best

**4.** cloth made from a plant

**5.** supper

**6.** season between spring and fall

Write the word spelled in the boxes. ____________________

Unit **25**

Name ____________________ **Test Master**

Read each sentence. Look at the underlined spelling word. Fill in a circle. Show if the word is spelled **Right** or **Wrong**.

**Sample**

**We have a large red baloon.** Right ○ Wrong ●

1. I think your picture is better than mine.
2. There was a penny on the bottum of the pool.
3. Her new dress was made of cotton.
4. We had roast beef for dinner.
5. Did you hapen to see my shoes?
6. The young kitten was very playful.
7. Jim climbed the ladder to paint the house.
8. That math lessen was fun.
9. I will mail my letter at the post office.
10. There was fur on the top of each mitten.
11. He put pepper on his corn.
12. We put a pink ribbon around the gift.
13. The sudden loud noise made me jump.
14. I had fun swimming this summer.
15. We had rice and beans for shuper.

**Answer Box**

| | Right | Wrong |
|---|---|---|
| 1. | ○ | ○ |
| 2. | ○ | ○ |
| 3. | ○ | ○ |
| 4. | ○ | ○ |
| 5. | ○ | ○ |
| 6. | ○ | ○ |
| 7. | ○ | ○ |
| 8. | ○ | ○ |
| 9. | ○ | ○ |
| 10. | ○ | ○ |
| 11. | ○ | ○ |
| 12. | ○ | ○ |
| 13. | ○ | ○ |
| 14. | ○ | ○ |
| 15. | ○ | ○ |

Name ______________________ **Homework Master** Unit **25**

Circle any small words you see in these spelling words.

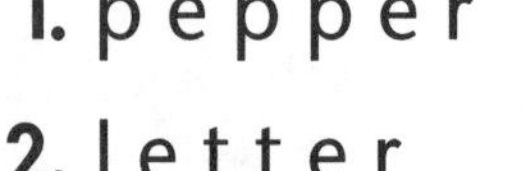

| | |
|---|---|
| 1. pepper | 5. ribbon |
| 2. letter | 6. lesson |
| 3. kitten | 7. summer |
| 4. cotton | 8. mitten |

Unscramble the letters. Use them to complete the spelling words. Write the spelling words on the lines.

1. esru ___ ___ pp ___ ___ ______________

2. ehan ___ ___ pp ___ ___ ______________

3. ried ___ ___ nn ___ ___ ______________

4. alre ___ ___ dd ___ ___ ______________

5. nuse ___ ___ dd ___ ___ ______________

6. eebr ___ ___ tt ___ ___ ______________

7. obom ___ ___ tt ___ ___ ______________

Name ______________________



## Double Consonants + y

### Color-a-Vowel

Pronounce each word and have your child write it with a crayon. Then ask your child to use another crayon to draw a ring around the letters that stand for the vowel sounds in the word. Be sure that your child understands that there are two vowel sounds in each of these words.

1. carry
2. bunny
3. happy
4. muddy
5. berry
6. furry
7. puppy
8. sorry
9. merry
10. jelly
11. hurry
12. pretty
13. cherry
14. worry
15. funny

1. ______
2. ______
3. ______
4. ______
5. ______
6. ______
7. ______
8. ______
9. ______
10. ______
11. ______
12. ______
13. ______
14. ______
15. ______

Name ____________________

Unit 26

**Hoja para estudiar en casa**

## Double Consonants + y

### Colorea vocales

Pronuncien cada palabra y pídanle a su hijo o hija que escriba la palabra con un creyón de pintar. Luego díganle que use un creyón de otro color para circular las letras que indican los sonidos vocálicos en cada palabra. Estén seguros de que su hijo o hija comprende que en estas palabras hay dos sonidos vocálicos.

1. carry — llevar
2. bunny — conejito
3. happy — contento; alegre
4. muddy — barroso; lodoso
5. berry — baya
6. furry — con piel (animal)
7. puppy — perrito
8. sorry — sentirlo
9. merry — alegre
10. jelly — jalea
11. hurry — apurarse
12. pretty — bonita; bastante
13. cherry — cereza
14. worry — preocuparse
15. funny — chistoso; raro

1. ____________________
2. ____________________
3. ____________________
4. ____________________
5. ____________________
6. ____________________
7. ____________________
8. ____________________
9. ____________________
10. ____________________
11. ____________________
12. ____________________
13. ____________________
14. ____________________
15. ____________________

Name ____________________

Unit 26 **Practice Master**

| | | | |
|---|---|---|---|
| 1. happy | 3. funny | 5. pretty | 7. worry |
| 2. puppy | 4. carry | 6. sorry | 8. hurry |

**A.** Write the base word for each of the following words.

**1.** happiest ____________ **5.** carries ____________

**2.** prettier ____________ **6.** worries ____________

**3.** funniest ____________ **7.** hurried ____________

**4.** puppies ____________ **8.** sorriest ____________

**B.** Replace the underlined part of each sentence with a spelling word.

**1.** That <u>baby dog</u> is so playful. ____________

**2.** "Jingle Bells" is a <u>jolly</u> tune. ____________

**3.** <u>Be quick</u> or we will miss the train! ____________

**4.** The garden had many <u>beautiful</u> flowers. ____________

Name ____________________

Unit 26 Practice Master

| happy | funny | pretty | worry |
|---|---|---|---|
| puppy | carry | sorry | hurry |

**C.** Complete each spelling word. Add the missing letters. Read each clue to help you write the correct word.

1. a young dog __ __ ppy
2. an antonym for sad __ __ ppy
3. nice looking __ __ __ tty
4. feeling sadness __ __ rry
5. rush __ __ rry
6. take from one place to another __ __ rry

**D.** Unscramble the letters to make spelling words. Write the words. The first letter of each word is in dark print to get you started.

1. n n **f** u y ____________________
2. o r **s** r y ____________________
3. r r y a **c** ____________________
4. y r r **h** u ____________________
5. t t e y r **p** ____________________
6. r r **w** o y ____________________
7. y p p **h** a ____________________
8. p p y **p** u ____________________

Unit **26**

**Test Master**

Name ______________________________

Read each sentence. Look at the underlined spelling word. Fill in a circle. Show if the word is spelled **Right** or **Wrong**.

**Sample**

Is that berry ripe yet? — Right ● Wrong ○

**Answer Box**

| | Right | Wrong |
|---|---|---|
| **1.** My friend told me a funny story. | ○ | ○ |
| **2.** All the lettuce was eaten by that bunny. | ○ | ○ |
| **3.** I helped my dad karry the bags. | ○ | ○ |
| **4.** I like chery pie the best. | ○ | ○ |
| **5.** The birds like the red bury the best. | ○ | ○ |
| **6.** She was very happy with her new toy. | ○ | ○ |
| **7.** We must herry to catch the bus. | ○ | ○ |
| **8.** Carol made jelly from those strawberries. | ○ | ○ |
| **9.** We had a marry time at the school picnic. | ○ | ○ |
| **10.** The water in the pond was muddie. | ○ | ○ |
| **11.** The city lights were a pretty sight. | ○ | ○ |
| **12.** I have two white kittens and one brown puppy. | ○ | ○ |
| **13.** I'm very sorry that I'm late. | ○ | ○ |
| **14.** The small zoo had a few fury animals. | ○ | ○ |
| **15.** I hope my grandmother doesn't worry about me. | ○ | ○ |

Name ______________________________

Complete each spelling word. Add the missing letters. Read each clue to help you write the correct word.

1. a young dog ___ ___ p p y

2. an antonym for sad ___ ___ p p y

3. a synonym for rabbit ___ ___ n n y

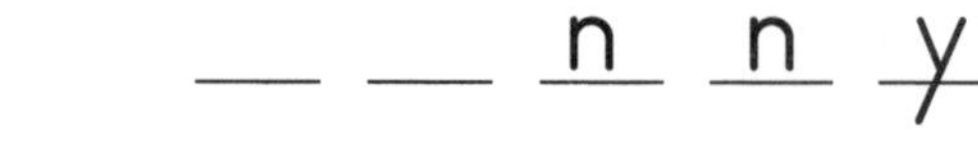

4. a red fruit with a pit ___ ___ ___ r r y

5. nice-looking ___ ___ ___ t t y

6. feeling sadness ___ ___ r r y

7. rush ___ ___ r r y

8. an antonym for serious ___ ___ n n y

9. a small red or blue fruit ___ ___ r r y

10. wet, soft earth ___ ___ d d y

Unscramble the letters to form spelling words. Write the words on the lines.

1. y j e l l ______________

2. r r e m y ______________

3. r r y o w ______________

4. c r r y a ______________

5. r r y u f ______________

Name ______________________

Unit 27 **Home Study Master**

## Adding -ing

### Spelling Banner

Help your child make a spelling banner. Have him or her write each spelling word on an index card and punch a hole in the top of the card. Provide shoelaces or yarn so that he or she can lace the cards together in groups according to the spellings of the long vowel sounds. Help your child hang the banner and encourage her or him to read and spell from it frequently. Occasionally you might also suggest that your child write the words.

1. coming
2. skating
3. taking
4. giving
5. choosing
6. smiling
7. baking
8. sliding
9. changing
10. waving
11. leaving
12. making
13. hoping
14. trading
15. having

1. ______
2. ______
3. ______
4. ______
5. ______
6. ______
7. ______
8. ______
9. ______
10. ______
11. ______
12. ______
13. ______
14. ______
15. ______

Unit 27

Name ____________________ **Hoja para estudiar en casa**

## Una banderola

Ayuden a su hijo o hija a hacer una banderola. Pídanle que escriba cada palabra en una ficha y perforen las fichas. Dénle lazos de zapato o hilaza para atar las fichas en grupos según el deletreo de los sonidos largos de las vocales. Ayúdenlo/a a colgar la banderola y anímenlo/a a que lea y deletree las palabras en la banderola a menudo. A veces pueden sugerir que su hijo o hija escriba los grupos de palabras.

## Adding -ing

1. *coming* viniendo
2. *skating* patinando
3. *taking* tomando
4. *giving* dando
5. *choosing* escogiendo
6. *smiling* sonriéndose
7. *baking* horneando
8. *sliding* deslizando
9. *changing* cambiando
10. *waving* haciendo señal con la mano
11. *leaving* saliendo; dejando
12. *making* haciendo
13. *hoping* esperando
14. *trading* trocando
15. *having* teniendo

1. ____________________
2. ____________________
3. ____________________
4. ____________________
5. ____________________
6. ____________________
7. ____________________
8. ____________________
9. ____________________
10. ____________________
11. ____________________
12. ____________________
13. ____________________
14. ____________________
15. ____________________

Name ____________________

Unit 27 Practice Master

| | | | |
|---|---|---|---|
| 1. taking | 3. having | 5. coming | 7. leaving |
| 2. baking | 4. making | 6. giving | 8. changing |

**A.** Write the spelling word that is a synonym for each word.

1. going ____________
2. arriving ____________
3. cooking ____________
4. creating ____________
5. presenting ____________
6. grabbing ____________

**B.** Write the spelling word that belongs in each sentence.

1. Carlos is ____ the flat tire on my bike tomorrow. ____________
2. Those old papers are ____ up too much space. ____________
3. Sandy had fun ____ a birthday card for her great-grandmother. ____________
4. I will be ____ early for school tomorrow. ____________
5. We are ____ fresh vegetables for dinner. ____________

Name ____________________

**Unit 27 Practice Master**

| taking | having | coming | leaving |
|---|---|---|---|
| baking | making | giving | changing |

**C.** Write the spelling word that is made from each base word.

1. have ____________
2. give ____________
3. change ____________
4. come ____________
5. take ____________
6. leave ____________

**D.** Read across and down to find spelling words hidden in the puzzle. Circle and write the words.

| g | a | f | c | o | m | i | n | g | n |
|---|---|---|---|---|---|---|---|---|---|
| i | h | j | l | e | a | v | i | n | g |
| v | b | l | t | a | k | i | n | g | m |
| i | k | h | a | v | i | n | g | o | c |
| n | b | a | k | i | n | g | d | g | i |
| g | c | h | a | n | g | i | n | g | e |

1. ____________
2. ____________
3. ____________
4. ____________
5. ____________
6. ____________
7. ____________
8. ____________

Test Master

Name ____________________

Read each sentence. Look at the underlined spelling word. Fill in a circle. Show if the word is spelled **Right** or **Wrong**.

**Sample**

**He was hopping to get home early.**

| | Right | Wrong |
|---|---|---|
| | ○ | ● |

Answer Box

| Sentence | | Right | Wrong |
|---|---|---|---|
| 1. Our neighbors are changing the flat tire. | 1. | ○ | ○ |
| 2. When are you chosing a puppy? | 2. | ○ | ○ |
| 3. My aunt is cuming here for a visit. | 3. | ○ | ○ |
| 4. We are giving a surprise to our teacher. | 4. | ○ | ○ |
| 5. Tomorrow we are having a party. | 5. | ○ | ○ |
| 6. They were hoping to win the big prize. | 6. | ○ | ○ |
| 7. When are you leafing to go home? | 7. | ○ | ○ |
| 8. Jan is baking something good for breakfast. | 8. | ○ | ○ |
| 9. We had fun makking a snowman. | 9. | ○ | ○ |
| 10. You should only go skateing on thick ice. | 10. | ○ | ○ |
| 11. It was fun sliding on the smooth ice. | 11. | ○ | ○ |
| 12. Everyone was smilin for the picture. | 12. | ○ | ○ |
| 13. We are takeing a trip in July. | 13. | ○ | ○ |
| 14. The farmer is trading corn for meat. | 14. | ○ | ○ |
| 15. The flag was waving in the wind. | 15. | ○ | ○ |

Name ____________________

Circle only the spelling words. Then write the nine spelling words. Begin here.

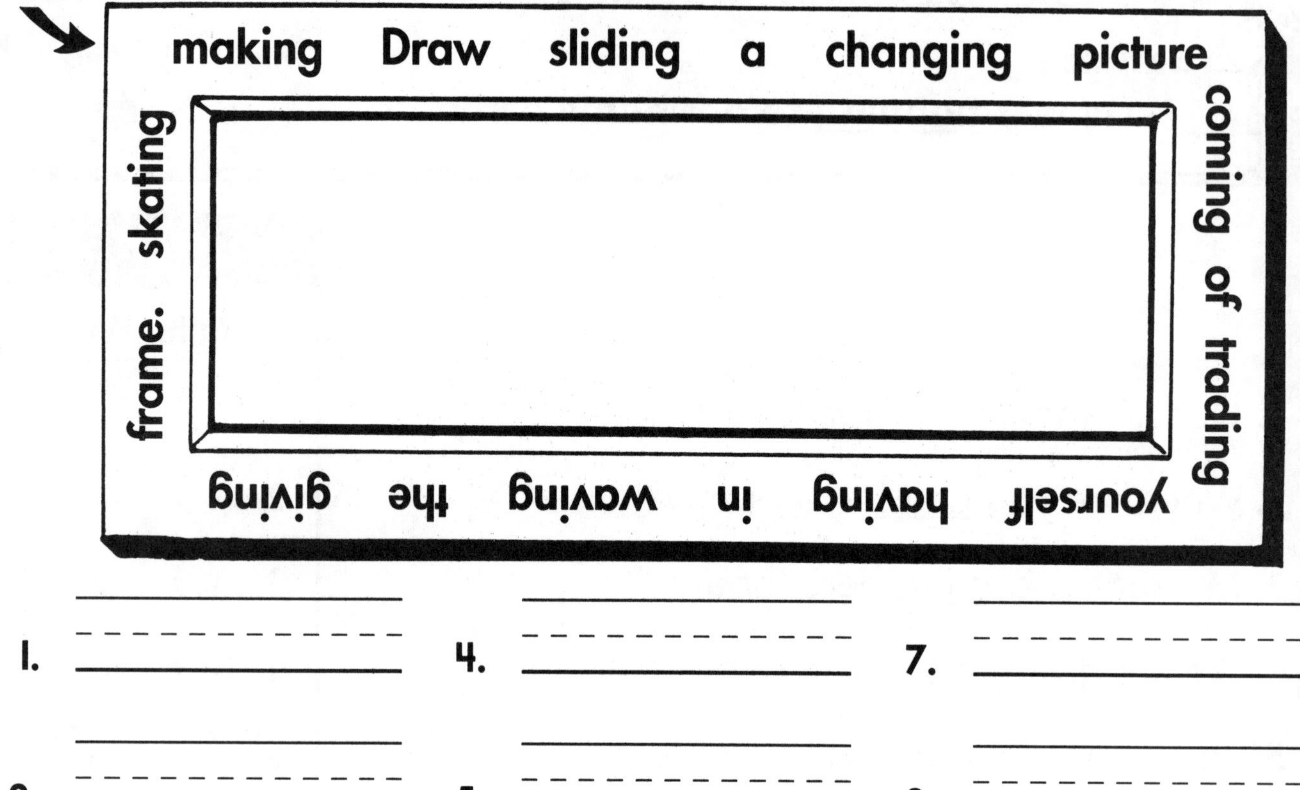


1. ____________ 4. ____________ 7. ____________

2. ____________ 5. ____________ 8. ____________

3. ____________ 6. ____________ 9. ____________

10. You will find a secret message if you write each word that is shown after a spelling word. Write the message as a sentence. Do what it says.

________________________________________

Write **S** if the words are synonyms. Write **A** if the words are antonyms.

1. smiling-crying ____
2. hoping-wishing ____
3. taking-giving ____
4. leaving-arriving ____
5. choosing-picking ____
6. baking-cooking ____

Name ____________________

# Home Study Master Unit 28

## Adding -ed and -ing

### Small Word Circles

Help your child form generalizations that will help him or her remember the spellings of the words in this unit. One such generalization is that each of the words is made up of a word plus a suffix. Then have your child write each spelling word and circle the smaller word in each.

1. stopped
2. digging
3. rubbed
4. sitting
5. planned
6. wrapping
7. sledding
8. dropped
9. scrubbing
10. hopped
11. putting
12. tripped
13. swimming
14. spotted
15. running

1. ____________________
2. ____________________
3. ____________________
4. ____________________
5. ____________________
6. ____________________
7. ____________________
8. ____________________
9. ____________________
10. ____________________
11. ____________________
12. ____________________
13. ____________________
14. ____________________
15. ____________________

Name ______________________

**Hoja para estudiar en casa**

Unit **28**

## Adding -ed and -ing

### Palabras pequeñas en círculos

Ayuden a su hijo o hija a encontrar un método que le ayudará a recordar el deletreo de las palabras en esta unidad. Una de estas reglas generales es que muchas veces una palabra se compone de dos palabras pequeñas o de una palabra y un sufijo. Luego pídanle a su hijo o hija que escriba cada palabra y que circule la palabra o palabras pequeñas en cada una de las palabras compuestas.

1. *stopped* — se detuvo; se paró
2. *digging* — cavando
3. *rubbed* — frotó
4. *sitting* — sentándose; sentado
5. *planned* — planeó
6. *wrapping* — envolviendo
7. *sledding* — deslizándose en luge
8. *dropped* — dejó caer
9. *scrubbing* — fregando
10. *hopped* — dio un salto
11. *putting* — poniendo
12. *tripped* — tropezó
13. *swimming* — nadando
14. *spotted* — pinto; descubrió
15. *running* — corriendo

1. ______________________
2. ______________________
3. ______________________
4. ______________________
5. ______________________
6. ______________________
7. ______________________
8. ______________________
9. ______________________
10. ______________________
11. ______________________
12. ______________________
13. ______________________
14. ______________________
15. ______________________

Name ______________________

| | | | |
|---|---|---|---|
| 1. stopped | 3. dropped | 5. sitting | 7. running |
| 2. tripped | 4. planned | 6. putting | 8. swimming |

**A.** Write the spelling word that is made from each base word.

1. plan ____________
2. drop ____________
3. stop ____________
4. trip ____________
5. swim ____________
6. run ____________
7. put ____________
8. sit ____________

**B.** Write the spelling word that goes with each meaning.

1. placing something ____________

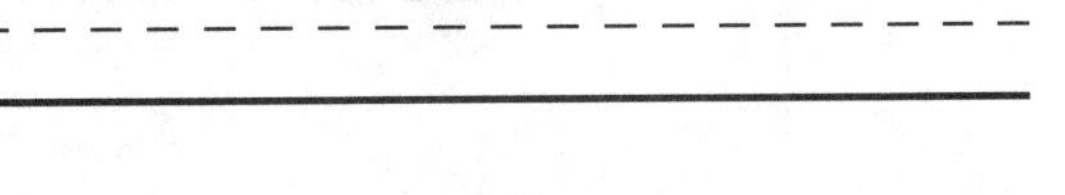

2. kept from moving ____________

3. stumbled ____________

4. let fall ____________

Name ____________________

Unit 28

Practice Master

| stopped | dropped | sitting | running |
|---|---|---|---|
| tripped | planned | putting | swimming |

**C.** Write the spelling word that does not belong in each group.

**1.** walking, jogging, running, sitting ____________________

**2.** swimming, putting, setting, placing ____________________

**3.** hopped, jumped, tripped, bounced ____________________

**4.** skated, walked, dropped, jogged ____________________

**D.** Add the ending shown to each base word to make four spelling words. Remember that the ending consonant of these base words doubles when **-ed** or **-ing** is added. Write the words.

**Add -ed**

**1.** stop ____________________

**2.** plan ____________________

**3.** trip ____________________

**4.** drop ____________________

**Add -ing**

**1.** swim ____________________

**2.** sit ____________________

**3.** run ____________________

**4.** put ____________________

Unit **28**

**Test Master**

Name ____________________________________

Read each sentence. Look at the underlined spelling word. Fill in a circle. Show if the word is spelled **Right** or **Wrong**.

**Sample** — Right / Wrong

**The students are <u>sitting</u> quietly at their desks.** ● ○

| | Answer Box | |
|---|---|---|
| | Right | Wrong |
| 1. My dog likes <u>diging</u> for bones. | 1. ○ | ○ |
| 2. He <u>dropped</u> the bone into the hole | 2. ○ | ○ |
| 3. The rabbit <u>hopt</u> across my front lawn. | 3. ○ | ○ |
| 4. After dinner we <u>plannd</u> to take a ride. | 4. ○ | ○ |
| 5. Where are you <u>putting</u> my coat? | 5. ○ | ○ |
| 6. My friend and I <u>rubbed</u> the magic lamp. | 6. ○ | ○ |
| 7. I will be <u>running</u> in the two-mile race. | 7. ○ | ○ |
| 8. Dad is <u>scrubbing</u> the walls of the garage. | 8. ○ | ○ |
| 9. Mr. and Mrs. Smith were <u>siting</u> on the park bench. | 9. ○ | ○ |
| 10. We went <u>sledding</u> down the steep hill. | 10. ○ | ○ |
| 11. A leopard has <u>spotted</u> fur. | 11. ○ | ○ |
| 12. After six hours we <u>stopped</u> for dinner. | 12. ○ | ○ |
| 13. We went <u>swimmin</u> in my friend's pool. | 13. ○ | ○ |
| 14. I <u>tript</u> over the rake in my yard. | 14. ○ | ○ |
| 15. My sister is <u>rapping</u> the present. | 15. ○ | ○ |

Unit 28

Name ____________________ **Homework Master**

Match each subject with a predicate to make a correct sentence. Draw lines to show the matches you make.

| | |
|---|---|
| 1. The cars • | • will go swimming in the pool. |
| 2. The rabbit • | • are sitting on a tree branch. |
| 3. The girl • | • stopped and honked their horns. |
| 4. The birds • | • have planned a trip to the zoo. |
| 5. We • | • rubbed her arm after she fell. |
| 6. The workers • | • tripped over his sister's toys. |
| 7. The boys and girls • | • hopped off into the woods. |
| 8. Joseph • | • are digging a hole for a well. |

| | |
|---|---|
| 9. That girl • | • went sledding with his son. |
| 10. Mom and Dad • | • are scrubbing their dog. |
| 11. The baby • | • is running as fast as she can. |
| 12. The firefighters • | • spotted his bib. |
| 13. They • | • dropped his books on the floor. |
| 14. Mr. Richards • | • are wrapping the presents for my party. |
| 15. Alan • | • are putting on boots and helmets. |

Now pick any subject and any predicate. Make a new sentence. It can be silly or serious.

______________________________________________

______________________________________________

Name ______________________

## Contractions

1. he's
2. what's
3. don't
4. I'm
5. that's
6. doesn't
7. there's
8. she's
9. isn't
10. I'll
11. won't
12. here's
13. didn't
14. who's
15. can't

## Spelling Code

Write the spelling words in code by replacing each letter with the corresponding number in the chart below. Keep the apostrophes, too. Then ask your child to use the chart to decode the words. You might also include spelling words written in code in "secret messages" to your child.

| | | |
|---|---|---|
| a=1 | b=2 | c=3 |
| d=4 | e=5 | f=6 |
| g=7 | h=8 | i=9 |
| j=10 | k=11 | l=12 |
| m=13 | n=14 | o=15 |
| p=16 | q=17 | r=18 |
| s=19 | t=20 | u=21 |
| v=22 | w=23 | x=24 |
| y=25 | z=26 | |

1. ______________________
2. ______________________
3. ______________________
4. ______________________
5. ______________________
6. ______________________
7. ______________________
8. ______________________
9. ______________________
10. ______________________
11. ______________________
12. ______________________
13. ______________________
14. ______________________
15. ______________________

Name ______________________

## Hoja para estudiar en casa

### Deletrear en claves

Deletreen las palabras en clave usando el número que corresponde a cada letra en el cuadro siguiente. Luego pídanle a su hjio o hija que use el cuadro para descifrar las palabras. Con su hijo o hija pueden usar también palabras escritas en claves en "mensajes secretos".

| | | |
|---|---|---|
| a=1 | b=2 | c=3 |
| d=4 | e=5 | f=6 |
| g=7 | h=8 | i=9 |
| j=10 | k=11 | l=12 |
| m=13 | n=14 | o=15 |
| p=16 | q=17 | r=18 |
| s=19 | t=20 | u=21 |
| v=22 | w=23 | x=24 |
| y=25 | z=26 | |

### Contractions

1. he's — (él) es, está
2. what's — ¿qué es, está?
3. don't — no
4. I'm — soy; estoy
5. that's — que es, está; eso es
6. doesn't — no
7. there's — allí está; hay
8. she's — (ella) es, está
9. isn't — no es, está
10. I'll — voy a ... (indica el futuro)
11. won't — no va a ... (indica el futuro)
12. here's — aquí está
13. didn't — no (lo hizo) (indica el pasado)
14. who's — quien es, está
15. can't — no puede

1. ______________
2. ______________
3. ______________
4. ______________
5. ______________
6. ______________
7. ______________
8. ______________
9. ______________
10. ______________
11. ______________
12. ______________
13. ______________
14. ______________
15. ______________

Name ______________________________

Unit 29 **Practice Master**

| | | | |
|---|---|---|---|
| 1. I'm | 3. he's | 5. can't | 7. won't |
| 2. I'll | 4. that's | 6. don't | 8. didn't |

**A.** Write the spelling word that belongs in each sentence.

**1.** Juan ____ take an umbrella yesterday. ______________

**2.** I'm sure it ____ rain tomorrow. ______________

**3.** I hope ____ be in your class. ______________

**4.** I ____ think there are any pencils left. ______________

**B.** Circle the words in each sentence that can be written as a contraction. Write the contractions.

**1.** She cannot find the missing key. ______________

**2.** That is the best joke that I have ever heard. ______________

**3.** He is my best friend. ______________

**4.** I am going tomorrow. ______________

Unit 29

Name ______________________

Practice Master

| I'm | he's | can't | won't |
|---|---|---|---|
| I'll | that's | don't | didn't |

**C.** Write the contraction that is an antonym for each word.

1. can ______________

3. will ______________

2. do ______________

4. did ______________

**D.** Write spelling words for the words shown on the plant.

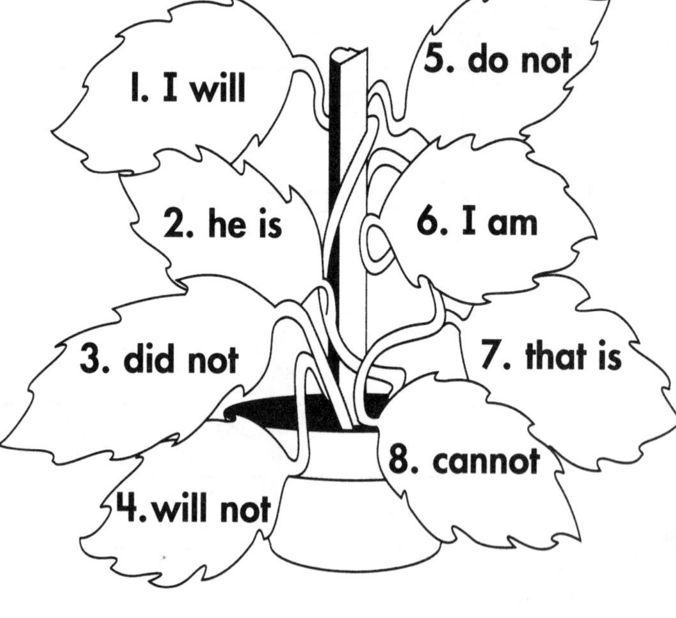


1. ______________

2. ______________

3. ______________

4. ______________

5. ______________

6. ______________

7. ______________

8. ______________

Name ______________________________

Read each sentence. Look at the underlined spelling word. Fill in a circle. Show if the word is spelled **Right** or **Wrong**.

**Sample** — Right / Wrong

**My brother cann't lift as much as I can.** ○ ●

## Answer Box

| Sentence | | Right | Wrong |
|---|---|---|---|
| 1. They din't like the last act of the play. | 1. | ○ | ○ |
| 2. We can't ride our bikes on that bumpy road. | 2. | ○ | ○ |
| 3. I am sure he deosn't mind if I sit here. | 3. | ○ | ○ |
| 4. We do'nt want to go swimming today. | 4. | ○ | ○ |
| 5. Mike is very good, but he's not the best player. | 5. | ○ | ○ |
| 6. Here's the ticket for the ride. | 6. | ○ | ○ |
| 7. I'll draw another picture of a farm. | 7. | ○ | ○ |
| 8. I do not know if I'm the winner. | 8. | ○ | ○ |
| 9. I know that Mary is'nt coming with us. | 9. | ○ | ○ |
| 10. Judy likes baseball, and she's a good batter. | 10. | ○ | ○ |
| 11. That's the best game I ever played. | 11. | ○ | ○ |
| 12. Do you know there's a parade next Saturday? | 12. | ○ | ○ |
| 13. What's the score of the football game? | 13. | ○ | ○ |
| 14. Do you know whoo's playing tonight? | 14. | ○ | ○ |
| 15. If we hurry we won't miss the bus. | 15. | ○ | ○ |

Name ______________________

Write the numerals for the two words that make the contraction shown below. The first one is done as an example.

| | | |
|---|---|---|
| 1. I | 5. there | 9. here |
| 2. does | 6. do | 10. will |
| 3. what | 7. am | 11. not |
| 4. who | 8. is | 12. he |

I'm 1 7 there's ___ ___ he's ___ ___ don't ___ ___

what's ___ ___ who's ___ ___ doesn't ___ ___ isn't ___ ___

Circle the words in each sentence that can be written as a contraction. Write the contraction on the line.

1. I will not be able to play football. ______________

2. I did not know her name. ______________

3. She cannot find the missing key. ______________

4. What is the answer to this problem? ______________

5. That is the best joke I have ever heard. ______________

6. She is my best friend. ______________

7. I will ask for help with this problem. ______________

8. Here is the lost cap. ______________

Name ____________________



## Assessment and Review

1. *happen*
2. *sudden*
3. *letter*
4. *summer*
5. *funny*
6. *pretty*
7. *happy*
8. *sorry*
9. *baking*
10. *having*
11. *coming*
12. *leaving*
13. *dropped*
14. *stopped*
15. *running*
16. *swimming*
17. *can't*
18. *that's*
19. *didn't*
20. *won't*

### Keeping in Touch

Ask your child to write a letter to a family member or a friend in another city or state about his or her activities during the past summer. Have him or her use as many words from the spelling list in this unit as possible. Not everything has to be true.

1. ____________________
2. ____________________
3. ____________________
4. ____________________
5. ____________________
6. ____________________
7. ____________________
8. ____________________
9. ____________________
10. ____________________
11. ____________________
12. ____________________
13. ____________________
14. ____________________
15. ____________________
16. ____________________
17. ____________________
18. ____________________
19. ____________________
20. ____________________

Name ______________________



## Hoja para estudiar en casa

### Mantenerse en contacto

Pidan a su hijo o hija que escriba una carta a un miembro de la familia que vive en otra ciudad o estado, describiendo sus actividades durante el verano pasado. Indíquenle que use tantas palabras de la lista de esta unidad como puede. No es necesario que todo sea verdad.

### Assessment and Review

1. *happen* ocurrir
2. *sudden* repentino
3. *letter* letra; carta
4. *summer* verano
5. *funny* chistoso; raro
6. *pretty* bonita; bastante
7. *happy* contento; alegre
8. *sorry* sentirlo
9. *baking* horneando
10. *having* teniendo
11. *coming* viniendo
12. *leaving* saliendo; dejando
13. *dropped* dejó caer
14. *stopped* se detuvo; se paró
15. *running* corriendo
16. *swimming* nadando
17. *can't* no puede
18. *that's* que es, está; eso es
19. *didn't* no (lo hizo) (indica el pasado)
20. *won't* no va a… (indica el futuro)

1. ______________________
2. ______________________
3. ______________________
4. ______________________
5. ______________________
6. ______________________
7. ______________________
8. ______________________
9. ______________________
10. ______________________
11. ______________________
12. ______________________
13. ______________________
14. ______________________
15. ______________________
16. ______________________
17. ______________________
18. ______________________
19. ______________________
20. ______________________

Unit **30**

Test **Master**

Name ______________________________

**A.** Look at these spelling words. Write **C** for each word that is spelled correctly. If the word is misspelled, write the word correctly below.

1. summer ☐
2. didn't ☐
3. hapy ☐
4. funny ☐
5. thats ☐
6. lettre ☐
7. pretty ☐
8. leaveing ☐
9. sudden ☐
10. running ☐
11. cano't ☐
12. swimming ☐
13. happen ☐
14. droped ☐
15. baking ☐

______________________________

______________________________

**B.** Find the spelling word in each sentence. If the word is misspelled, write **NC** (not correct). If the word is spelled correctly, write **C**.

1. She is haveing lunch with Beth. ☐
2. I won't be late. ☐
3. Our bus stopped at the crosswalk. ☐
4. I'm sorey that I bumped into you. ☐
5. Are you comeing with me? ☐

Unit 31

Name ______________________________ **Home Study Master**

## Plurals: -s, -es

## Concentration

Write the spelling words on index cards or slips of paper with blank spaces in place of the letters that spell the vowels **a, e, i, o, u**. Write the letters that are missing from each word on separate cards. Make two sets. Place each set of cards facedown in three stacks. Have your child draw one card from each stack and try to make a spelling word from the parts. If a spelling word can be made, have your child read the word and then write it. If no spelling word can be made, have him or her return the cards to the stacks. Shuffle the cards and continue until all the cards have been used.

1. flags
2. inches
3. dresses
4. pies
5. bushes
6. classes
7. apples
8. colors
9. drums
10. branches
11. things
12. buses
13. benches
14. tracks
15. brushes

1. ______________________
2. ______________________
3. ______________________
4. ______________________
5. ______________________
6. ______________________
7. ______________________
8. ______________________
9. ______________________
10. ______________________
11. ______________________
12. ______________________
13. ______________________
14. ______________________
15. ______________________

Name ____________________

# Hoja para estudiar en casa

## Plurals: -s, -es

### Concentración

Deletreen las palabras en fichas o en cuadros de papel dejando en blanco las letras para las vocales **a, e, i, o, u**. Escriban las letras que faltan en otras fichas. Pongan cada serie de fichas boca abajo en tres montones. Díganle a su hijo o hija que tome una ficha de cada montón y que trate de componer una palabra usando las tres fichas. Si es posible componer una palabra, díganle a su hijo o hija que lea la palabra y luego que la escriba. Si es imposible componer una palabra, déjenle poner las tres fichas en los tres montones, barajar las fichas de cada montón, y continuar el juego hasta que no queden fichas.

1. *flags* banderas
2. *inches* pulgadas
3. *dresses* vestidos; se viste
4. *pies* pasteles; empanadas
5. *bushes* arbustos
6. *classes* clases
7. *apples* manzanas
8. *colors* colores
9. *drums* tambores
10. *branches* ramas
11. *things* cosas
12. *buses* autobuses
13. *benches* bancos (para sentarse)
14. *tracks* rieles; carriles; huellas
15. *brushes* cepillos

1. ____________________
2. ____________________
3. ____________________
4. ____________________
5. ____________________
6. ____________________
7. ____________________
8. ____________________
9. ____________________
10. ____________________
11. ____________________
12. ____________________
13. ____________________
14. ____________________
15. ____________________

Name ______________________________

| | | | |
|---|---|---|---|
| 1. colors | 3. tracks | 5. branches | 7. dresses |
| 2. things | 4. inches | 6. buses | 8. classes |

**A.** Add either **-s** or **-es** to make the words plural. Write the spelling words.

**1.** color ____________________

**2.** class ____________________

**3.** track ____________________

**4.** inch ____________________

**5.** bus ____________________

**6.** dress ____________________

**7.** thing ____________________

**8.** branch ____________________

**B.** Write the spelling word that belongs in each group.

**1.** miles, yards, feet, ____ ____________________

**2.** cars, trucks, trains, ____ ____________________

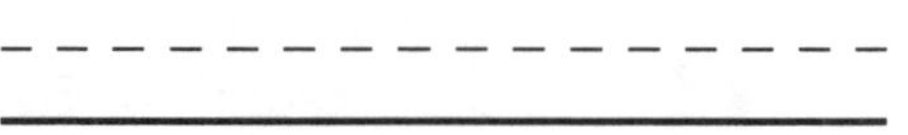

**3.** skirts, pants, ____ ____________________

**4.** roots, bark, leaves, ____ ____________________

Unit 31

**Practice Master**

Name ______________________

| colors | tracks | branches | dresses |
|---|---|---|---|
| things | inches | buses | classes |

**C.** Write the spelling word that goes with each meaning.

1. the rails on which a train moves ______________

2. groups of people learning together ______________

3. red, green, and blue ______________

**D.** Write the spelling word that fits each shape.

1. ______________ 5. ______________

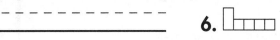

2. ______________ 6. ______________

3. ______________ 7. ______________

4. ______________ 8. ______________

Unit 31

Test Master

Name ____________________

Read each sentence. Look at the underlined spelling word. Fill in a circle. Show if the word is spelled **Right** or **Wrong**.

**Sample** — **Right** / **Wrong**

**We put the boxes in a row.** ● ○

## Answer Box

| | Right | Wrong |
|---|---|---|
| 1. We picked aples to make cider. | ○ | ○ |
| 2. They put benches all around the park. | ○ | ○ |
| 3. The storm had broken many branches off that tree. | ○ | ○ |
| 4. We cleaned the brusches in the water. | ○ | ○ |
| 5. All the school busez were ready to go. | ○ | ○ |
| 6. The little birds hid in the bushes. | ○ | ○ |
| 7. How many classes are going on the trip? | ○ | ○ |
| 8. His new shirt had many colors in it. | ○ | ○ |
| 9. I bought two new dresess last week. | ○ | ○ |
| 10. We heard the durms playing in the band. | ○ | ○ |
| 11. The park had flags from many places. | ○ | ○ |
| 12. One foot is the same as 12 inches. | ○ | ○ |
| 13. My mom made six pumpkin piez. | ○ | ○ |
| 14. My father told me to put my things away. | ○ | ○ |
| 15. We saw the traks of a fox. | ○ | ○ |

Name ______________________________

Look at the picture of a pie. Next to it is another picture of a pie. The label reads **pies**. Finish the other pictures. Draw one more. Label each set of pictures.

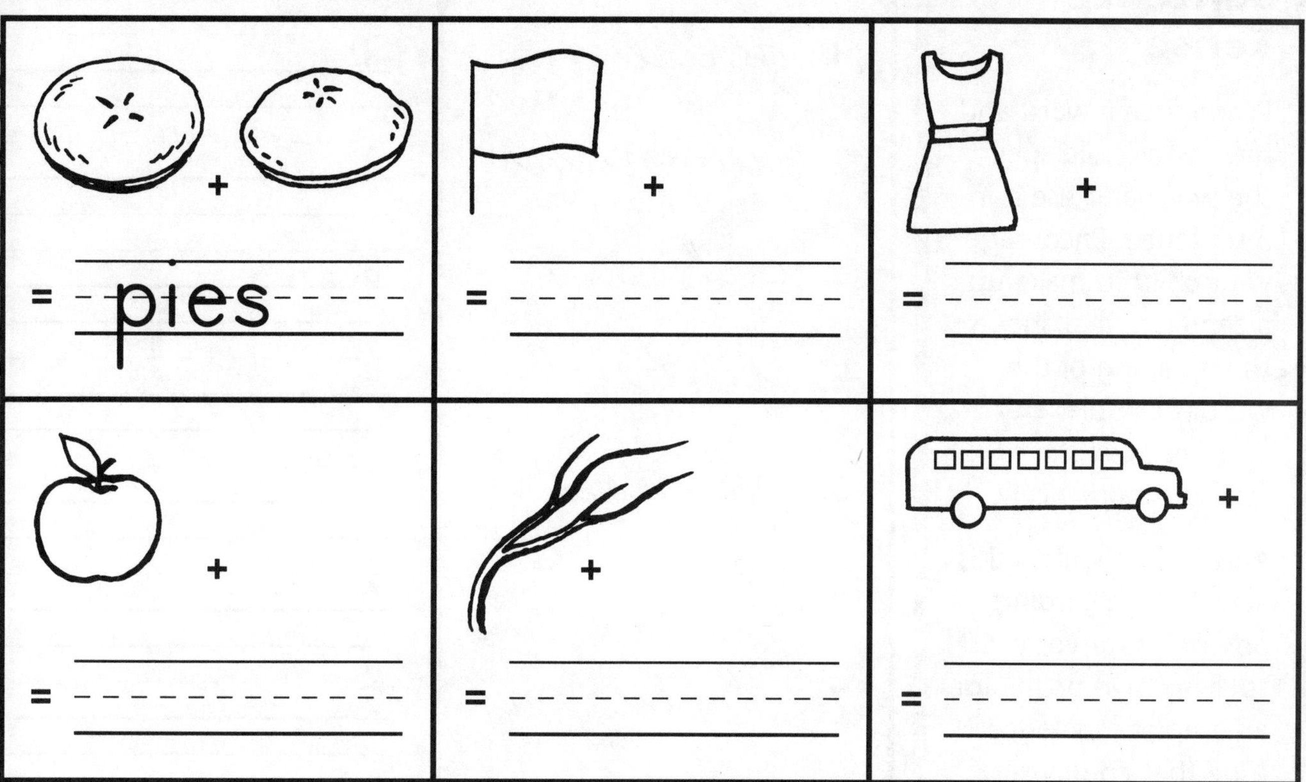


Unscramble the letters to make spelling words. Write the words on the lines.

1. a l s c s e s
2. n c e s b e h
3. n h i c e s
4. h u r e s s b
5. o o c l r s
6. s a t k c r
7. m d r s u
8. h g i t n s
9. u e s s h b

1. ______________
2. ______________
3. ______________
4. ______________
5. ______________
6. ______________
7. ______________
8. ______________
9. ______________

Name ____________________

Unit 32

**Home Study Master**

## Irregular Plurals

### Sentence Sense

Pronounce a word and have your child spell the word and use it in a sentence. Encourage your child to make up a sentence that shows the meaning of the word. Example: **calf**. *The small calf stayed near the mother cow.*

Add excitement to this activity by awarding one point for correct spelling, two points for a complete sentence (one that contains a noun phrase and a verb phrase), and three points if the sentence clearly shows the meaning of the word.

1. goose
2. woman
3. calf
4. fish
5. mouse
6. leaf
7. children
8. geese
9. calves
10. leaves
11. half
12. child
13. women
14. mice
15. halves

1. ____________________
2. ____________________
3. ____________________
4. ____________________
5. ____________________
6. ____________________
7. ____________________
8. ____________________
9. ____________________
10. ____________________
11. ____________________
12. ____________________
13. ____________________
14. ____________________
15. ____________________

Name ____________________

**Hoja para estudiar en casa**

## Irregular Plurals

1. goose
ganso
2. woman
mujer
3. calf
ternero
4. fish
pescado; pez, peces; pescar
5. mouse
ratoncito
6. leaf
hoja
7. children
hijos
8. geese
gansos
9. calves
terneros
10. leaves
hojas
11. half
medio; mitad
12. child
hijo/a
13. women
mujeres
14. mice
ratoncitos
15. halves
dos partes iguales

1. ____________________
2. ____________________
3. ____________________
4. ____________________
5. ____________________
6. ____________________
7. ____________________
8. ____________________
9. ____________________
10. ____________________
11. ____________________
12. ____________________
13. ____________________
14. ____________________
15. ____________________

### Frases buenas

Pronuncien una palabra y díganle a su hijo o hija que deletree la palabra y luego que la use en una frase. Animen a su hijo o hija a que componga una frase que indica el significado de la palabra. Por ejemplo: **calf**. *The small calf stayed near the mother cow.* (**ternero**. *El pequeño ternero se quedó cerca de la vaca madre.*)

Para hacer la actividad más interesante, premien con un punto al niño o a la niña por el deletreo correcto, dénle dos puntos por una frase completa, y dénle tres puntos si la frase indica claramente el significado de la palabra.

Unit **32**

**Practice Master**

Name ______________________________

| | | | |
|---|---|---|---|
| 1. half | 3. mouse | 5. women | 7. children |
| 2. leaves | 4. woman | 6. child | 8. fish |

**A.** Write the spelling words in a-b-c order.

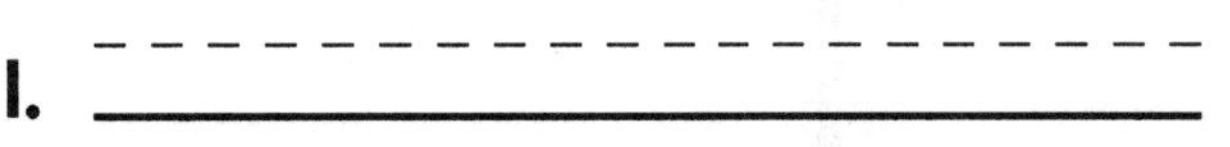

1. ______________ 5. ______________

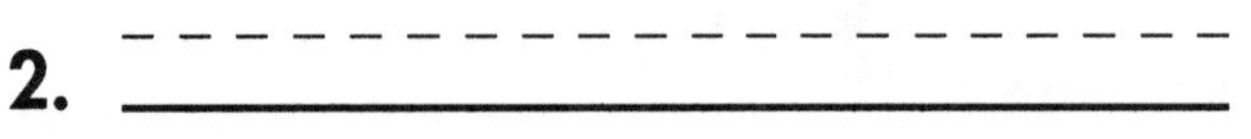

2. ______________ 6. ______________

3. ______________ 7. ______________

4. ______________ 8. ______________

**B.** Write the spelling word that is the plural form of each word.

1. leaf ______________

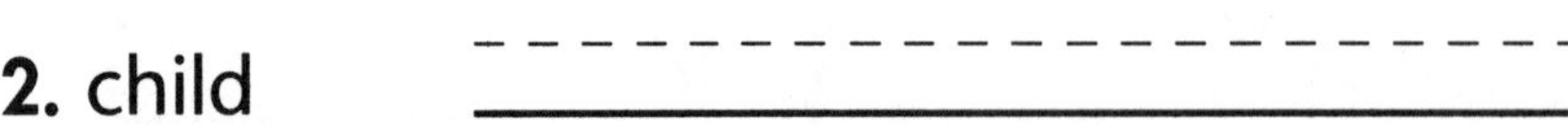

2. child ______________

3. woman ______________

Name ______________________________

| half | mouse | women | children |
|---|---|---|---|
| leaves | woman | child | fish |

**C.** Write the spelling word that belongs in each group.

**1.** quarter, third, ____ ______________________

**2.** man, woman, ____ ______________________

**3.** trunks, branches, ____ ______________________

**D.** Use spelling words to complete the puzzle. Letters are given to get you started.

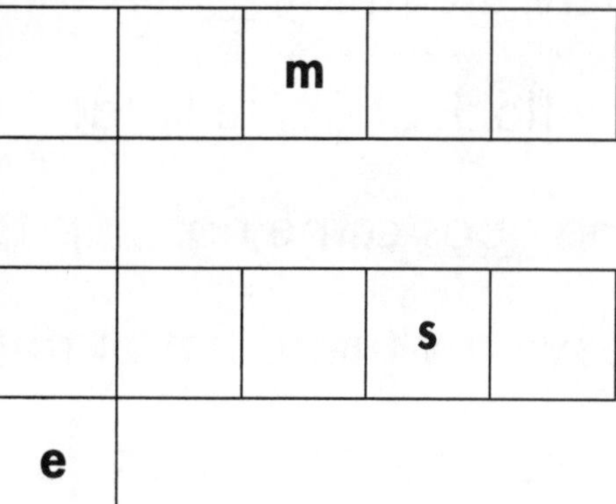


c

e

f

Name ______________________ **Test Master**

Read each sentence. Look at the underlined spelling word. Fill in a circle. Show if the word is spelled **Right** or **Wrong**.

**Sample**

**We saw a herd of <u>dear</u> in the field.** Right ○ Wrong ●

**Answer Box**

| | Sentence | Right | Wrong |
|---|---|---|---|
| **1.** | The young <u>caf</u> played near its mother. | ○ | ○ |
| **2.** | All the <u>calves</u> are in the field. | ○ | ○ |
| **3.** | This pretty picture was drawn by that <u>child</u>. | ○ | ○ |
| **4.** | The third-grade class has 20 <u>childern</u>. | ○ | ○ |
| **5.** | There are many <u>fish</u> in that pond. | ○ | ○ |
| **6.** | The flock of <u>geese</u> landed on our pond. | ○ | ○ |
| **7.** | One <u>goos</u> came right up to us for bits of bread. | ○ | ○ |
| **8.** | I gave my friend <u>haf</u> of my apple. | ○ | ○ |
| **9.** | We cut the cake into two <u>haves</u>. | ○ | ○ |
| **10.** | The <u>leaf</u> has a strange shape. | ○ | ○ |
| **11.** | In fall the <u>leafes</u> change to pretty colors. | ○ | ○ |
| **12.** | The cat chased the <u>mice</u> into the barn. | ○ | ○ |
| **13.** | One <u>mouse</u> stayed behind the boxes. | ○ | ○ |
| **14.** | A <u>woman</u> with a broom chased the cat away. | ○ | ○ |
| **15.** | She then went back and told the other <u>women</u>. | ○ | ○ |

Unit 32

Name ______________________ **Homework Master**

Write the missing spelling word to complete each sentence.

1. **Boy** is to **man** as **girl** is to ____.

2. **Deer** is to **fawn** as **cow** is to ____.

3. **Roar** is to **lion** as **squeak** is to ____.

4. **Job** is to a **worker** as **school** is to a ____.

5. **Animal** is to **tiger** as **bird** is to ____.

6. **Arm** is to **hand** as **branch** is to ____.

7. **Sky** is to **bird** as **water** is to ____.

Use spelling words to complete each puzzle. Letters are given in each puzzle to get you started.

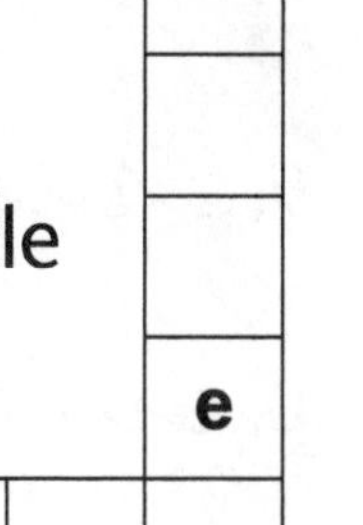


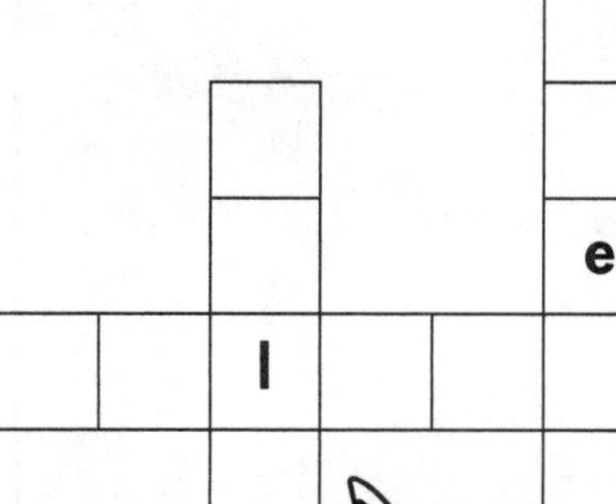


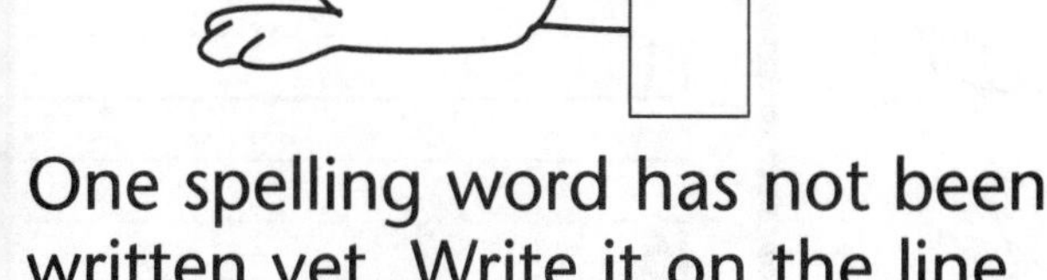

One spelling word has not been written yet. Write it on the line.

Name ______________________

Unit 33

**Home Study Master**

## Record-a-Word

Encourage your child to say and spell each of the spelling words into a tape recorder. Replay the tape so that you and your child can check the spelling against the word list.

## Suffixes: -er, -est

1. larger
2. sadder
3. widest
4. sharper
5. closest
6. hotter
7. saddest
8. redder
9. reddest
10. wider
11. later
12. largest
13. closer
14. hottest
15. latest

1. ______
2. ______
3. ______
4. ______
5. ______
6. ______
7. ______
8. ______
9. ______
10. ______
11. ______
12. ______
13. ______
14. ______
15. ______

Name ______________________

**Hoja para estudiar en casa**

## Suffixes: -er, -est

### Grabar una palabra

Animen a su hijo o hija a que diga y a que deletree cada una de las palabras usando una grabadora. Luego pongan la cinta y escuchen las palabras. Miren la lista de palabras de esta lección para comprobar su deletreo.

1. *larger* — más grande
2. *sadder* — más triste
3. *widest* — el más ancho
4. *sharper* — más agudo
5. *closest* — el más cercano
6. *hotter* — más caliente
7. *saddest* — el más triste
8. *redder* — más rojo
9. *reddest* — el más rojo
10. *wider* — más ancho
11. *later* — más tarde
12. *largest* — el más grande
13. *closer* — más cerca
14. *hottest* — el más caliente
15. *latest* — el último; el más tarde

1. ____________________
2. ____________________
3. ____________________
4. ____________________
5. ____________________
6. ____________________
7. ____________________
8. ____________________
9. ____________________
10. ____________________
11. ____________________
12. ____________________
13. ____________________
14. ____________________
15. ____________________

Name ______________________

Unit 33 **Practice Master**

| | | | |
|---|---|---|---|
| 1. widest | 3. closer | 5. hottest | 7. sadder |
| 2. later | 4. largest | 6. reddest | 8. sharper |

**A.** Write the spelling word that is made from each base word.

**1.** sharp ______________

**2.** hot ______________

**3.** late ______________

**4.** red ______________

**5.** large ______________

**6.** close ______________

**7.** wide ______________

**8.** sad ______________

**B.** Write the spelling word that is an antonym for each word.

**1.** happier ______________

**2.** narrowest ______________

**3.** smallest ______________

**4.** coldest ______________

**5.** earlier ______________

**6.** farther ______________

Name ____________________

Unit **33** **Practice Master**

| widest | closer | hottest | sadder |
|---|---|---|---|
| later | largest | reddest | sharper |

**C.** Write the word that would be the dictionary entry word for each spelling word.

**1.** widest ____________________

**2.** later ____________________

**3.** largest ____________________

**4.** sharper ____________________

**D.** Use the code to find spelling words. Write the words.

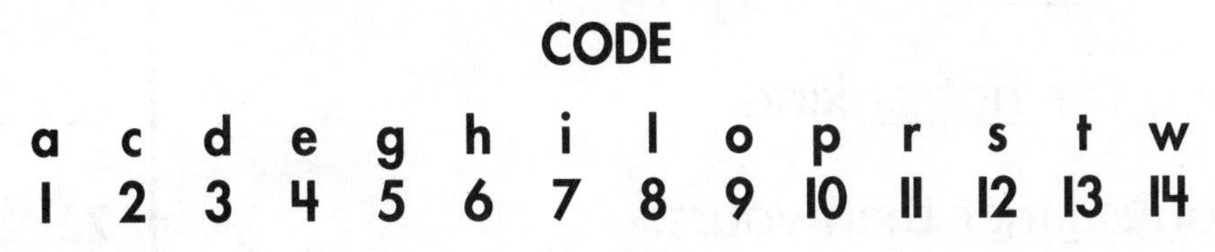

**CODE**

| a | c | d | e | g | h | i | l | o | p | r | s | t | w |
|---|---|---|---|---|---|---|---|---|---|---|---|---|---|
| 1 | 2 | 3 | 4 | 5 | 6 | 7 | 8 | 9 | 10 | 11 | 12 | 13 | 14 |

**1.** 6 + 9 + 13 + 13 + 4 + 12 + 13 = ____ ____________________

**2.** 8 + 1 + 11 + 5 + 4 + 12 + 13 = ____ ____________________

**3.** 11 + 4 + 3 + 3 + 4 + 12 + 13 = ____ ____________________

**4.** 2 + 8 + 9 + 12 + 4 + 11 = ____ ____________________

**5.** 12 + 1 + 3 + 3 + 4 + 11 = ____ ____________________

Unit **33**

Name ______________________ **Test Master**

Read each sentence. Look at the underlined spelling word. Fill in a circle. Show if the word is spelled **Right** or **Wrong**.

**Sample**

That clown has a sadder face than this one. Right ● Wrong ○

**Answer Box**

| Sentence | | Right | Wrong |
|---|---|---|---|
| 1. You are closer to the door than I am. | 1. | ○ | ○ |
| 2. That was the closess we ever came to winning. | 2. | ○ | ○ |
| 3. Your paint is reder than mine. | 3. | ○ | ○ |
| 4. That clay is the reddest of all. | 4. | ○ | ○ |
| 5. That stove is hottre than your fire. | 5. | ○ | ○ |
| 6. An oil fire is the hotest kind. | 6. | ○ | ○ |
| 7. My balloon is larjer than yours. | 7. | ○ | ○ |
| 8. My friend has the largest balloon of all. | 8. | ○ | ○ |
| 9. I will help you with your homework later. | 9. | ○ | ○ |
| 10. That is the latest my dad ever had to work. | 10. | ○ | ○ |
| 11. I'm sader today than I was yesterday. | 11. | ○ | ○ |
| 12. My teacher told us the sattest tale I've ever heard. | 12. | ○ | ○ |
| 13. To write better, you need a sharper pencil. | 13. | ○ | ○ |
| 14. The river is whider than that brook. | 14. | ○ | ○ |
| 15. That is the widest pool I've ever seen. | 15. | ○ | ○ |

Name ____________________

Write the antonym for each word. Then write spelling words to show the **-er** and **-est** form of the words.

| | Antonym | -er form | -est form |
|---|---|---|---|
| 1. far | | | |
| 2. narrow | | | |
| 3. early | | | |
| 4. small | | | |
| 5. happy | | | |
| 6. cold | | | |

Draw a picture of something that is red. Next to it, draw a picture of something that is even redder. Then draw the reddest thing you have ever seen. Label each picture!

**7.**

**8.**

**9.**

**10.** What is the matter with the point of this pencil? Write your answer in a sentence.

Unit 34

Home Study Master

Name ____________________

## Suffix Take-Away

Ask your child to write each spelling word without the **-ly** suffix. (For example, **badly** becomes **bad**.) Remind your child that this is the base word of each spelling word. Ask your child to use both the base words and the spelling words in sentences.

### Suffix: -ly

1. slowly
2. mainly
3. badly
4. hourly
5. suddenly
6. lately
7. partly
8. closely
9. really
10. lastly
11. plainly
12. loudly
13. shortly
14. monthly
15. softly

1. ____________________
2. ____________________
3. ____________________
4. ____________________
5. ____________________
6. ____________________
7. ____________________
8. ____________________
9. ____________________
10. ____________________
11. ____________________
12. ____________________
13. ____________________
14. ____________________
15. ____________________

Name

## Hoja para estudiar en casa

### Quitar un sufijo

Pidan a su hijo o hija que escriba cada palabra para deletrear sin el sufijo **-ly**. (Por ejemplo: **badly** se convierte en **bad**.) Recuérdenle a su hijo o hija que esta es la palabra primitiva de cada palabra en la lista. Indiquen a su hijo o hija que escriba oraciones usando las palabras primitivas y las palabras de esta unidad.

### Suffix: -ly

1. *slowly* lentamente
2. *mainly* principalmente
3. *badly* mal
4. *hourly* por hora
5. *suddenly* de repente
6. *lately* últimamente
7. *partly* en parte
8. *closely* íntimamente
9. *really* realmente
10. *lastly* finalmente
11. *plainly* claramente
12. *loudly* ruidosamente
13. *shortly* dentro de poco
14. *monthly* mensualmente
15. *softly* suavemente

1. __________
2. __________
3. __________
4. __________
5. __________
6. __________
7. __________
8. __________
9. __________
10. __________
11. __________
12. __________
13. __________
14. __________
15. __________

Name ______________________

**Unit 34**
**Practice Master**

| | | | |
|---|---|---|---|
| 1. slowly | 3. really | 5. shortly | 7. monthly |
| 2. partly | 4. lastly | 6. hourly | 8. suddenly |

**A.** Add the suffix **-ly** to the base words to make spelling words. Write the words.

**1.** month ______________

**2.** part ______________

**3.** sudden ______________

**4.** hour ______________

**5.** short ______________

**6.** real ______________

**7.** slow ______________

**8.** last ______________

**B.** Write the spelling word that belongs in each sentence.

**1.** It will be ____ sunny today. ______________

**2.** Turtles move very ____. ______________

**3.** The clock chimes ____. ______________

**4.** ____ the rain stopped. ______________

Name ____________________

| slowly | really | shortly | monthly |
|---|---|---|---|
| partly | lastly | hourly | suddenly |

**C.** Write the spelling word that goes with each dictionary definition.

**1.** in part ____________

**2.** in fact, actually ____________

**3.** once every month ____________

**4.** done every hour ____________

**D.** Use spelling words to complete the puzzle.

**Across**
1. in a short time
4. not fast
5. once a month

**Down**
2. once an hour
3. at the end
4. quickly

Unit 34

**Test Master**

Name ____________________

Read each sentence. Look at the underlined spelling word. Fill in a circle. Show if the word is spelled **Right** or **Wrong**.

**Sample**

**Make sure that you drive sloly.** — Right ○ Wrong ●

1. The dog behaved badly in front of our visitors.
2. I worked closly with my teacher.
3. Please check the time on the clock hourly.
4. Lastly, I brushed my teeth.
5. Have you seen Pam laetly?
6. The man played his horn lowdly.
7. My house is mainly white.
8. We pay our rent monthly.
9. The plane was partly hidden by clouds.
10. The elephant was planely the largest animal.
11. The young girl reely enjoys fishing.
12. I will be ready to go shortly.
13. He came up to the stop sign sloely.
14. Please play the piano sofly.
15. The storm came up very suddenly.

**Answer Box**

| | Right | Wrong |
|---|---|---|
| 1. | ○ | ○ |
| 2. | ○ | ○ |
| 3. | ○ | ○ |
| 4. | ○ | ○ |
| 5. | ○ | ○ |
| 6. | ○ | ○ |
| 7. | ○ | ○ |
| 8. | ○ | ○ |
| 9. | ○ | ○ |
| 10. | ○ | ○ |
| 11. | ○ | ○ |
| 12. | ○ | ○ |
| 13. | ○ | ○ |
| 14. | ○ | ○ |
| 15. | ○ | ○ |

Name ______________________________

Choose spelling words to complete the sentences. Write the words on the lines.

| loudly | monthly | shortly | really | softly |
|---|---|---|---|---|
| closely | badly | partly | slowly | |

1. A turtle moves ____.
2. The people will cheer ____.
3. I will tiptoe ____.
4. The gas bill comes ____.
5. You should listen ____.
6. Never treat a pet ____.
7. I am just ____ finished.
8. I know I will finish ____.
9. This plant ____ needs water.

1. ______________
2. ______________
3. ______________
4. ______________
5. ______________
6. ______________
7. ______________
8. ______________
9. ______________

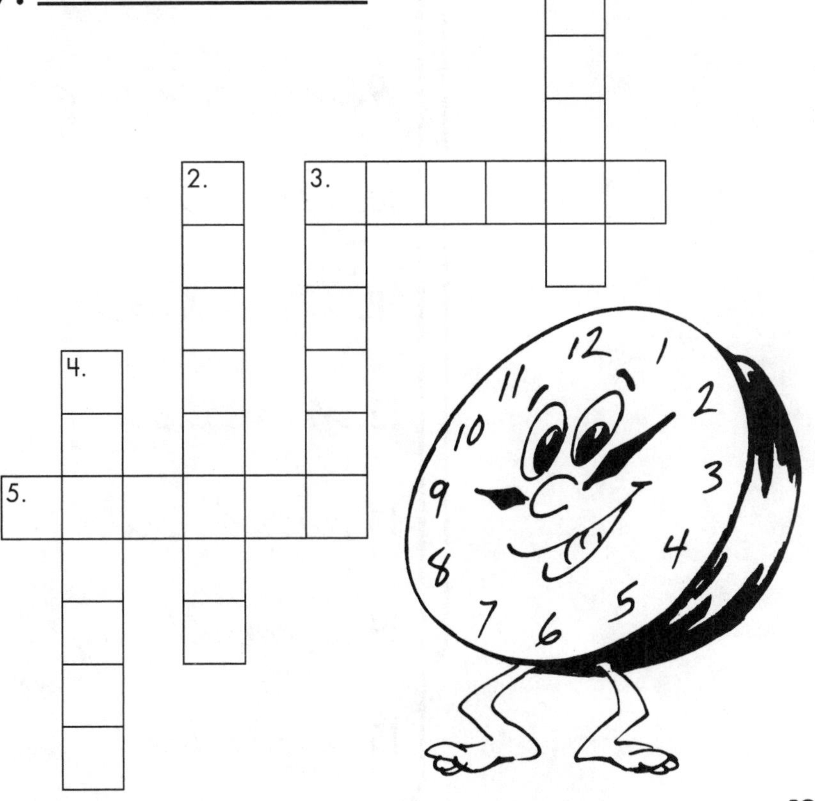


Read each clue. Then use spelling words to complete the puzzle.

**Across**

3. a little while ago
5. mostly

**Down**

1. once an hour
2. quickly
3. at the end
4. clearly

Name ____________________

Unit 35

**Home Study Master**

## Compound Words

1. herself
2. nobody
3. airplane
4. grandfather
5. someone
6. rainbow
7. anything
8. grandmother
9. everything
10. afternoon
11. sunshine
12. himself
13. anybody
14. something
15. without

1. ____________________
2. ____________________
3. ____________________
4. ____________________
5. ____________________
6. ____________________
7. ____________________
8. ____________________
9. ____________________
10. ____________________
11. ____________________
12. ____________________
13. ____________________
14. ____________________
15. ____________________

### Thank You!

Thank you for helping your child practice spelling at home this year. I hope that you have enjoyed the activities as well as the knowledge that you have been an integral part of your child's progress in school. During the summer months, please continue to use the activities to help your child develop his or her writing skills.

Unit 35

Name ____________________

# Hoja para estudiar en casa

## ¡Muchas gracias!

Muchas gracias por haber ayudado a su hijo o hija a practicar el deletreo de palabras en casa este año. Espero que se hayan divertido con los ejercicios y que se alegren también de saber que Uds. han contribuido al progreso de su hijo o hija en la escuela. Durante los meses del verano, por favor continúen el uso de estas actividades para ayudar a su hijo o hija a desarrollar y ampliar sus habilidades de escribir.

## Compound Words

1. *herself* se (ella)
2. *nobody* nadie
3. *airplane* avión
4. *grandfather* abuelo
5. *someone* alguna persona
6. *rainbow* arco iris
7. *anything* cualquier cosa
8. *grandmother* abuela
9. *everything* todo
10. *afternoon* la tarde
11. *sunshine* brillo del sol
12. *himself* se (él)
13. *anybody* cualquier persona
14. *something* algo
15. *without* sin

1. ____________________
2. ____________________
3. ____________________
4. ____________________
5. ____________________
6. ____________________
7. ____________________
8. ____________________
9. ____________________
10. ____________________
11. ____________________
12. ____________________
13. ____________________
14. ____________________
15. ____________________

Name ______________________

Unit 35 **Practice Master**

| | | | |
|---|---|---|---|
| 1. nobody | 3. anything | 5. herself | 7. afternoon |
| 2. someone | 4. everything | 6. without | 8. grandfather |

**A.** Write the spelling words in a-b-c order.

1. ______________________
2. ______________________
3. ______________________
4. ______________________
5. ______________________
6. ______________________
7. ______________________
8. ______________________

**B.** Put words together to make compound words from the spelling list.

| | | | |
|---|---|---|---|
| **out** | **noon** | **no** | **with** |
| **father** | **grand** | **after** | **body** |

1. ______________________
2. ______________________
3. ______________________
4. ______________________

Name ____________________

| | | | |
|---|---|---|---|
| nobody | anything | herself | afternoon |
| someone | everything | without | grandfather |

**C.** Write the spelling word that belongs in each group.

**1.** son, father, ____ ____________________

**2.** morning, ____, night ____________________

**D.** Match the puzzle pieces to form compound words. Then write the spelling words.

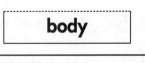

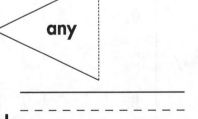

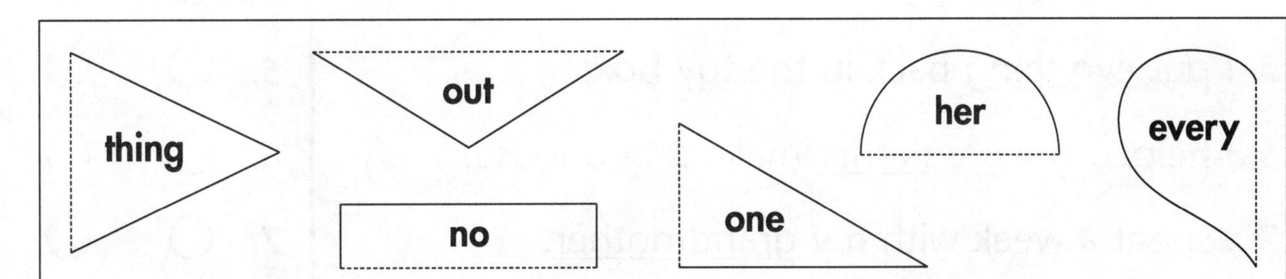


any

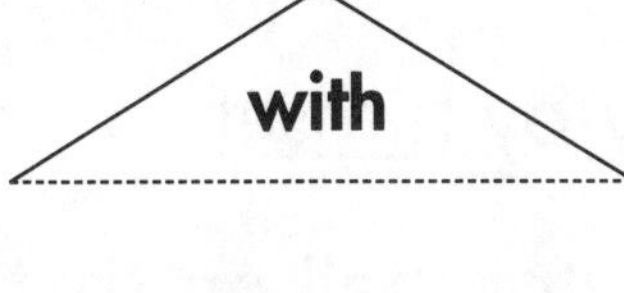


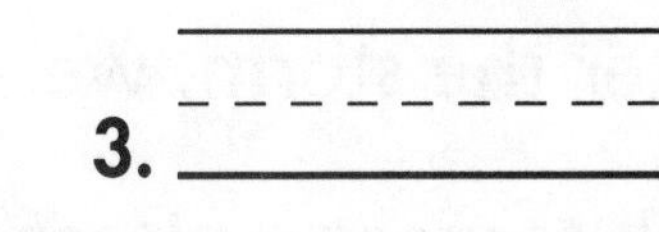


**1.** ____________________ **2.** ____________________ **3.** ____________________

some

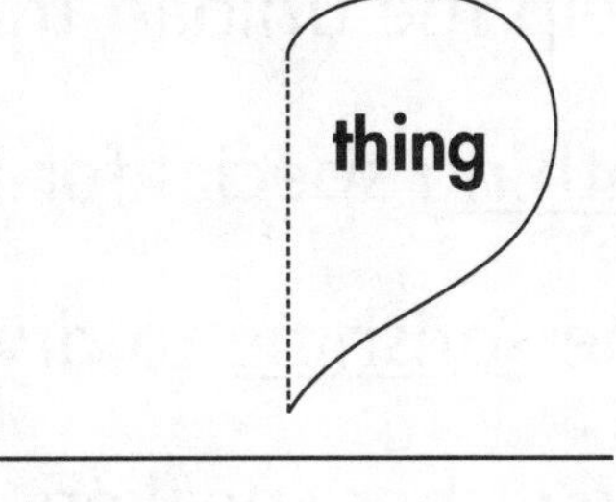


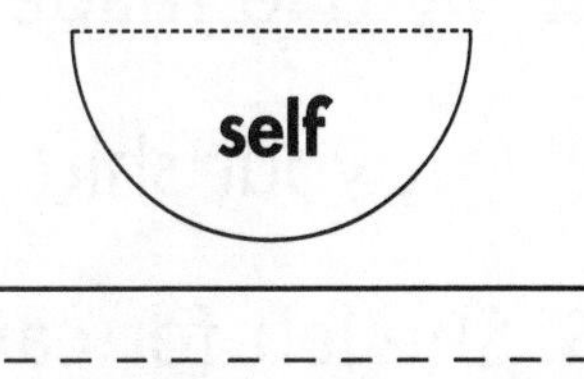


**4.** ____________________ **5.** ____________________ **6.** ____________________

Unit **35**

Name ______________________________ **Test Master**

Read each sentence. Look at the underlined spelling word. Fill in a circle. Show if the word is spelled **Right** or **Wrong**.

**Sample**
I have to clean my bedrum before I go. Right ○ Wrong ●

**Answer Box**

| | Sentence | Right | Wrong |
|---|---|---|---|
| 1. | I will go for a swim this afternoon. | ○ | ○ |
| 2. | We went on a trip in an airplain. | ○ | ○ |
| 3. | I don't know anybodie who wants this chair. | ○ | ○ |
| 4. | Is there anything you need at the store? | ○ | ○ |
| 5. | I put evrything back in the toy box. | ○ | ○ |
| 6. | I helped my granfather make a birdhouse. | ○ | ○ |
| 7. | I spent a week with my grandmother. | ○ | ○ |
| 8. | Susan can make a cake all by herself. | ○ | ○ |
| 9. | He walked to the library by himsef. | ○ | ○ |
| 10. | Nobody wanted to play football on that hot day. | ○ | ○ |
| 11. | After the storm, we saw a beautiful reinbow. | ○ | ○ |
| 12. | Will someone please help me unload the car? | ○ | ○ |
| 13. | My dad made me sumthing special for lunch. | ○ | ○ |
| 14. | Put your shirt out in the sonshine to dry. | ○ | ○ |
| 15. | She left for camp withowt her sneakers. | ○ | ○ |

Name ______________________ **Homework Master**

Match the puzzle pieces to form compound words. Draw in the missing pieces where they belong. Then write the spelling words as labels.

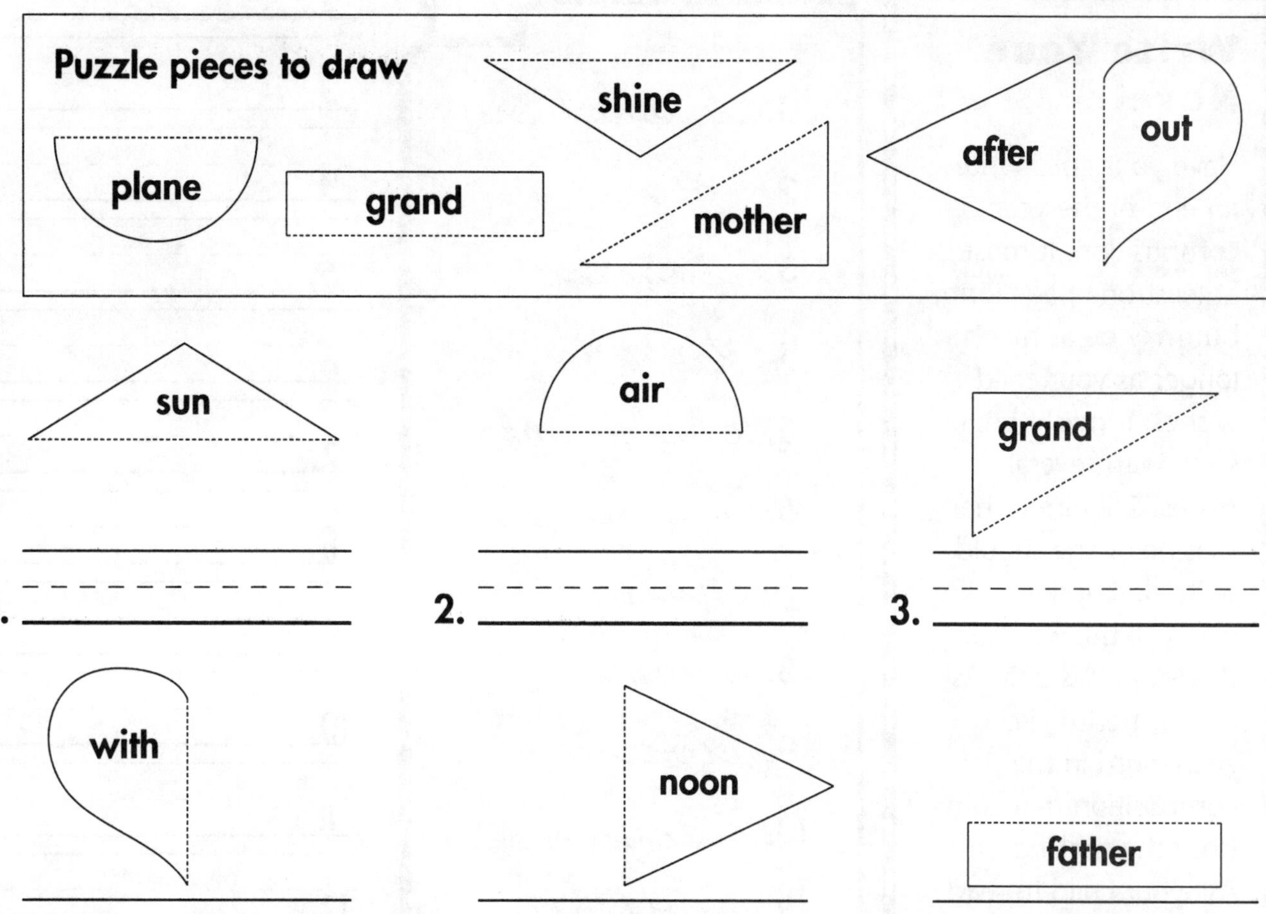


Finish each compound word by adding the part that is missing.

1. __ __ __ self

__ __ __ self

2. __ __ body

__ __ __ body

3. some __ __ __

some __ __ __ __ __

4. __ __ __ thing

__ __ __ __ __ thing

Write the compound word that has not been written yet. ______________

Name ________________________________

Home Study **Master** Unit **36**

## Assessment and Review

### Write Your Novel

Have your child write an end-of-the-year composition. It must be at least one page long, but may be as much longer as your child wishes. It might be a story with several pages. Tell him or her that he or she should write descriptively, using all the words in the list in this unit. Ask him or her to circle each word in the composition that came from the spelling list. Ask your child to read his or her "novel" to other members of the family. Perhaps he or she could "publish" it on the computer and create illustrations from clip art. Otherwise, he or she could draw illustrations and place the finished composition with a title page in a notebook.

1. branches
2. colors
3. classes
4. things
5. children
6. leaves
7. half
8. woman
9. closer
10. largest
11. hottest
12. sadder
13. hourly
14. really
15. monthly
16. shortly
17. afternoon
18. nobody
19. everything
20. without

1. ____________
2. ____________
3. ____________
4. ____________
5. ____________
6. ____________
7. ____________
8. ____________
9. ____________
10. ____________
11. ____________
12. ____________
13. ____________
14. ____________
15. ____________
16. ____________
17. ____________
18. ____________
19. ____________
20. ____________

Name ______________________

Unit 36

## Hoja para estudiar en casa

### Assessment and Review

1. *branches* ramas
2. *colors* colores
3. *classes* clases
4. *things* cosas
5. *children* hijos
6. *leaves* hojas
7. *half* medio; mitad
8. *woman* mujer
9. *closer* más cerca
10. *largest* el más grande
11. *hottest* el más caliente
12. *sadder* más triste
13. *hourly* por hora
14. *really* realmente
15. *monthly* mensualmente
16. *shortly* dentro de poco
17. *afternoon* la tarde
18. *nobody* nadie
19. *everything* todo
20. *without* sin

### Escribe tu novela

Indiquen a su hijo o hija que escriba una composición para el fin del año escolar. Debe ser de una página, como mínimo, o más, según el interés que su hijo o hija muestre. Pudiera ser un cuento de varias páginas. Díganle que debe escribir de una manera descriptiva, usando todas las palabras de la lista en esta unidad. Pídanle que encierre en un círculo todas las palabras en su composición que están en la lista en esta unidad. Pídanle que lea su "novela" a otros miembros de la familia. Quizás pudiera "publicar" la novela, escribiéndola en la computadora y creando ilustraciones usando arte gráfico de la computadora. De otra manera, él o ella pudiera dibujar las ilustraciones y poner la composición, incluyendo una página con el título, en un cuaderno.

1. ______
2. ______
3. ______
4. ______
5. ______
6. ______
7. ______
8. ______
9. ______
10. ______
11. ______
12. ______
13. ______
14. ______
15. ______
16. ______
17. ______
18. ______
19. ______
20. ______

Name ______________________________

Unit 36 **Test Master**

**A.** Look at the two underlined spelling words in each sentence. Decide which word is misspelled. Write it correctly.

1. Nobody was around to help me rake leves. ______________

2. I must do three tings before the hourly bell rings. ______________

3. Evrythng seemed small next to the largest statue. ______________

4. Red is thought of as one of the hotest colors. ______________

5. The puppy seemed sadder whithout her owner. ______________

6. Please trim the branches that are kloser to the ground. ______________

7. The clases will visit the factory this afternoon. ______________

**B.** One word in each list is misspelled. Write the letter of each misspelled word.

1. **a.** woman **b.** shortly **c.** haf **d.** without ☐

2. **a.** colors **b.** childran **c.** monthly **d.** hottest ☐

3. **a.** reely **b.** hourly **c.** monthly **d.** sadder ☐

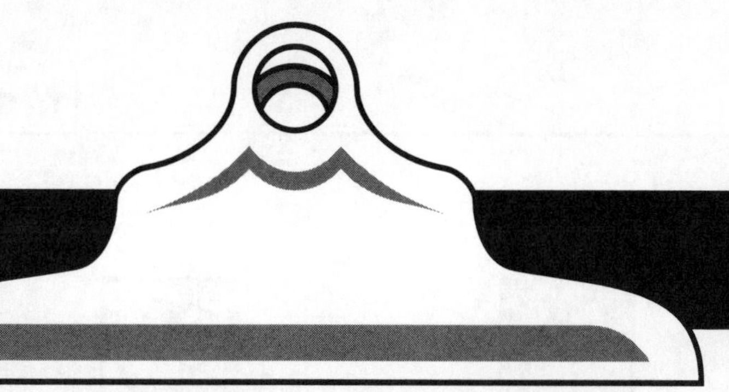

# APPENDIX

## Table of Contents

Student Name ______________________________

Date __________

# Modality Checklist

| |  Visual | 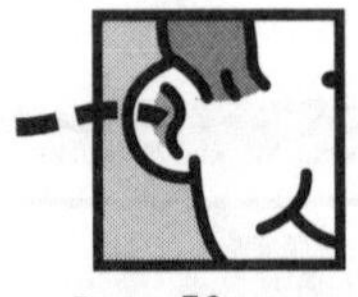 Auditory |  Kinesthetic |
|---|---|---|---|
| **Learning Style** | Learns by seeing, watching demonstrations ☐ | Learns through verbal instructions from others or self ☐ | Learns by doing, direct involvement ☐ |
| **Reading** | Likes description; sometimes stops reading to stare into space and imagine scene; intense concentration ☐ | Enjoys dialogue, avoids lengthy description, unaware of illustrations; moves lips or subvocalizes ☐ | Prefers stories where action occurs early; fidgets when reading; handles books; not an avid reader ☐ |
| **Spelling** | Recognizes words by sight; relies on configuration of words ☐ | Uses a phonics approach; has auditory word attack skills ☐ | Often is a poor speller; writes words to determine whether they "feel" right ☐ |
| **Handwriting** | Tends to be good, particularly in early years; spacing and size are good; appearance is important ☐ | Has more difficulty learning in initial stages; tends to write lightly; says strokes when writing ☐ | Good initially, deteriorates when space becomes smaller; pushes harder on writing instrument ☐ |
| **Memory** | Remembers faces, forgets names; writes things down; takes notes ☐ | Remembers names, forgets faces; remembers by auditory repetition ☐ | Remembers best what was done, not what was seen or talked about ☐ |
| **Imagery** | Vivid imagination; thinks in pictures, visualizes in detail ☐ | Subvocalizes, thinks in sounds; details less important ☐ | Imagery not important; images that do occur are accompanied by movement ☐ |
| **Distractibility** | Generally unaware of sounds; distracted by visual disorder or movement ☐ | Easily distracted by sounds ☐ | Not attentive to visual, auditory presentation, so seems distractible ☐ |

## To the Teacher:

Use the Modality Checklist on pages 204–205 to help you identify each student's modality strengths. Place a check mark in the box for each item that describes that student. The completed checklist may be filed with the student's personal records. It may be helpful as a reference when you are planning special activities during parent/teacher conferences.

Remember, however, that no student is totally driven by only one of the modality strengths. Because of the wide variety of skills in a single child—and within the class as a whole—you should teach by involving as many modality-centered strategies as possible. Additional modality information and strategies are included in each unit in the Teacher Edition.

Student Name ______________________________

Date __________

# Modality Checklist

| | Visual | Auditory | Kinesthetic |
|---|---|---|---|
| **Problem Solving** | Deliberate; plans in advance; organizes thoughts by writing them; lists problems ☐ | Talks problems out, tries solutions orally, subvocally; talks self through problem ☐ | Attacks problems physically; impulsive; often selects solution involving greatest activity ☐ |
| **Response to Periods of Inactivity** | Stares; doodles; finds something to watch ☐ | Hums; talks to self or to others ☐ | Fidgets; finds reasons to move; holds up hand ☐ |
| **Response to New Situations** | Looks around; examines structure ☐ | Talks about situation, pros and cons, what to do ☐ | Tries things out; touches, feels, manipulates ☐ |
| **Emotionality** | Somewhat repressed; stares when angry, cries easily, beams when happy; facial expression is a good index of emotion ☐ | Shouts with joy or anger; blows up verbally but soon calms down; expresses emotion through words and through changes in volume and pitch of voice ☐ | Jumps for joy; hugs, tugs, and pulls when happy; stamps, jumps, pounds, and stomps off when angry; general body tone is a good index of emotion ☐ |
| **Communication** | Quiet; does not talk at length; becomes impatient when extensive listening is required; may use words clumsily; describes without embellishment; uses words such as *see* and *look* ☐ | Enjoys listening but cannot wait to talk; descriptions are long but repetitive; likes hearing self and others talk; uses words such as *listen* and *hear* ☐ | Gestures when speaking; does not listen well; stands close when speaking or listening; quickly loses interest in detailed oral discourse; uses words such as *get* and *take* ☐ |
| **General Appearance** | Neat, meticulous, likes order; may choose not to vary appearance ☐ | Matching clothes not so important, can explain choices of clothes ☐ | Neat but soon becomes wrinkled through activity ☐ |
| **Response to the Arts** | Not particularly responsive to music; prefers the visual arts; tends not to voice appreciation of art of any kind, but can be deeply affected by visual displays; focuses on details and components rather than on the work as a whole ☐ | Favors music; finds less appeal in visual art, but is readily able to discuss it; misses significant detail but appreciates the work as a whole; is able to develop verbal association for all art forms; spends more time talking about pieces than looking at them ☐ | Responds to music by physical movement; prefers sculpture; touches statues and paintings; at exhibits stops only at those in which he or she can become physically involved; comments very little on any art form ☐ |

______________________________________________
(Name of Piece)

written by ______________________ read by ______________________
(Writer's Name) (Reader's Name)

1. This is what I liked best about this writing: ______________________

______________________________________________

2. There are spelling mistakes on lines ______________________

______________________________________________

3. There are mistakes in the way words are used on lines ____________

______________________________________________

4. There are mistakes in capitalization on lines ______________________

______________________________________________

5. There are mistakes in punctuation on lines ______________________

______________________________________________

6. I think the main idea is ______________________

______________________________________________

7. Do all of the sentences support that main idea? ______________
(yes/no)

8. The sentences on these lines need to be rewritten so they support the main idea: ______________________

9. Additional suggestions: ______________________

______________________________________________

______________________________________________

______________________________________________

______________________________________________

# Make Your Own Word Sort **Master**

Making a word sort can help you inspect words. Identify the spelling patterns in this week's unit. Pick a word that fits each pattern to be a **Master Word** and write it on a **Master Word** strip. Write each spelling word on a blank strip. Write other pattern words on the other strips. Cut on the dotted lines to make word strips for sorting. Then use the sounds you hear and the spelling patterns you see to match each word to a **Master Word**. Check your final word sort with your teacher.

| Master Word | Master Word | Master Word |
|---|---|---|
| | | |

## Directions

Write spelling words you want to study in the first column. Cover the first word and write it in the second column. Check your spelling. Cover the word again and rewrite it in the last column. Check your spelling. Use a **Flip Folder** with this page if you have one.

# Answer Key

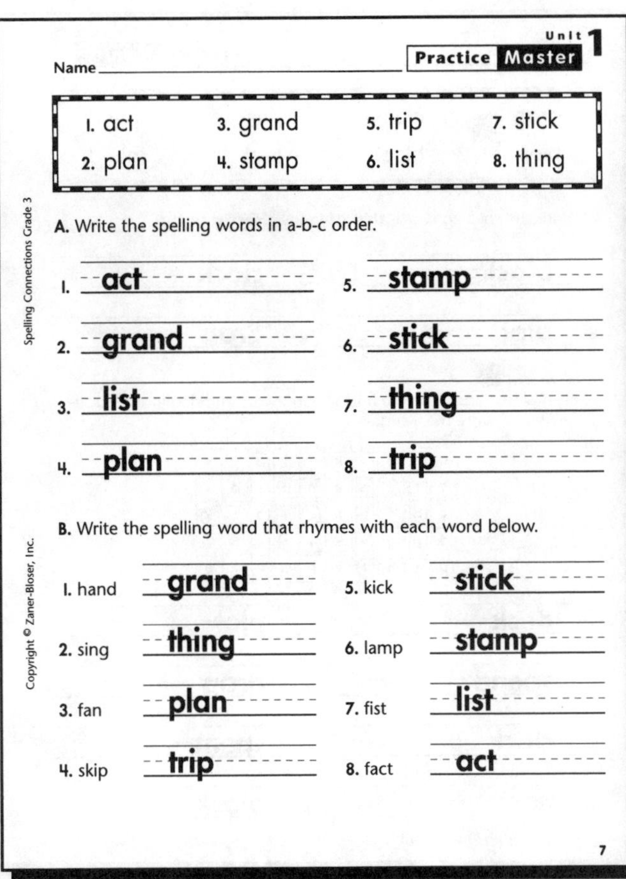

Unit 1 **Practice Master**

Name ____________________

| | | | |
|---|---|---|---|
| 1. act | 3. grand | 5. trip | 7. stick |
| 2. plan | 4. stamp | 6. list | 8. thing |

**A.** Write the spelling words in a-b-c order.

1. act
2. grand
3. list
4. plan
5. stamp
6. stick
7. thing
8. trip

**B.** Write the spelling word that rhymes with each word below.

1. hand — grand
2. sing — thing
3. fan — plan
4. skip — trip
5. kick — stick
6. lamp — stamp
7. fist — list
8. fact — act





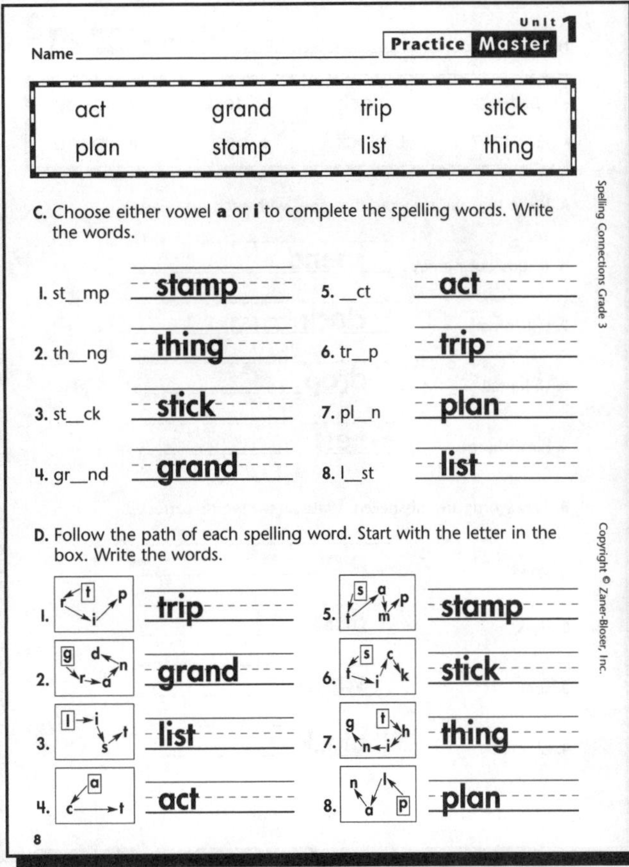

Unit 1 **Practice Master**

Name ____________________

| | | | |
|---|---|---|---|
| act | grand | trip | stick |
| plan | stamp | list | thing |

**C.** Choose either vowel **a** or **i** to complete the spelling words. Write the words.

1. st__mp — stamp
2. th__ng — thing
3. st__ck — stick
4. gr__nd — grand
5. __ct — act
6. tr__p — trip
7. pl__n — plan
8. l__st — list

**D.** Follow the path of each spelling word. Start with the letter in the box. Write the words.

1. trip
2. grand
3. list
4. act
5. stamp
6. stick
7. thing
8. plan





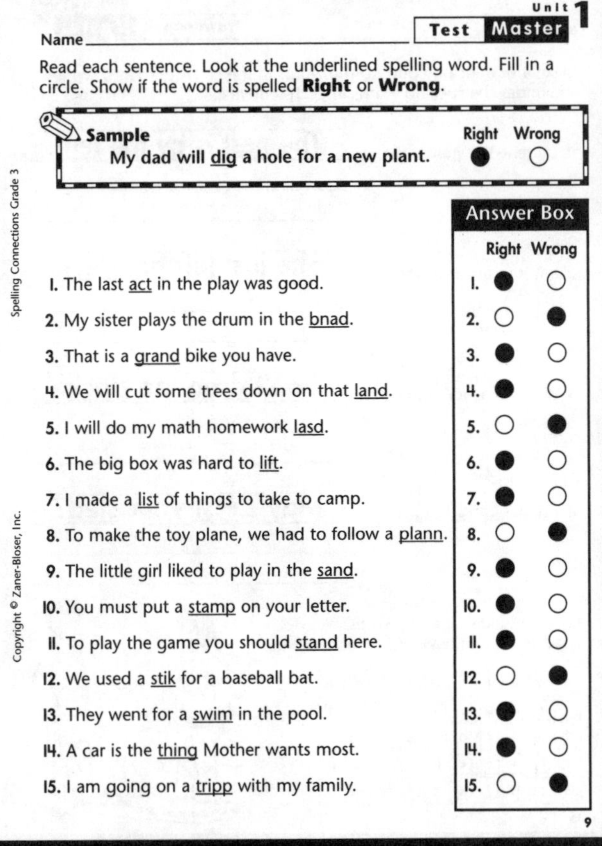

Unit 1 **Test Master**

Name ____________________

Read each sentence. Look at the underlined spelling word. Fill in a circle. Show if the word is spelled **Right** or **Wrong**.

**Sample**
My dad will dig a hole for a new plant. Right ● Wrong ○

**Answer Box**

| Sentence | | Right | Wrong |
|---|---|---|---|
| 1. The last act in the play was good. | 1. | ● | ○ |
| 2. My sister plays the drum in the bnad. | 2. | ○ | ● |
| 3. That is a grand bike you have. | 3. | ● | ○ |
| 4. We will cut some trees down on that land. | 4. | ● | ○ |
| 5. I will do my math homework lasd. | 5. | ○ | ● |
| 6. The big box was hard to lift. | 6. | ● | ○ |
| 7. I made a list of things to take to camp. | 7. | ● | ○ |
| 8. To make the toy plane, we had to follow a plann. | 8. | ○ | ● |
| 9. The little girl liked to play in the sand. | 9. | ● | ○ |
| 10. You must put a stamp on your letter. | 10. | ● | ○ |
| 11. To play the game you should stand here. | 11. | ● | ○ |
| 12. We used a stik for a baseball bat. | 12. | ○ | ● |
| 13. They went for a swim in the pool. | 13. | ● | ○ |
| 14. A car is the thing Mother wants most. | 14. | ● | ○ |
| 15. I am going on a tripp with my family. | 15. | ○ | ● |





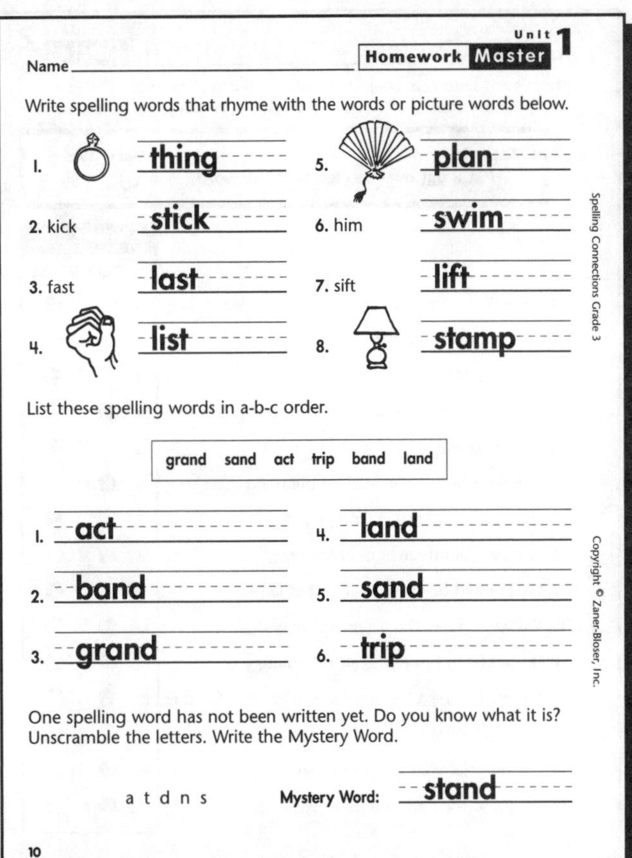

Unit 1 **Homework Master**

Name ____________________

Write spelling words that rhyme with the words or picture words below.

1. (picture) — thing
2. kick — stick
3. fast — last
4. (picture) — list
5. (picture) — plan
6. him — swim
7. sift — lift
8. (picture) — stamp

List these spelling words in a-b-c order.

grand sand act trip band land

1. act
2. band
3. grand
4. land
5. sand
6. trip

One spelling word has not been written yet. Do you know what it is? Unscramble the letters. Write the Mystery Word.

a t d n s **Mystery Word:** stand

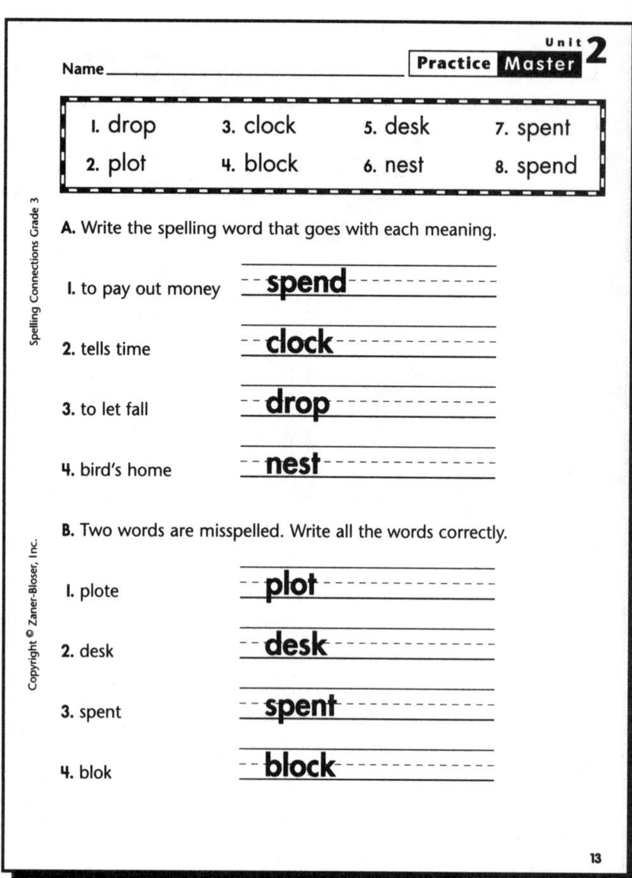
Name ______ Unit 2 Practice Master

| | | | |
|---|---|---|---|
| 1. drop | 3. clock | 5. desk | 7. spent |
| 2. plot | 4. block | 6. nest | 8. spend |

**A.** Write the spelling word that goes with each meaning.

1. to pay out money — spend
2. tells time — clock
3. to let fall — drop
4. bird's home — nest

**B.** Two words are misspelled. Write all the words correctly.

1. plote — plot
2. desk — desk
3. spent — spent
4. blok — block

Spelling Connections Grade 3

Copyright © Zaner-Bloser, Inc.

13

Name ______ Unit 2 Practice Master

| | | | |
|---|---|---|---|
| drop | clock | desk | spent |
| plot | block | nest | spend |

**C.** Write the spelling words that have the **short o** sound.

1. block
2. plot
3. clock
4. drop

**D.** Read across and down to find spelling words hidden in the puzzle. Circle and write the words.

| | | | | | | | | | |
|---|---|---|---|---|---|---|---|---|---|
| a | d | e | s | k | j | l | b | n | e |
| b | r | s | p | e | n | d | l | o | s |
| c | o | f | e | h | c | l | o | c | k |
| d | p | g | n | e | s | t | c | p | t |
| p | l | o | t | i | k | m | k | q | u |

1. desk
2. spend
3. clock
4. nest
5. plot
6. drop
7. spent
8. block

Spelling Connections Grade 3

Copyright © Zaner-Bloser, Inc.

14

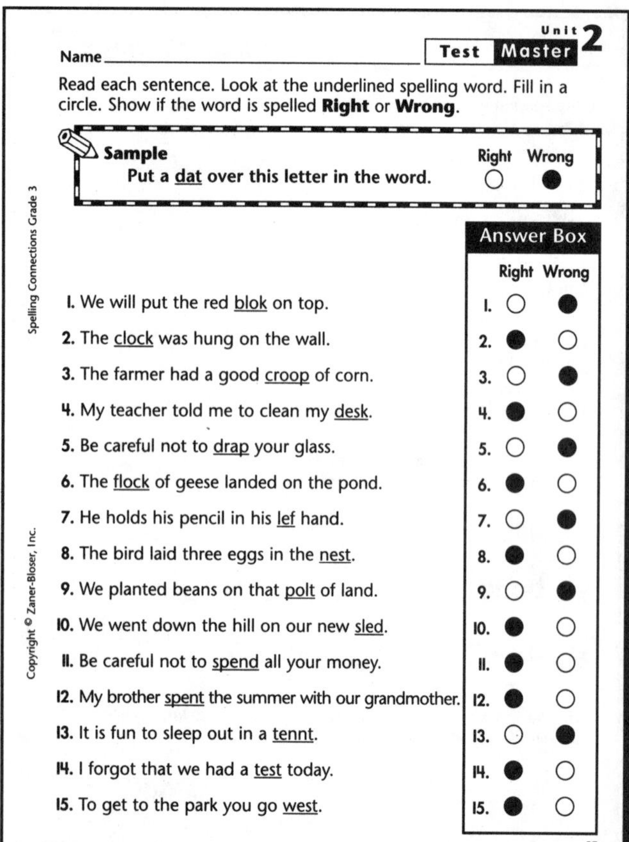
Name ______ Unit 2 Test Master

Read each sentence. Look at the underlined spelling word. Fill in a circle. Show if the word is spelled **Right** or **Wrong**.

**Sample** Put a dat over this letter in the word. Right ○ Wrong ●

Answer Box

| Sentence | Right | Wrong |
|---|---|---|
| 1. We will put the red blok on top. | ○ | ● |
| 2. The clock was hung on the wall. | ● | ○ |
| 3. The farmer had a good croop of corn. | ○ | ● |
| 4. My teacher told me to clean my desk. | ● | ○ |
| 5. Be careful not to drap your glass. | ○ | ● |
| 6. The flock of geese landed on the pond. | ● | ○ |
| 7. He holds his pencil in his lef hand. | ○ | ● |
| 8. The bird laid three eggs in the nest. | ● | ○ |
| 9. We planted beans on that polt of land. | ○ | ● |
| 10. We went down the hill on our new sled. | ● | ○ |
| 11. Be careful not to spend all your money. | ● | ○ |
| 12. My brother spent the summer with our grandmother. | ● | ○ |
| 13. It is fun to sleep out in a tennt. | ○ | ● |
| 14. I forgot that we had a test today. | ● | ○ |
| 15. To get to the park you go west. | ● | ○ |

Spelling Connections Grade 3

Copyright © Zaner-Bloser, Inc.

15

Name ______ Unit 2 Homework Master

Make a sentence by putting the words in the correct order. Draw a line under the spelling words in each sentence.

1. by tent The nest is the. — The nest is by the tent.
2. left her just desk She. — She just left her desk.
3. drop the clock Don't. — Don't drop the clock.
4. I sled your test May? — May I test your sled?

Look for hidden spelling words. Read across and down. Circle each word.

| | | | | | | | | | |
|---|---|---|---|---|---|---|---|---|---|
| e | g | h | i | f | a | s | f | d | g |
| c | r | o | p | l | s | p | e | n | t |
| t | a | c | l | o | w | e | s | t | u |
| r | b | l | o | c | k | n | s | u | b |
| s | e | p | t | k | z | d | y | m | o |

Spelling Connections Grade 3

Copyright © Zaner-Bloser, Inc.

16

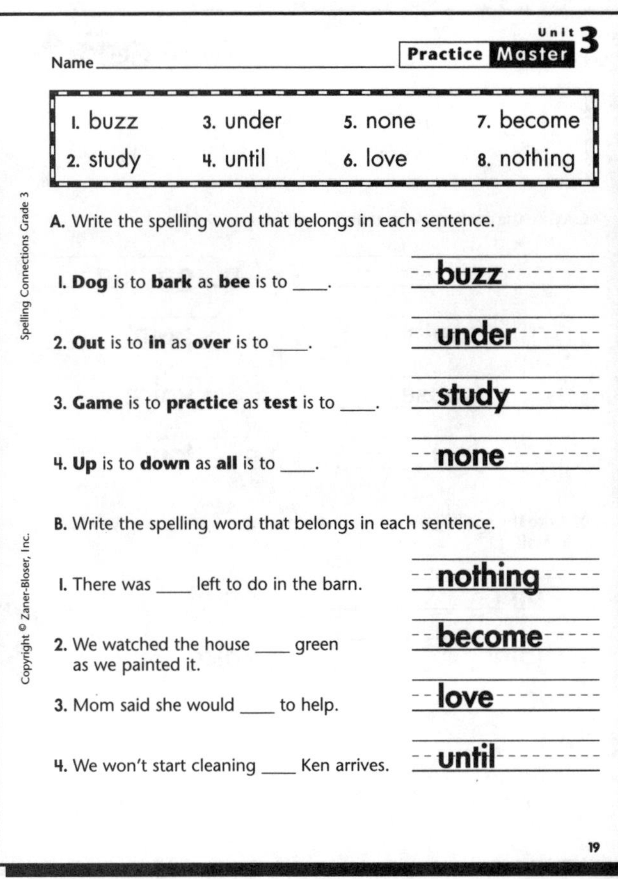

Unit 3 Practice Master

Name ____________________

1. buzz  2. study  3. under  4. until  5. none  6. love  7. become  8. nothing

**A.** Write the spelling word that belongs in each sentence.

1. **Dog** is to **bark** as **bee** is to ____. **buzz**
2. **Out** is to **in** as **over** is to ____. **under**
3. **Game** is to **practice** as **test** is to ____. **study**
4. **Up** is to **down** as **all** is to ____. **none**

**B.** Write the spelling word that belongs in each sentence.

1. There was ____ left to do in the barn. **nothing**
2. We watched the house ____ green as we painted it. **become**
3. Mom said she would ____ to help. **love**
4. We won't start cleaning ____ Ken arrives. **until**



19

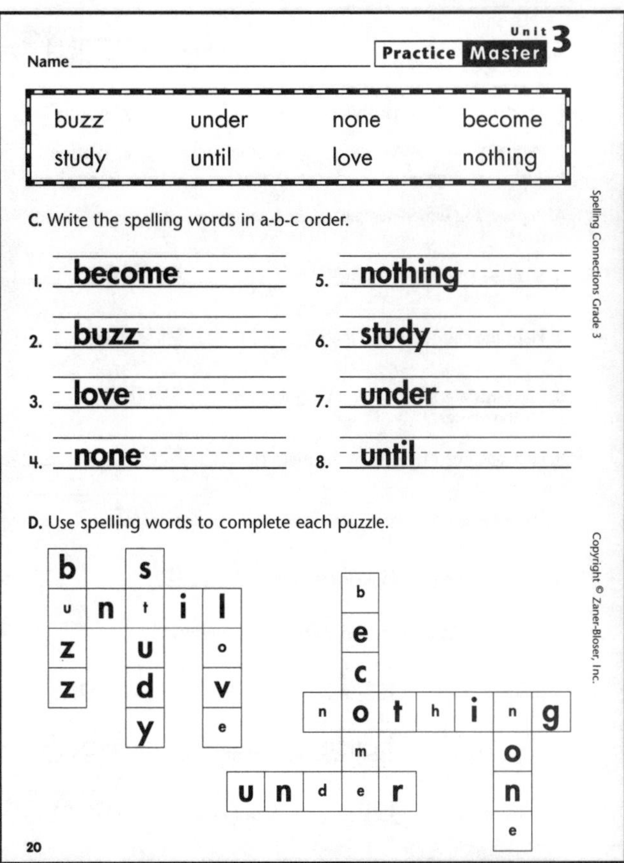

Unit 3 Practice Master

Name ____________________

buzz  under  none  become
study  until  love  nothing

**C.** Write the spelling words in a-b-c order.

1. **become**
2. **buzz**
3. **love**
4. **none**
5. **nothing**
6. **study**
7. **under**
8. **until**

**D.** Use spelling words to complete each puzzle.



20

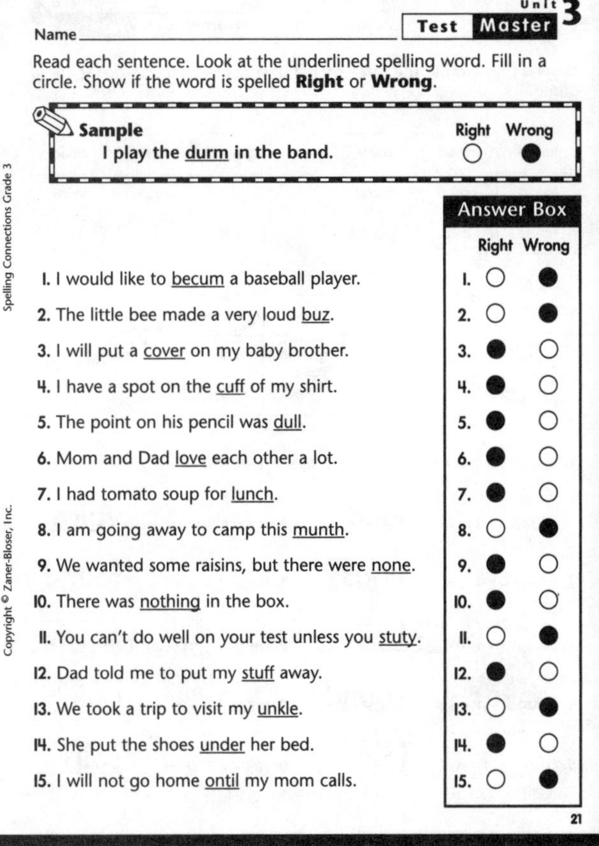

Unit 3 Test Master

Name ____________________

Read each sentence. Look at the underlined spelling word. Fill in a circle. Show if the word is spelled **Right** or **Wrong**.

**Sample**
**I play the durm in the band.** Right ○ Wrong ●

| Sentence | Right | Wrong |
|---|---|---|
| 1. I would like to becum a baseball player. | ○ | ● |
| 2. The little bee made a very loud buz. | ○ | ● |
| 3. I will put a cover on my baby brother. | ● | ○ |
| 4. I have a spot on the cuff of my shirt. | ● | ○ |
| 5. The point on his pencil was dull. | ● | ○ |
| 6. Mom and Dad love each other a lot. | ● | ○ |
| 7. I had tomato soup for lunch. | ● | ○ |
| 8. I am going away to camp this munth. | ○ | ● |
| 9. We wanted some raisins, but there were none. | ● | ○ |
| 10. There was nothing in the box. | ● | ○ |
| 11. You can't do well on your test unless you stuty. | ○ | ● |
| 12. Dad told me to put my stuff away. | ● | ○ |
| 13. We took a trip to visit my unkle. | ○ | ● |
| 14. She put the shoes under her bed. | ● | ○ |
| 15. I will not go home ontil my mom calls. | ○ | ● |



21

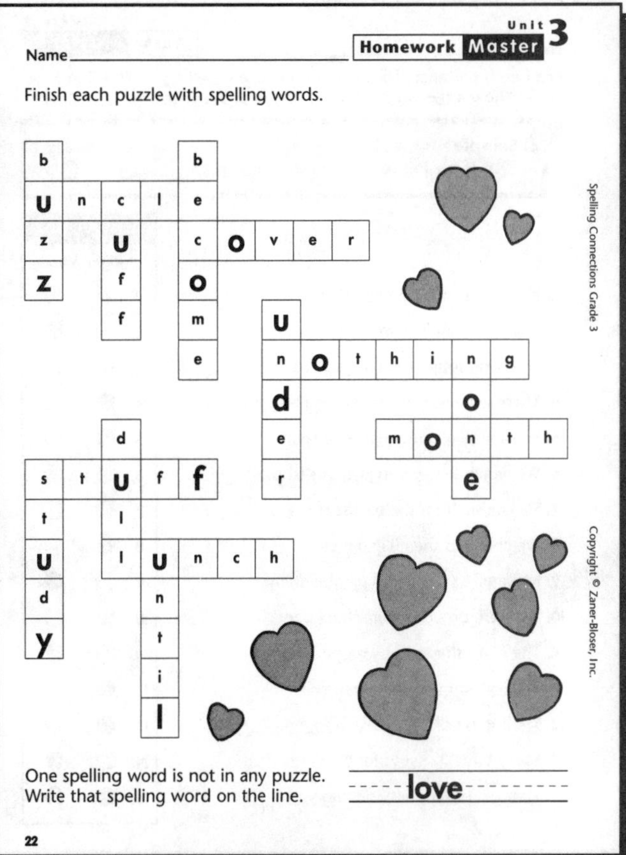

Unit 3 Homework Master

Name ____________________

Finish each puzzle with spelling words.

One spelling word is not in any puzzle. Write that spelling word on the line. **love**



22

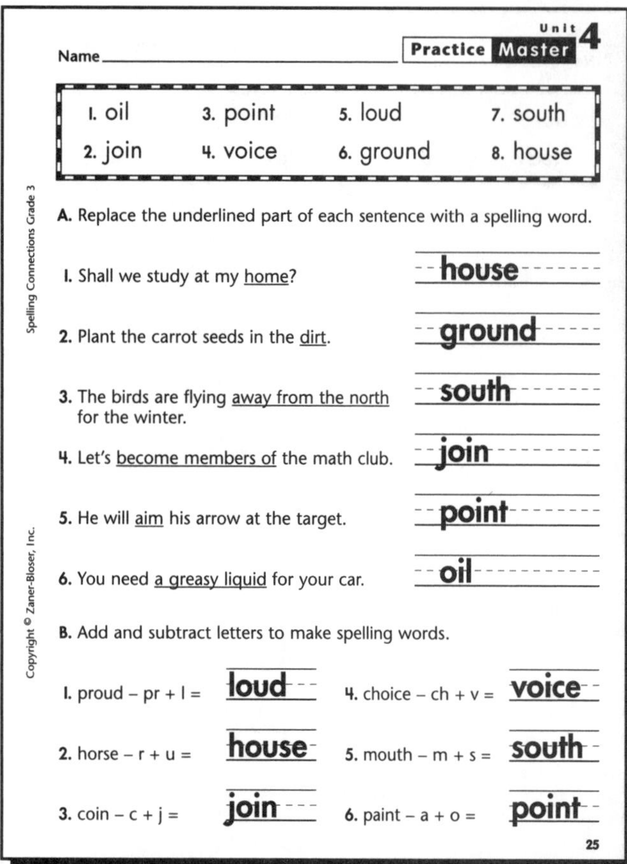

Name ______________ Practice Master Unit 4

| | | | |
|---|---|---|---|
| 1. oil | 3. point | 5. loud | 7. south |
| 2. join | 4. voice | 6. ground | 8. house |

**A.** Replace the underlined part of each sentence with a spelling word.

1. Shall we study at my home? **house**
2. Plant the carrot seeds in the dirt. **ground**
3. The birds are flying away from the north for the winter. **south**
4. Let's become members of the math club. **join**
5. He will aim his arrow at the target. **point**
6. You need a greasy liquid for your car. **oil**

**B.** Add and subtract letters to make spelling words.

1. proud – pr + l = **loud**
2. horse – r + u = **house**
3. coin – c + j = **join**
4. choice – ch + v = **voice**
5. mouth – m + s = **south**
6. paint – a + o = **point**

Spelling Connections Grade 3



25

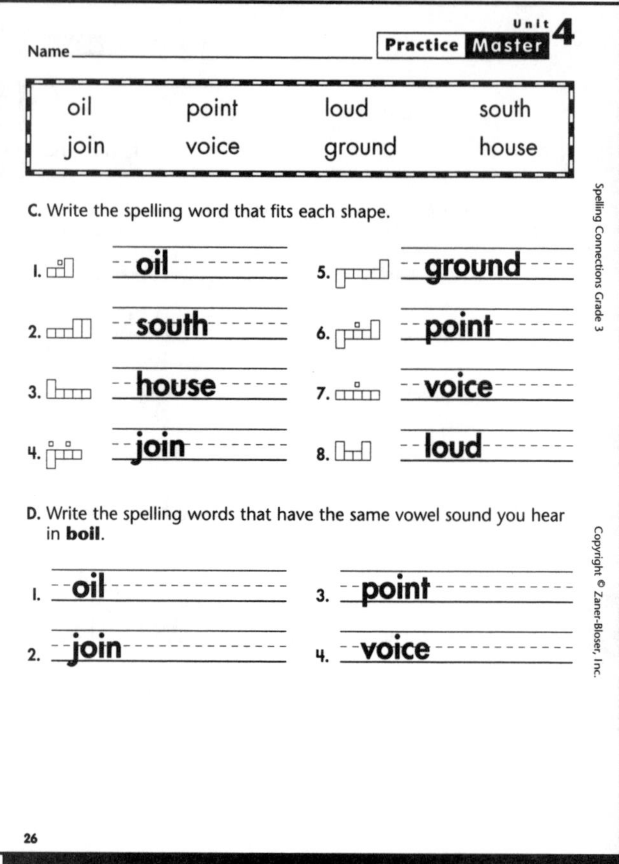

Name ______________ Practice Master Unit 4

| | | | |
|---|---|---|---|
| oil | point | loud | south |
| join | voice | ground | house |

**C.** Write the spelling word that fits each shape.

1. **oil**
2. **south**
3. **house**
4. **join**
5. **ground**
6. **point**
7. **voice**
8. **loud**

**D.** Write the spelling words that have the same vowel sound you hear in **boil**.

1. **oil**
2. **join**
3. **point**
4. **voice**

Spelling Connections Grade 3



26

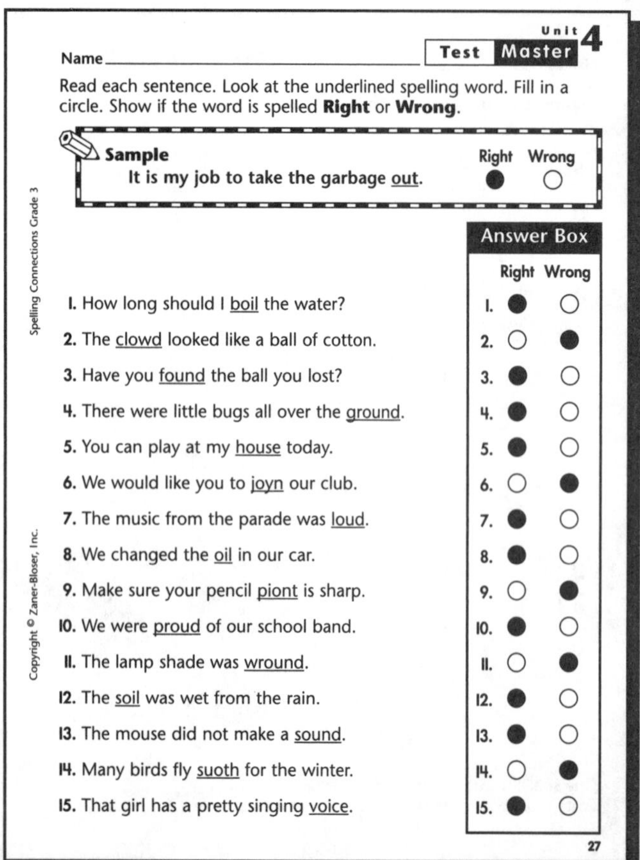

Name ______________ Test Master Unit 4

Read each sentence. Look at the underlined spelling word. Fill in a circle. Show if the word is spelled **Right** or **Wrong**.

**Sample**
It is my job to take the garbage out. Right ● Wrong ○

**Answer Box**

| | Sentence | Right | Wrong |
|---|---|---|---|
| 1. | How long should I boil the water? | ● | ○ |
| 2. | The clowd looked like a ball of cotton. | ○ | ● |
| 3. | Have you found the ball you lost? | ● | ○ |
| 4. | There were little bugs all over the ground. | ● | ○ |
| 5. | You can play at my house today. | ● | ○ |
| 6. | We would like you to joyn our club. | ○ | ● |
| 7. | The music from the parade was loud. | ● | ○ |
| 8. | We changed the oil in our car. | ● | ○ |
| 9. | Make sure your pencil piont is sharp. | ○ | ● |
| 10. | We were proud of our school band. | ● | ○ |
| 11. | The lamp shade was wround. | ○ | ● |
| 12. | The soil was wet from the rain. | ● | ○ |
| 13. | The mouse did not make a sound. | ● | ○ |
| 14. | Many birds fly suoth for the winter. | ○ | ● |
| 15. | That girl has a pretty singing voice. | ● | ○ |

Spelling Connections Grade 3



27

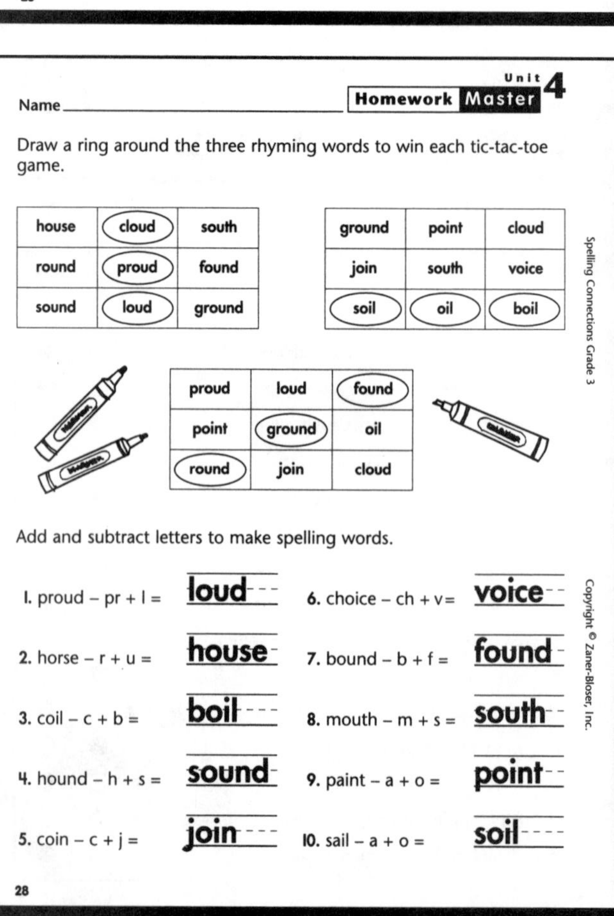

Name ______________ Homework Master Unit 4

Draw a ring around the three rhyming words to win each tic-tac-toe game.

| | | |
|---|---|---|
| house | (cloud) | south |
| round | (proud) | found |
| sound | (loud) | ground |

| | | |
|---|---|---|
| ground | point | cloud |
| join | south | voice |
| (soil) | (oil) | (boil) |

| | | |
|---|---|---|
| proud | loud | (found) |
| point | (ground) | oil |
| (round) | join | cloud |

Add and subtract letters to make spelling words.

1. proud – pr + l = **loud**
2. horse – r + u = **house**
3. coil – c + b = **boil**
4. hound – h + s = **sound**
5. coin – c + j = **join**
6. choice – ch + v= **voice**
7. bound – b + f = **found**
8. mouth – m + s = **south**
9. paint – a + o = **point**
10. sail – a + o = **soil**

Spelling Connections Grade 3



28

# Answer Key

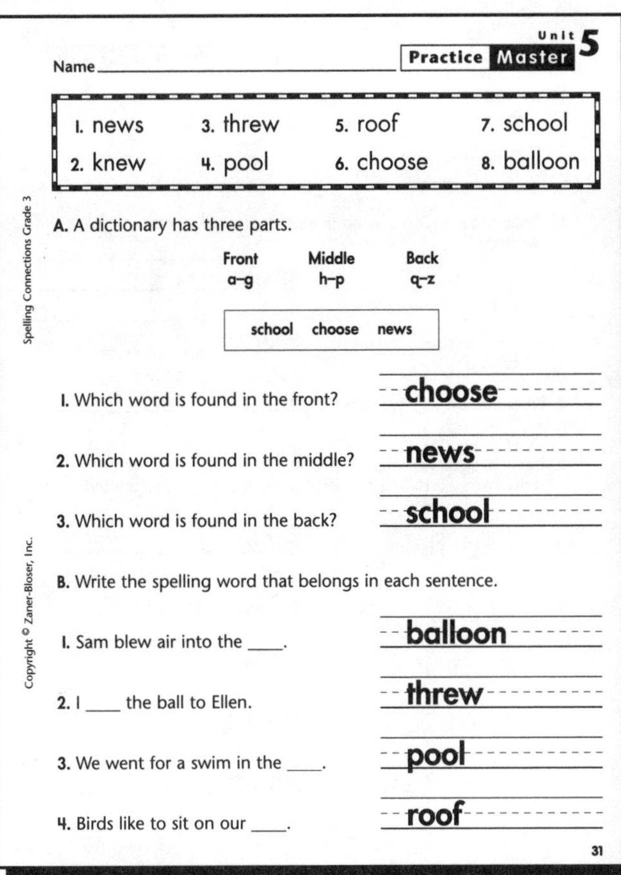

Unit 5 **Practice Master**

Name

| | | | |
|---|---|---|---|
| 1. news | 3. threw | 5. roof | 7. school |
| 2. knew | 4. pool | 6. choose | 8. balloon |

**A.** A dictionary has three parts.

| Front | Middle | Back |
|---|---|---|
| a–g | h–p | q–z |

school choose news

1. Which word is found in the front? **choose**
2. Which word is found in the middle? **news**
3. Which word is found in the back? **school**

**B.** Write the spelling word that belongs in each sentence.

1. Sam blew air into the ____. **balloon**
2. I ____ the ball to Ellen. **threw**
3. We went for a swim in the ____. **pool**
4. Birds like to sit on our ____. **roof**




31

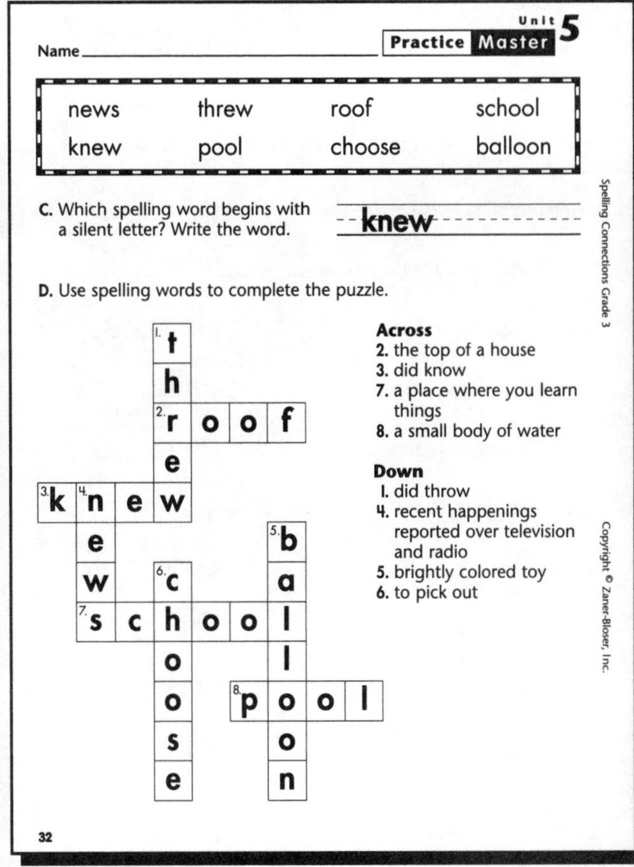

Unit 5 **Practice Master**

Name

| | | | |
|---|---|---|---|
| news | threw | roof | school |
| knew | pool | choose | balloon |

**C.** Which spelling word begins with a silent letter? Write the word. **knew**

**D.** Use spelling words to complete the puzzle.



**Across**
2. the top of a house
3. did know
7. a place where you learn things
8. a small body of water

**Down**
1. did throw
4. recent happenings reported over television and radio
5. brightly colored toy
6. to pick out




32

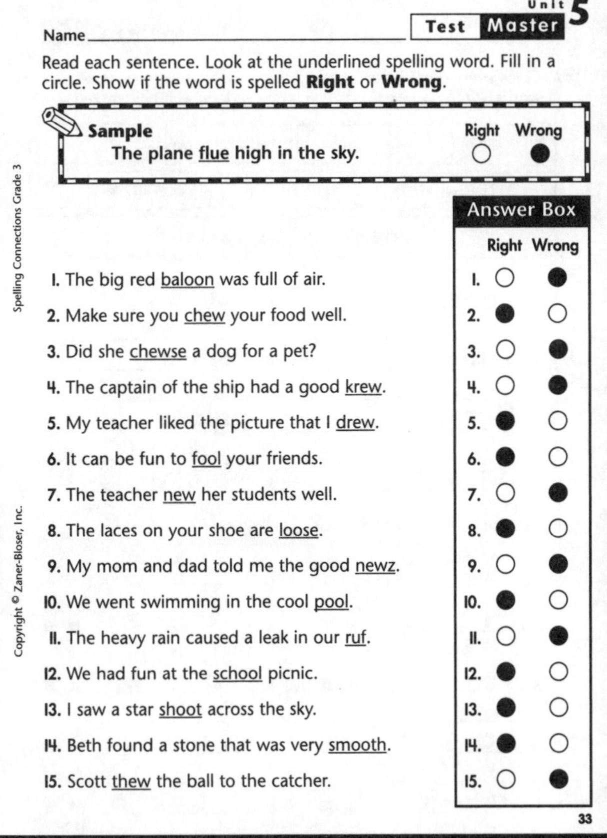

Unit 5 **Test Master**

Name

Read each sentence. Look at the underlined spelling word. Fill in a circle. Show if the word is spelled **Right** or **Wrong**.

**Sample** The plane flue high in the sky. Right ○ Wrong ●

**Answer Box**

| | Sentence | Right | Wrong |
|---|---|---|---|
| 1. | The big red baloon was full of air. | ○ | ● |
| 2. | Make sure you chew your food well. | ● | ○ |
| 3. | Did she chewse a dog for a pet? | ○ | ● |
| 4. | The captain of the ship had a good krew. | ○ | ● |
| 5. | My teacher liked the picture that I drew. | ● | ○ |
| 6. | It can be fun to fool your friends. | ● | ○ |
| 7. | The teacher new her students well. | ○ | ● |
| 8. | The laces on your shoe are loose. | ● | ○ |
| 9. | My mom and dad told me the good newz. | ○ | ● |
| 10. | We went swimming in the cool pool. | ● | ○ |
| 11. | The heavy rain caused a leak in our ruf. | ○ | ● |
| 12. | We had fun at the school picnic. | ● | ○ |
| 13. | I saw a star shoot across the sky. | ● | ○ |
| 14. | Beth found a stone that was very smooth. | ● | ○ |
| 15. | Scott thew the ball to the catcher. | ○ | ● |




33

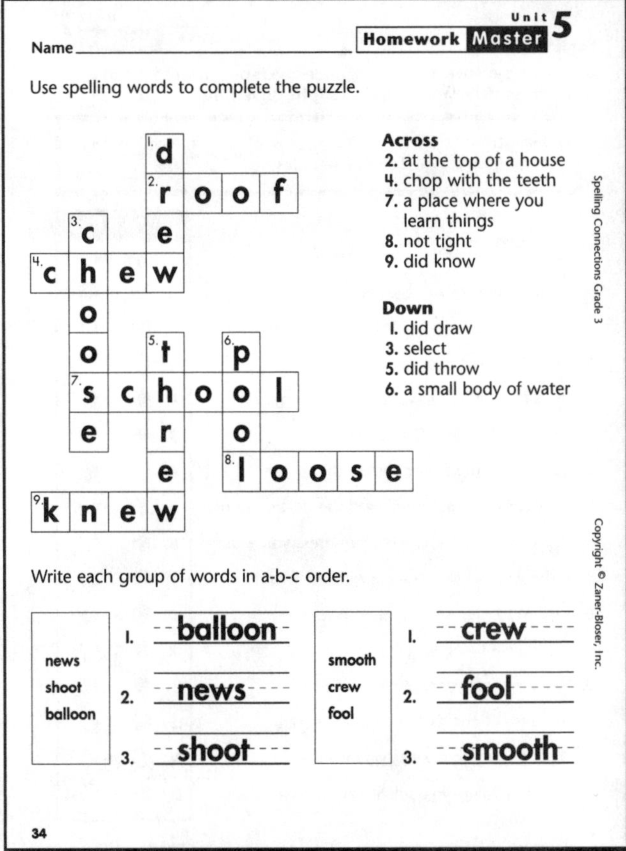

Unit 5 **Homework Master**

Name

Use spelling words to complete the puzzle.



**Across**
2. at the top of a house
4. chop with the teeth
7. a place where you learn things
8. not tight
9. did know

**Down**
1. did draw
3. select
5. did throw
6. a small body of water

Write each group of words in a-b-c order.

news, shoot, balloon
1. **balloon**
2. **news**
3. **shoot**

smooth, crew, fool
1. **crew**
2. **fool**
3. **smooth**




34

# Answer Key

Name ______________ **Practice Master** Unit 7

| | | | |
|---|---|---|---|
| 1. face | 3. plane | 5. smile | 7. close |
| 2. state | 4. size | 6. broke | 8. stone |

**A.** Write a spelling word for each clue.

1. I am found on the front of your head. **face**
2. I fly through the air. **plane**
3. I am something your face does. **smile**
4. I can also be called a rock. **stone**

**B.** Write the spelling word that belongs in each sentence.

1. The fans all wanted to be ____ to the star player. **close**
2. What ____ sneaker do you wear? **size**
3. The runner just ____ the world record time! **broke**
4. I'll show you on the ____ map where our team will travel. **state**



40

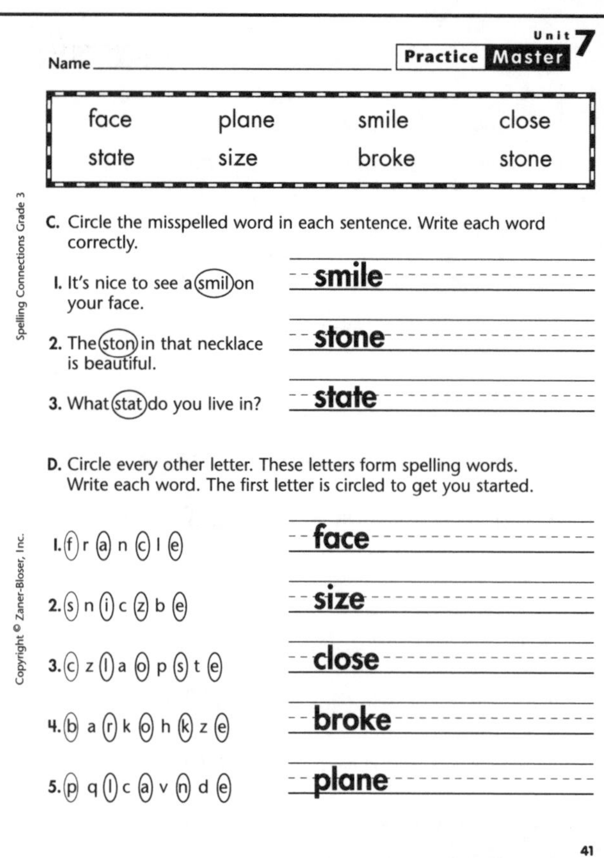

Name ______________ **Practice Master** Unit 7

| | | | |
|---|---|---|---|
| face | plane | smile | close |
| state | size | broke | stone |

**C.** Circle the misspelled word in each sentence. Write each word correctly.

1. It's nice to see a (smil) on your face. **smile**
2. The (ston) in that necklace is beautiful. **stone**
3. What (stat) do you live in? **state**

**D.** Circle every other letter. These letters form spelling words. Write each word. The first letter is circled to get you started.

1. (f) r (a) n (c) l (e) **face**
2. (s) n (i) c (z) b (e) **size**
3. (c) z (l) a (o) p (s) t (e) **close**
4. (b) a (r) k (o) h (k) z (e) **broke**
5. (p) q (l) c (a) v (n) d (e) **plane**



41

Name ______________ **Test Master** Unit 7

Read each sentence. Look at the underlined spelling word. Fill in a circle. Show if the word is spelled **Right** or **Wrong**.

**Sample**
A nickel is equal to five pennies. Right ● Wrong ○

**Answer Box**

| | Sentence | Right | Wrong |
|---|---|---|---|
| 1. | My brother brok our best vase. | ○ | ● |
| 2. | The score was klose near the end of the game. | ○ | ● |
| 3. | The clown had a funny fase. | ○ | ● |
| 4. | The campfire had a warm orange flame. | ● | ○ |
| 5. | A model of the earth is called a globe. | ● | ○ |
| 6. | This jet was much larger than that palne. | ○ | ● |
| 7. | Chris won a prize for wearing the best costume. | ● | ○ |
| 8. | Mom wants to know what size dress you wear. | ● | ○ |
| 9. | In the winter I like to skate with my friends. | ● | ○ |
| 10. | It is fun to slidd on the smooth ice. | ○ | ● |
| 11. | You have a friendly smile. | ● | ○ |
| 12. | The heavy gray smoke filled the sky. | ● | ○ |
| 13. | The trees in our state are beautiful. | ● | ○ |
| 14. | The little boy threw a stoan into the pond. | ○ | ● |
| 15. | The crew will pave Bank Street next week. | ● | ○ |



42

Name ______________ **Homework Master** Unit 7

**A.** Circle every other letter on the stone wall. These letters form spelling words. Write each word. The first one is done as an example.

(p) i (l) c (a) d (n) t (e) | (s) a (k) f (a) u (t) m (e) | (f) e (l) p (a) t (m) l (e)
(p) o (r) t (i) l (z) f (e) | (s) j (t) b (a) f (t) c (e) | (s) g (m) r (i) z (l) h (e)
(g) t (l) d (o) i (b) u (e) | (b) a (r) k (o) h (k) z (e)

1. plane
2. **skate**
3. **flame**
4. **prize**
5. **state**
6. **smile**
7. **globe**
8. **broke**

**B.** Use the code to complete each spelling word.

▲ = a ■ = e ● = i ♥ = o

1. s l **i** d **e** ● ■
2. s m **o** k **e** ♥ ■
3. p l **a** n **e** ▲ ■
4. f **a** c **e** ▲ ■
5. s **i** z **e** ● ■
6. p **a** v **e** ▲ ■
7. c l **o** s **e** ♥ ■
8. s t **o** n **e** ♥ ■



43

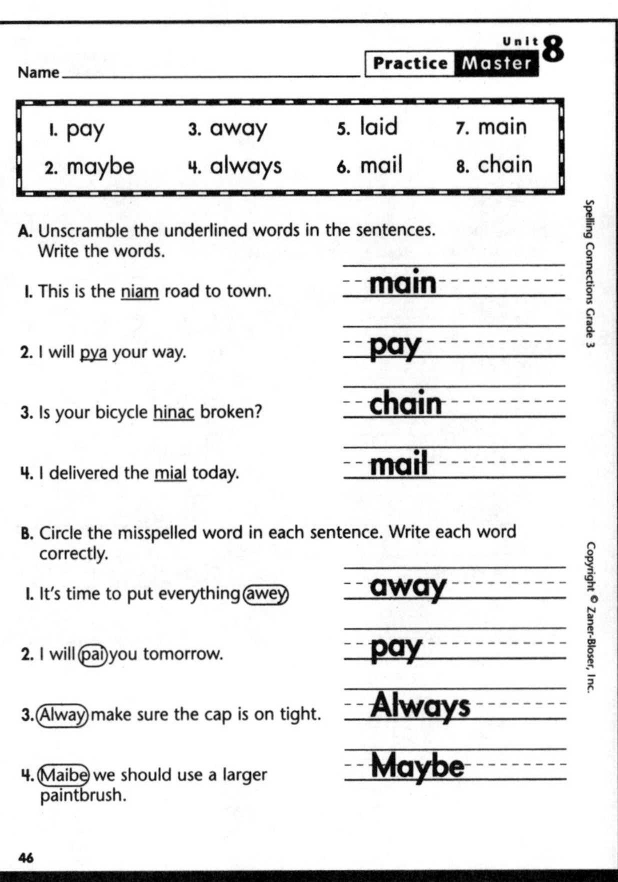

Unit 8

Name ____________ **Practice Master**

| | | | |
|---|---|---|---|
| 1. pay | 3. away | 5. laid | 7. main |
| 2. maybe | 4. always | 6. mail | 8. chain |

**A.** Unscramble the underlined words in the sentences. Write the words.

1. This is the niam road to town. **main**
2. I will pya your way. **pay**
3. Is your bicycle hinac broken? **chain**
4. I delivered the mial today. **mail**

**B.** Circle the misspelled word in each sentence. Write each word correctly.

1. It's time to put everything (awey) **away**
2. I will (pai) you tomorrow. **pay**
3. (Alway) make sure the cap is on tight. **Always**
4. (Maibe) we should use a larger paintbrush. **Maybe**







Unit 8

Name ____________ **Practice Master**

| | | | |
|---|---|---|---|
| pay | away | laid | main |
| maybe | always | mail | chain |

**C.** Write the spelling word that belongs in each sentence.

1. Someone ____ a book on my chair. **laid**
2. Our projects will be shown in the ____ hallway. **main**
3. My mobile is the one hanging from a ____. **chain**
4. I will ____ the letter. **mail**

**D.** Use the letters in the box to write five spelling words. You can use a letter more than once.

| | | |
|---|---|---|
| a | d | w |
| y | l | p |
| i | s | m |

1. **pay**
2. **mail**
3. **always**
4. **away**
5. **laid**







Unit 8

Name ____________ **Test Master**

Read each sentence. Look at the underlined spelling word. Fill in a circle. Show if the word is spelled **Right** or **Wrong**.

**Sample**
**My big brother played a game with me.** Right ● Wrong ○

**Answer Box**

| | Sentence | Right | Wrong |
|---|---|---|---|
| 1. | We will give aid to help needy people. | ● | ○ |
| 2. | My sister always wins in tennis. | ● | ○ |
| 3. | I went away to camp for the summer. | ● | ○ |
| 4. | He lade his school books on the table. | ○ | ● |
| 5. | Where did you lay your homework? | ● | ○ |
| 6. | Did you check for mayl yet? | ○ | ● |
| 7. | The tent is held up by one mane pole. | ○ | ● |
| 8. | Mom said that maybee we could go swimming. | ○ | ● |
| 9. | I paid for the book myself. | ● | ○ |
| 10. | Ted put sand in his pael. | ○ | ● |
| 11. | I will paint my wagon red. | ● | ○ |
| 12. | My dad will paye the clerk for the food. | ○ | ● |
| 13. | We ordered a tray of plain pizza. | ● | ○ |
| 14. | The gate was kept closed with a chain. | ● | ○ |
| 15. | She put her plate on a tray. | ● | ○ |







Unit 8

Name ____________ **Homework Master**

Unscramble the underlined word in the sentence. Write the spelling word.

1. Can you carry this rtya? **tray**
2. Why are you laywas smiling? **always**
3. This is the niam road to town. **main**
4. Please don't spill the iptna. **paint**
5. Have you diap for this milk? **paid**
6. The kitten ran ywaa from home. **away**
7. Mybae it will rain tonight. **Maybe**
8. We got lots of mial today. **mail**
9. I will pya your way. **pay**
10. Jill wanted to carry water in a lipa. **pail**

Use the letters in the box to write five other spelling words. You can use a letter more than once.

| | | |
|---|---|---|
| a | c | d |
| h | i | l |
| n | p | y |

11. **lay**
12. **chain**
13. **laid**
14. **aid**
15. **plain**

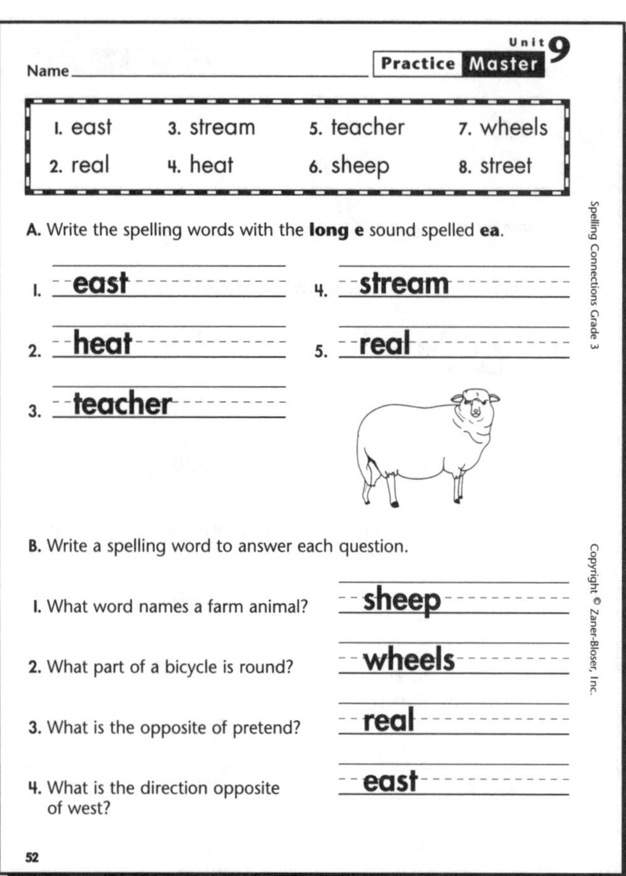

Unit 9 Practice Master

Name ______________________

| 1. east | 3. stream | 5. teacher | 7. wheels |
|---|---|---|---|
| 2. real | 4. heat | 6. sheep | 8. street |

**A.** Write the spelling words with the **long e** sound spelled **ea**.

1. east
2. heat
3. teacher
4. stream
5. real

**B.** Write a spelling word to answer each question.

1. What word names a farm animal? sheep
2. What part of a bicycle is round? wheels
3. What is the opposite of pretend? real
4. What is the direction opposite of west? east



52

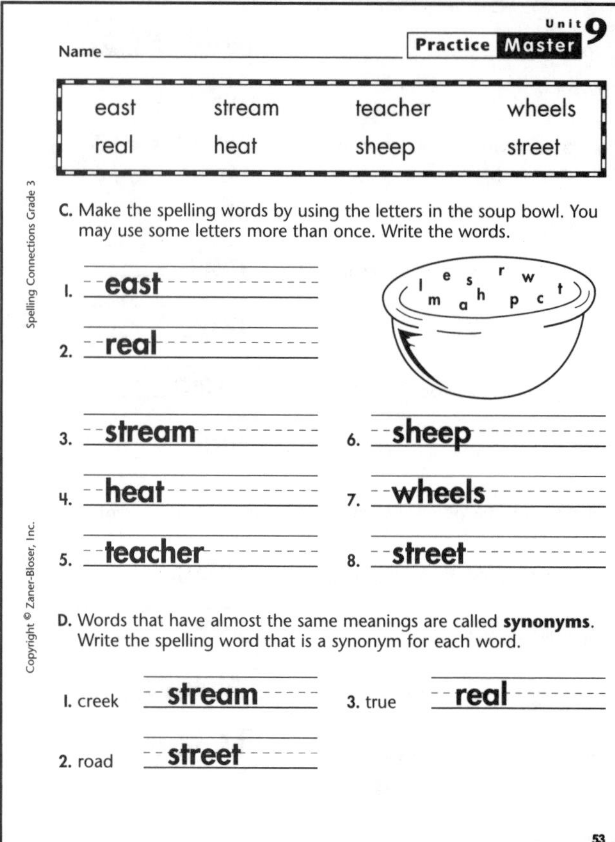

Unit 9 Practice Master

Name ______________________

| east | stream | teacher | wheels |
|---|---|---|---|
| real | heat | sheep | street |

**C.** Make the spelling words by using the letters in the soup bowl. You may use some letters more than once. Write the words.



1. east
2. real
3. stream
4. heat
5. teacher
6. sheep
7. wheels
8. street

**D.** Words that have almost the same meanings are called **synonyms**. Write the spelling word that is a synonym for each word.

1. creek stream
2. road street
3. true real



53

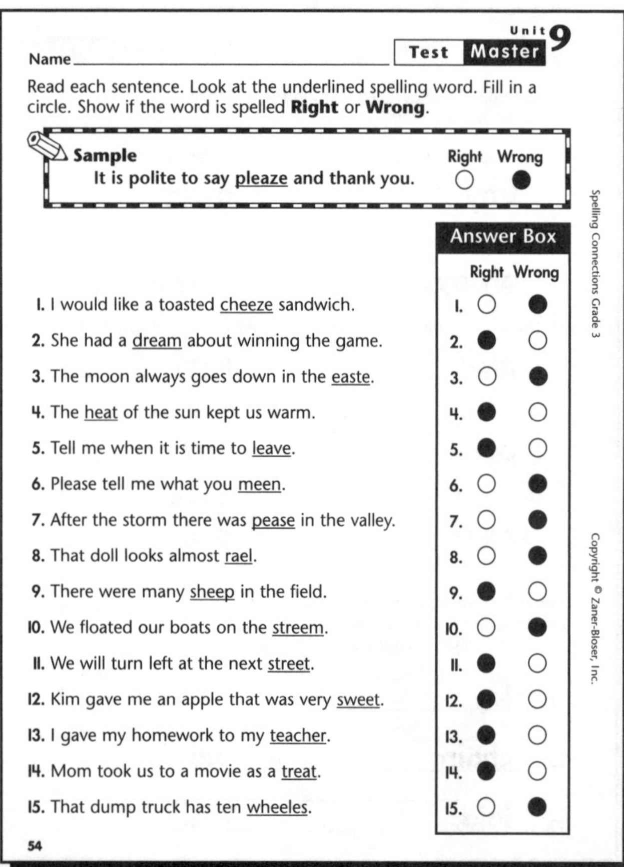

Unit 9 Test Master

Name ______________________

Read each sentence. Look at the underlined spelling word. Fill in a circle. Show if the word is spelled **Right** or **Wrong**.

**Sample**
It is polite to say pleaze and thank you. Right ○ Wrong ●

**Answer Box**

| Sentence | | Right | Wrong |
|---|---|---|---|
| 1. I would like a toasted cheeze sandwich. | 1. | ○ | ● |
| 2. She had a dream about winning the game. | 2. | ● | ○ |
| 3. The moon always goes down in the easte. | 3. | ○ | ● |
| 4. The heat of the sun kept us warm. | 4. | ● | ○ |
| 5. Tell me when it is time to leave. | 5. | ● | ○ |
| 6. Please tell me what you meen. | 6. | ○ | ● |
| 7. After the storm there was pease in the valley. | 7. | ○ | ● |
| 8. That doll looks almost rael. | 8. | ○ | ● |
| 9. There were many sheep in the field. | 9. | ● | ○ |
| 10. We floated our boats on the streem. | 10. | ○ | ● |
| 11. We will turn left at the next street. | 11. | ● | ○ |
| 12. Kim gave me an apple that was very sweet. | 12. | ● | ○ |
| 13. I gave my homework to my teacher. | 13. | ● | ○ |
| 14. Mom took us to a movie as a treat. | 14. | ● | ○ |
| 15. That dump truck has ten wheeles. | 15. | ○ | ● |



54

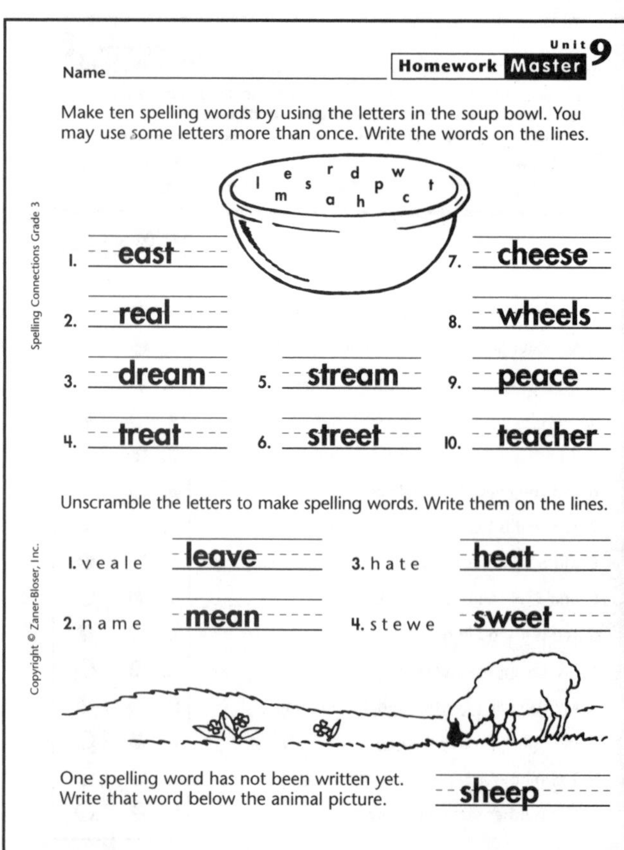

Unit 9 Homework Master

Name ______________________

Make ten spelling words by using the letters in the soup bowl. You may use some letters more than once. Write the words on the lines.



1. east
2. real
3. dream
4. treat
5. stream
6. street
7. cheese
8. wheels
9. peace
10. teacher

Unscramble the letters to make spelling words. Write them on the lines.

1. v e a l e leave
2. n a m e mean
3. h a t e heat
4. s t e w e sweet

One spelling word has not been written yet. Write that word below the animal picture. sheep



55

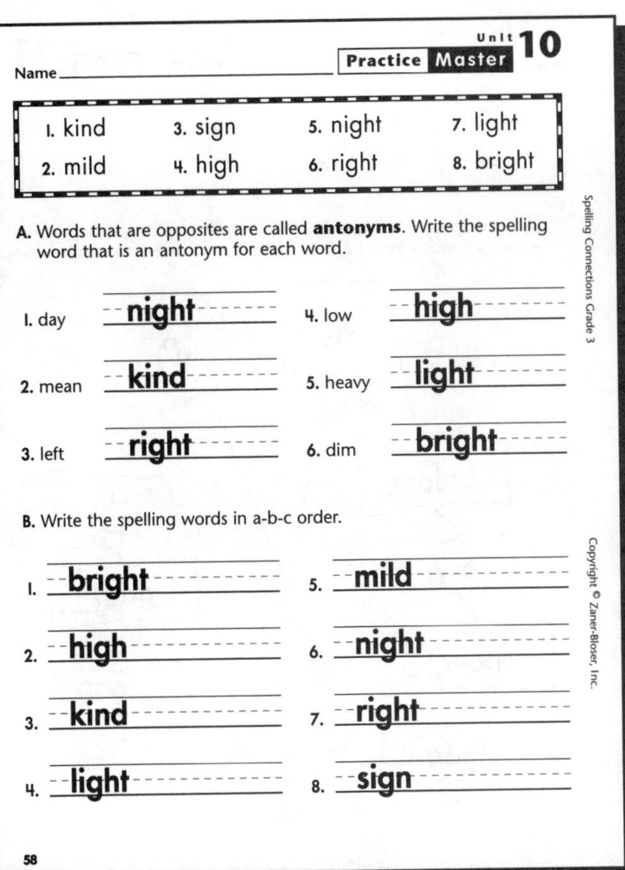

Unit 10 Practice Master

Name ______________________

| 1. kind | 3. sign | 5. night | 7. light |
|---|---|---|---|
| 2. mild | 4. high | 6. right | 8. bright |

**A.** Words that are opposites are called **antonyms**. Write the spelling word that is an antonym for each word.

1. day **night**
2. mean **kind**
3. left **right**
4. low **high**
5. heavy **light**
6. dim **bright**

**B.** Write the spelling words in a-b-c order.

1. **bright**
2. **high**
3. **kind**
4. **light**
5. **mild**
6. **night**
7. **right**
8. **sign**

Spelling Connections Grade 3

Copyright © Zaner-Bloser, Inc.

58

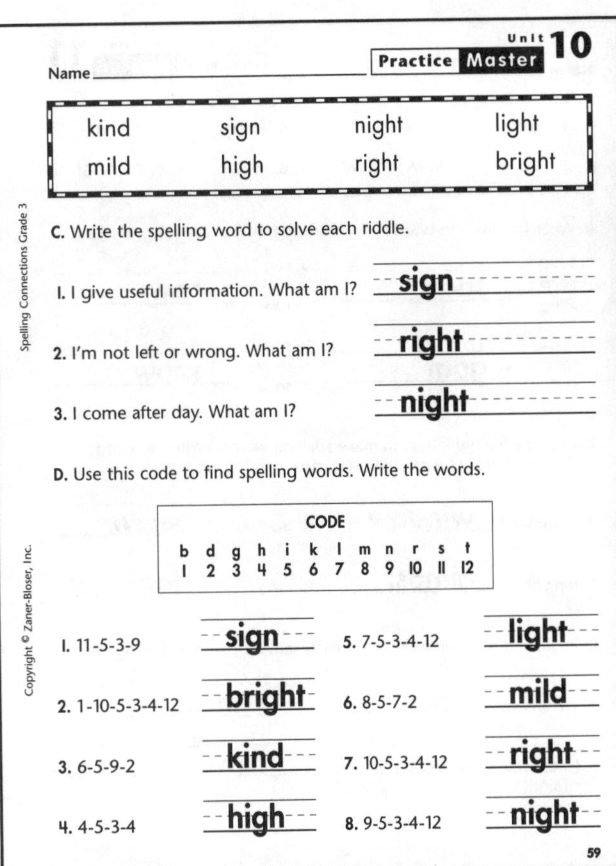

Unit 10 Practice Master

Name ______________________

| kind | sign | night | light |
|---|---|---|---|
| mild | high | right | bright |

**C.** Write the spelling word to solve each riddle.

1. I give useful information. What am I? **sign**
2. I'm not left or wrong. What am I? **right**
3. I come after day. What am I? **night**

**D.** Use this code to find spelling words. Write the words.

CODE

| b | d | g | h | i | k | l | m | n | r | s | t |
|---|---|---|---|---|---|---|---|---|---|---|---|
| 1 | 2 | 3 | 4 | 5 | 6 | 7 | 8 | 9 | 10 | 11 | 12 |

1. 11-5-3-9 **sign**
2. 1-10-5-3-4-12 **bright**
3. 6-5-9-2 **kind**
4. 4-5-3-4 **high**
5. 7-5-3-4-12 **light**
6. 8-5-7-2 **mild**
7. 10-5-3-4-12 **right**
8. 9-5-3-4-12 **night**

Spelling Connections Grade 3

Copyright © Zaner-Bloser, Inc.

59

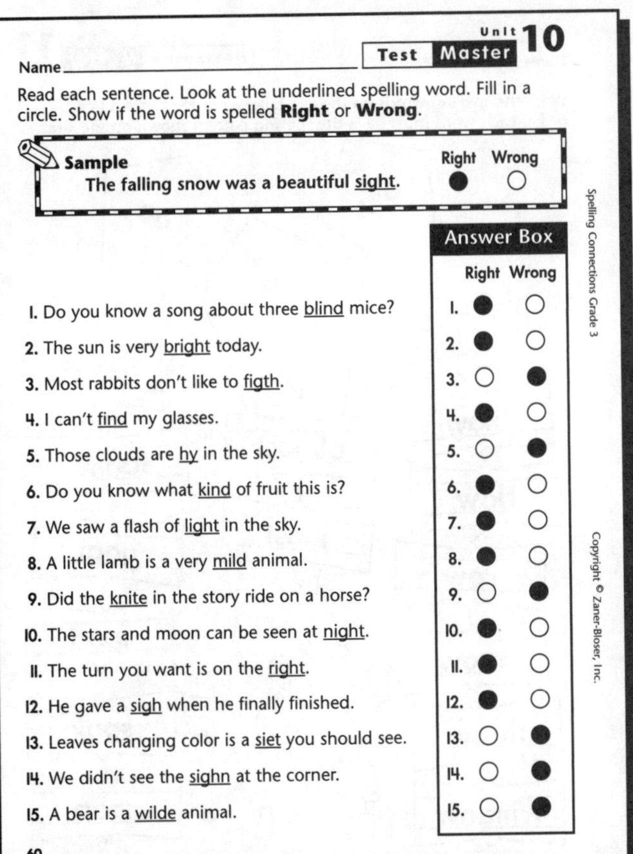

Unit 10 Test Master

Name ______________________

Read each sentence. Look at the underlined spelling word. Fill in a circle. Show if the word is spelled **Right** or **Wrong**.

**Sample** The falling snow was a beautiful sight. Right ● Wrong ○

Answer Box

| Sentence | Right | Wrong |
|---|---|---|
| 1. Do you know a song about three blind mice? | ● | ○ |
| 2. The sun is very bright today. | ● | ○ |
| 3. Most rabbits don't like to figth. | ○ | ● |
| 4. I can't find my glasses. | ● | ○ |
| 5. Those clouds are hy in the sky. | ○ | ● |
| 6. Do you know what kind of fruit this is? | ● | ○ |
| 7. We saw a flash of light in the sky. | ● | ○ |
| 8. A little lamb is a very mild animal. | ● | ○ |
| 9. Did the knite in the story ride on a horse? | ○ | ● |
| 10. The stars and moon can be seen at night. | ● | ○ |
| 11. The turn you want is on the right. | ● | ○ |
| 12. He gave a sigh when he finally finished. | ● | ○ |
| 13. Leaves changing color is a siet you should see. | ○ | ● |
| 14. We didn't see the sighn at the corner. | ○ | ● |
| 15. A bear is a wilde animal. | ○ | ● |

Spelling Connections Grade 3

Copyright © Zaner-Bloser, Inc.

60

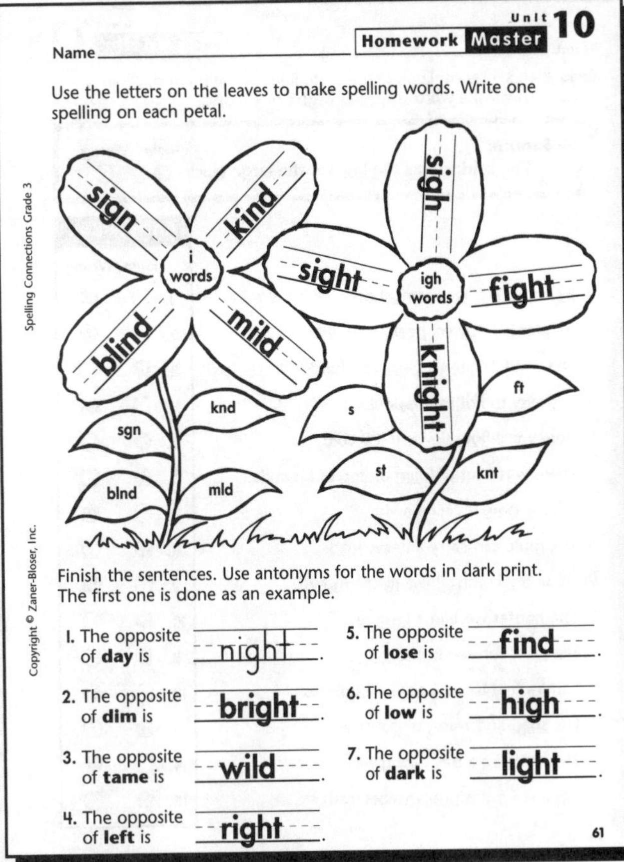

Unit 10 Homework Master

Name ______________________

Use the letters on the leaves to make spelling words. Write one spelling on each petal.



Finish the sentences. Use antonyms for the words in dark print. The first one is done as an example.

1. The opposite of **day** is night.
2. The opposite of **dim** is **bright**.
3. The opposite of **tame** is **wild**.
4. The opposite of **left** is **right**.
5. The opposite of **lose** is **find**.
6. The opposite of **low** is **high**.
7. The opposite of **dark** is **light**.

Spelling Connections Grade 3

Copyright © Zaner-Bloser, Inc.

61

# Answer Key

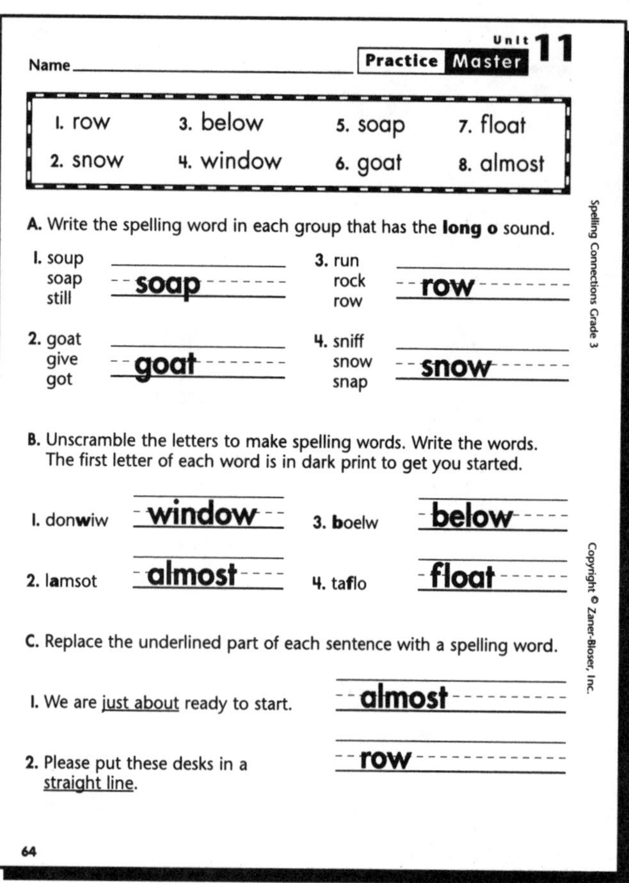

Name ____________ **Practice Master** Unit 11

| | | | |
|---|---|---|---|
| 1. row | 3. below | 5. soap | 7. float |
| 2. snow | 4. window | 6. goat | 8. almost |

**A.** Write the spelling word in each group that has the **long o** sound.

1. soup, soap, still — **soap**
2. goat, give, got — **goat**
3. run, rock, row — **row**
4. sniff, snow, snap — **snow**

**B.** Unscramble the letters to make spelling words. Write the words. The first letter of each word is in dark print to get you started.

1. donw**w**iw — **window**
2. l**a**msot — **almost**
3. **b**oelw — **below**
4. ta**f**lo — **float**

**C.** Replace the underlined part of each sentence with a spelling word.

1. We are <u>just about</u> ready to start. — **almost**
2. Please put these desks in a <u>straight line</u>. — **row**

64

Spelling Connections Grade 3



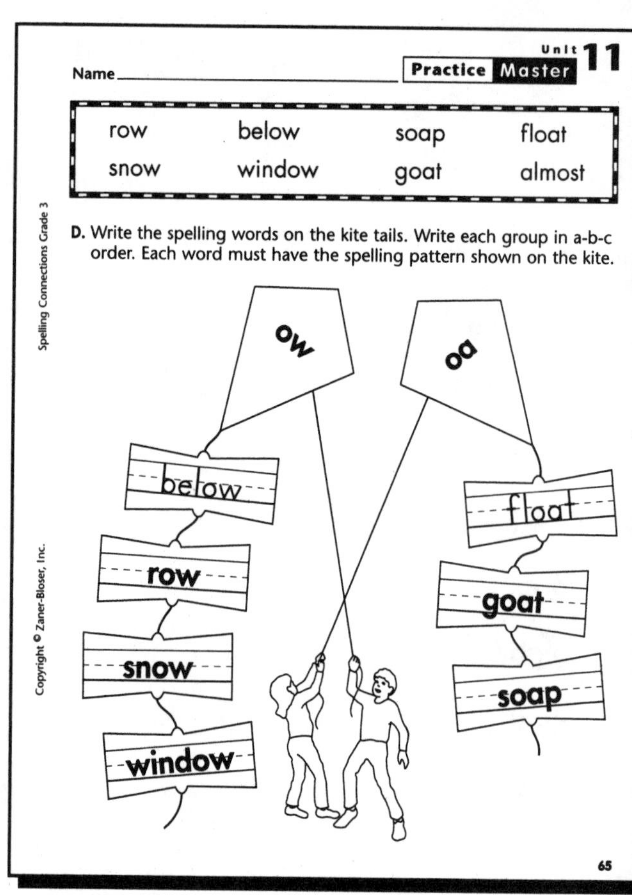

Name ____________ **Practice Master** Unit 11

| | | | |
|---|---|---|---|
| row | below | soap | float |
| snow | window | goat | almost |

**D.** Write the spelling words on the kite tails. Write each group in a-b-c order. Each word must have the spelling pattern shown on the kite.



65

Spelling Connections Grade 3



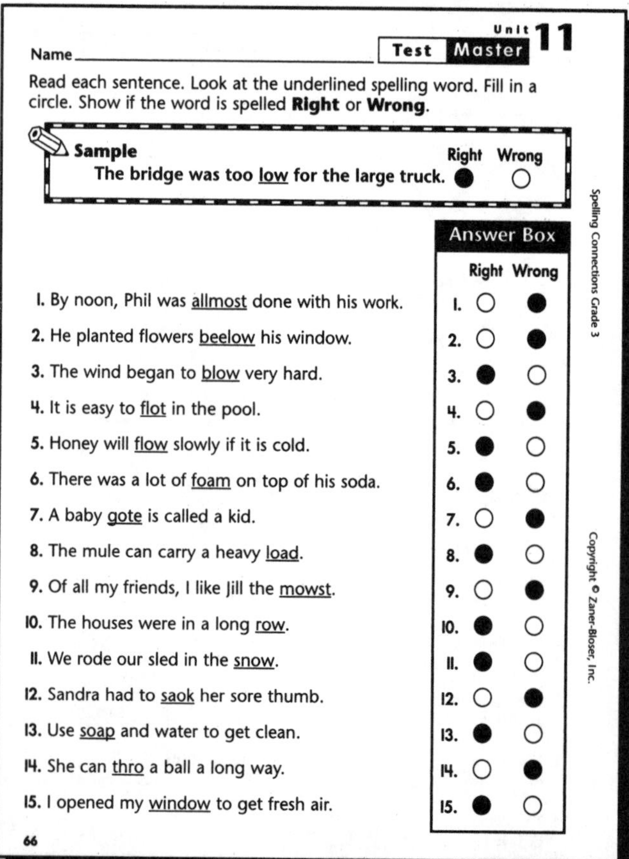

Name ____________ **Test Master** Unit 11

Read each sentence. Look at the underlined spelling word. Fill in a circle. Show if the word is spelled **Right** or **Wrong**.

**Sample** The bridge was too <u>low</u> for the large truck. Right ● Wrong ○

| Sentence | Right | Wrong |
|---|---|---|
| 1. By noon, Phil was <u>allmost</u> done with his work. | ○ | ● |
| 2. He planted flowers <u>beelow</u> his window. | ○ | ● |
| 3. The wind began to <u>blow</u> very hard. | ● | ○ |
| 4. It is easy to <u>flot</u> in the pool. | ○ | ● |
| 5. Honey will <u>flow</u> slowly if it is cold. | ● | ○ |
| 6. There was a lot of <u>foam</u> on top of his soda. | ● | ○ |
| 7. A baby <u>gote</u> is called a kid. | ○ | ● |
| 8. The mule can carry a heavy <u>load</u>. | ● | ○ |
| 9. Of all my friends, I like Jill the <u>mowst</u>. | ○ | ● |
| 10. The houses were in a long <u>row</u>. | ● | ○ |
| 11. We rode our sled in the <u>snow</u>. | ● | ○ |
| 12. Sandra had to <u>saok</u> her sore thumb. | ○ | ● |
| 13. Use <u>soap</u> and water to get clean. | ● | ○ |
| 14. She can <u>thro</u> a ball a long way. | ○ | ● |
| 15. I opened my <u>window</u> to get fresh air. | ● | ○ |

66

Spelling Connections Grade 3



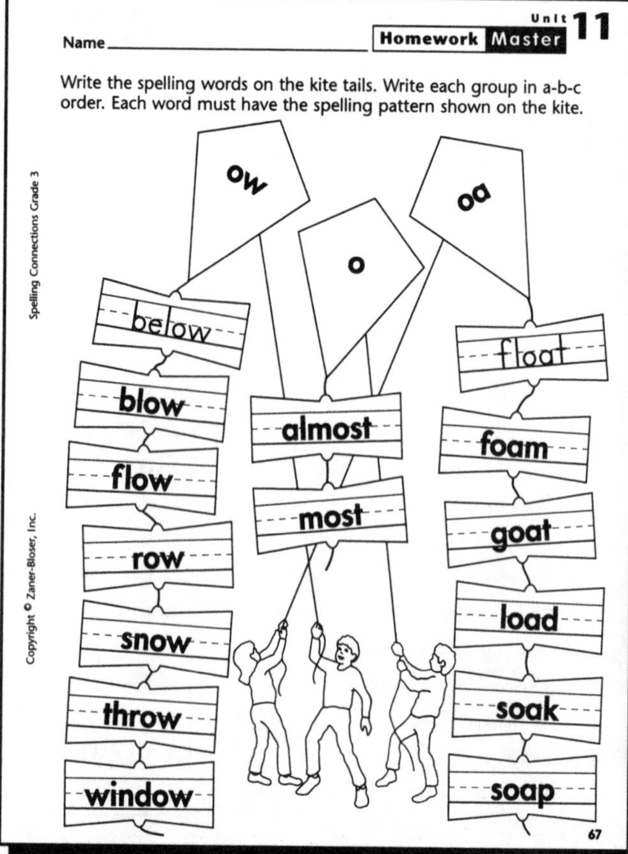

Name ____________ **Homework Master** Unit 11

Write the spelling words on the kite tails. Write each group in a-b-c order. Each word must have the spelling pattern shown on the kite.



67

Spelling Connections Grade 3

# Answer Key

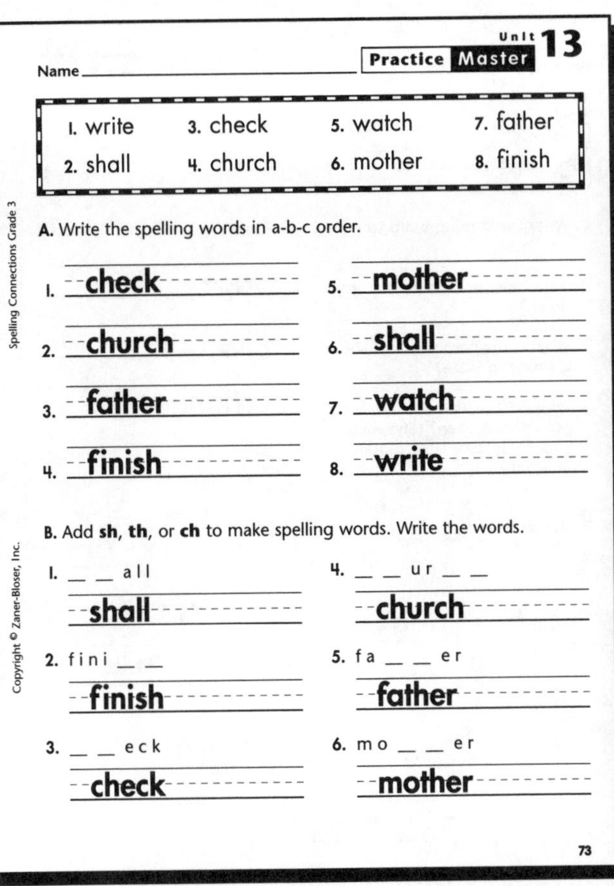

Unit 13 Practice Master

Name ______________________

1. write 3. check 5. watch 7. father
2. shall 4. church 6. mother 8. finish

**A.** Write the spelling words in a-b-c order.

1. check
2. church
3. father
4. finish
5. mother
6. shall
7. watch
8. write

**B.** Add **sh**, **th**, or **ch** to make spelling words. Write the words.

1. _ _ a l l — shall
2. f i n i _ _ — finish
3. _ _ e c k — check
4. _ _ u r _ _ — church
5. f a _ _ e r — father
6. m o _ _ e r — mother

Spelling Connections Grade 3

Copyright © Zaner-Bloser, Inc.

73

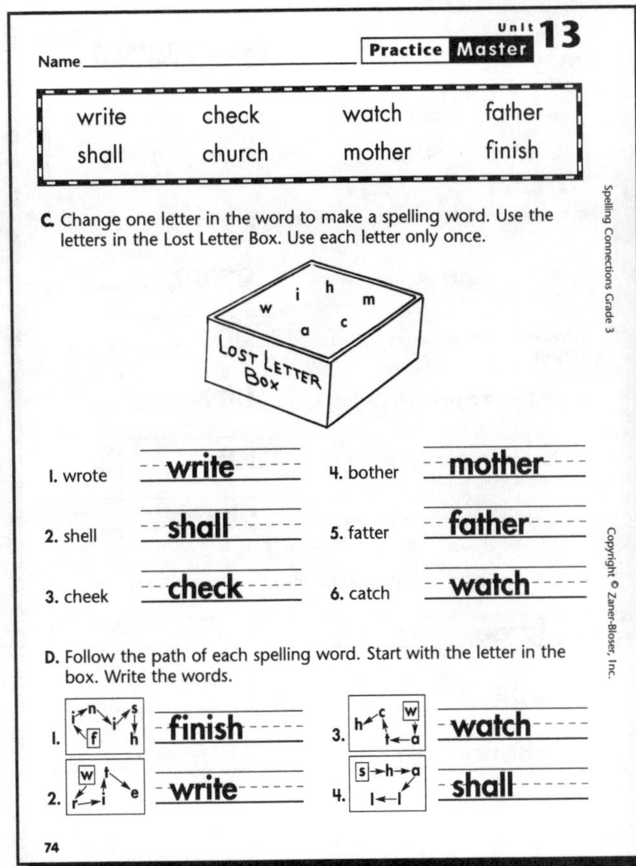

Unit 13 Practice Master

Name ______________________

write check watch father
shall church mother finish

**C.** Change one letter in the word to make a spelling word. Use the letters in the Lost Letter Box. Use each letter only once.



1. wrote — write
2. shell — shall
3. cheek — check
4. bother — mother
5. fatter — father
6. catch — watch

**D.** Follow the path of each spelling word. Start with the letter in the box. Write the words.

1. finish
2. write
3. watch
4. shall

Spelling Connections Grade 3

Copyright © Zaner-Bloser, Inc.

74

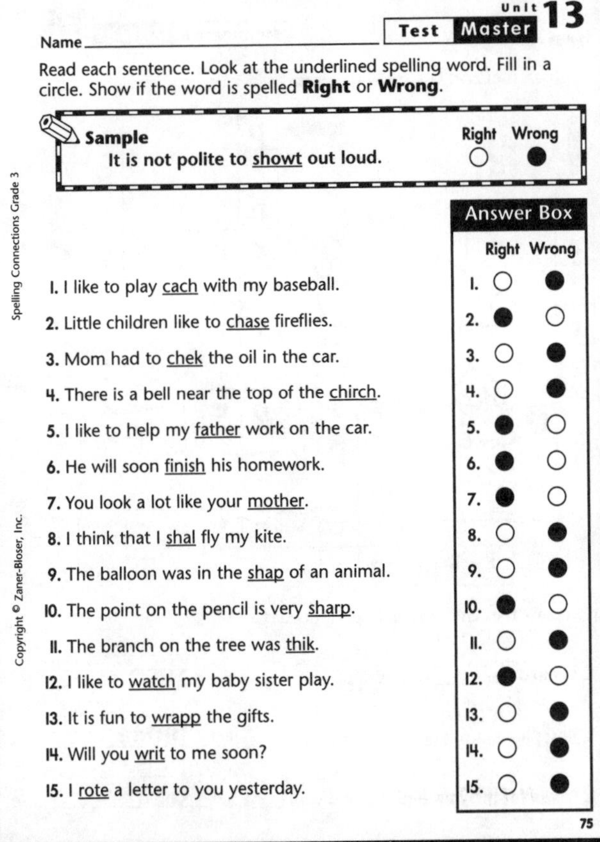

Unit 13 Test Master

Name ______________________

Read each sentence. Look at the underlined spelling word. Fill in a circle. Show if the word is spelled **Right** or **Wrong**.

**Sample** It is not polite to showt out loud. Right ○ Wrong ●

Answer Box

| | Sentence | Right | Wrong |
|---|---|---|---|
| 1. | I like to play cach with my baseball. | ○ | ● |
| 2. | Little children like to chase fireflies. | ● | ○ |
| 3. | Mom had to chek the oil in the car. | ○ | ● |
| 4. | There is a bell near the top of the chirch. | ○ | ● |
| 5. | I like to help my father work on the car. | ● | ○ |
| 6. | He will soon finish his homework. | ● | ○ |
| 7. | You look a lot like your mother. | ● | ○ |
| 8. | I think that I shal fly my kite. | ○ | ● |
| 9. | The balloon was in the shap of an animal. | ○ | ● |
| 10. | The point on the pencil is very sharp. | ● | ○ |
| 11. | The branch on the tree was thik. | ○ | ● |
| 12. | I like to watch my baby sister play. | ● | ○ |
| 13. | It is fun to wrapp the gifts. | ○ | ● |
| 14. | Will you writ to me soon? | ○ | ● |
| 15. | I rote a letter to you yesterday. | ○ | ● |

Spelling Connections Grade 3

Copyright © Zaner-Bloser, Inc.

75

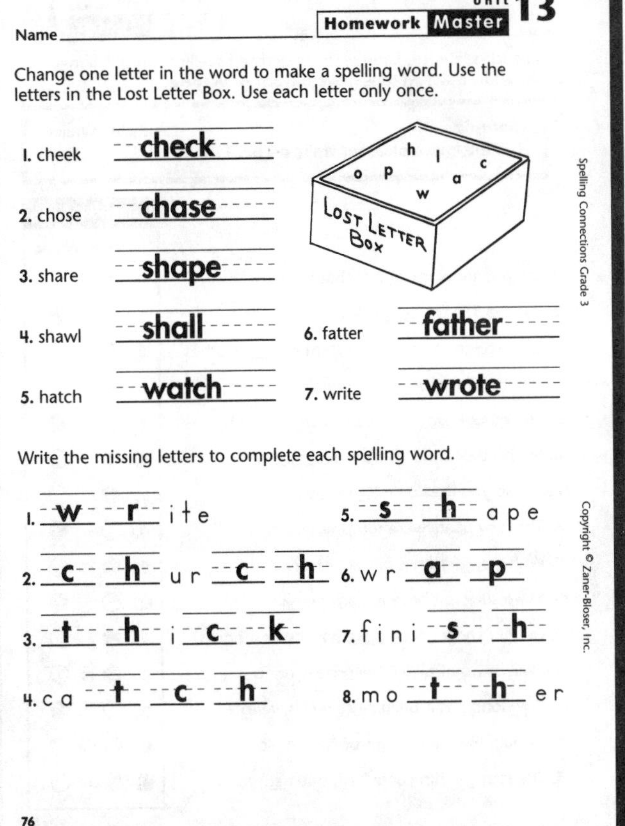

Unit 13 Homework Master

Name ______________________

Change one letter in the word to make a spelling word. Use the letters in the Lost Letter Box. Use each letter only once.



1. cheek — check
2. chose — chase
3. share — shape
4. shawl — shall
5. hatch — watch
6. fatter — father
7. write — wrote

Write the missing letters to complete each spelling word.

1. w r i t e
2. c h u r c h
3. t h i c k
4. c a t c h
5. s h a p e
6. w r a p
7. f i n i s h
8. m o t h e r

Spelling Connections Grade 3

Copyright © Zaner-Bloser, Inc.

76

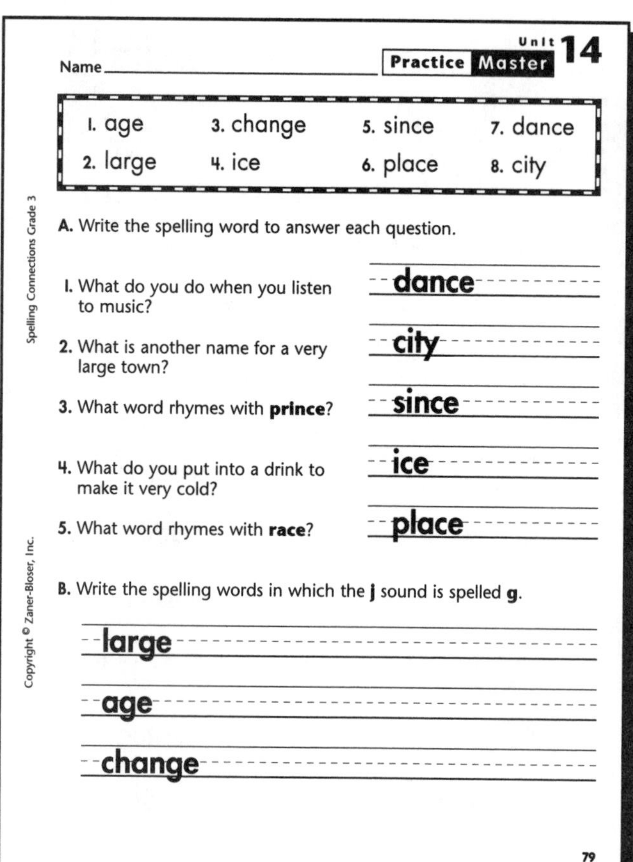

Name ____________ **Practice Master** Unit 14

| | | | |
|---|---|---|---|
| 1. age | 3. change | 5. since | 7. dance |
| 2. large | 4. ice | 6. place | 8. city |

**A.** Write the spelling word to answer each question.

1. What do you do when you listen to music? **dance**
2. What is another name for a very large town? **city**
3. What word rhymes with **prince**? **since**
4. What do you put into a drink to make it very cold? **ice**
5. What word rhymes with **race**? **place**

**B.** Write the spelling words in which the **j** sound is spelled **g**.

**large**

**age**

**change**




79

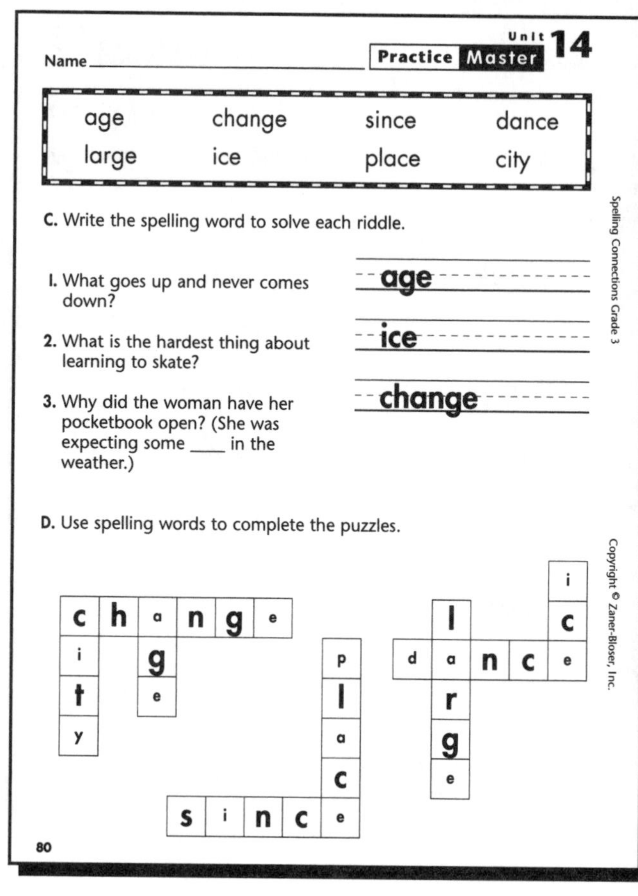

Name ____________ **Practice Master** Unit 14

| | | | |
|---|---|---|---|
| age | change | since | dance |
| large | ice | place | city |

**C.** Write the spelling word to solve each riddle.

1. What goes up and never comes down? **age**
2. What is the hardest thing about learning to skate? **ice**
3. Why did the woman have her pocketbook open? (She was expecting some ____ in the weather.) **change**

**D.** Use spelling words to complete the puzzles.




80

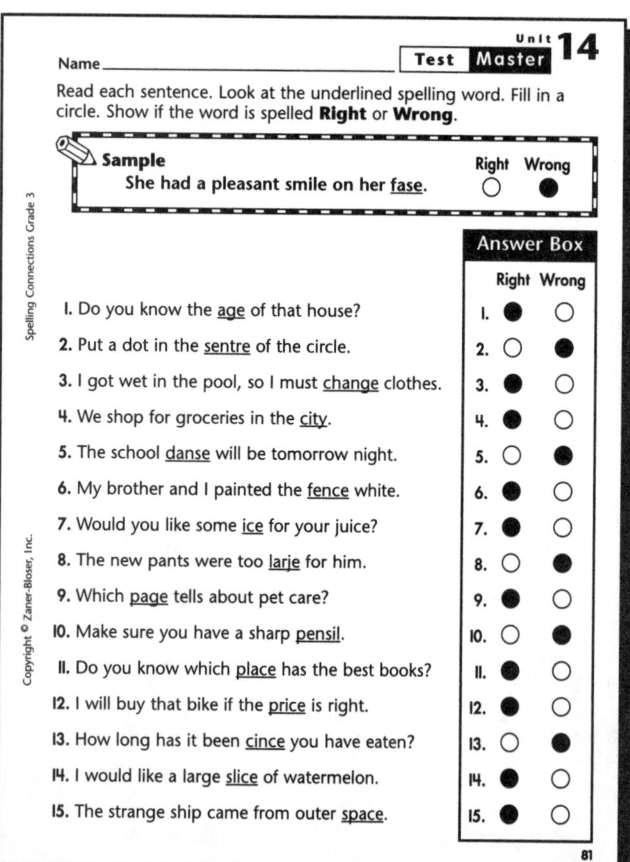

Name ____________ **Test Master** Unit 14

Read each sentence. Look at the underlined spelling word. Fill in a circle. Show if the word is spelled **Right** or **Wrong**.

**Sample** She had a pleasant smile on her fase. Right ○ Wrong ●

Answer Box

| | | Right | Wrong |
|---|---|---|---|
| 1. Do you know the age of that house? | 1. | ● | ○ |
| 2. Put a dot in the sentre of the circle. | 2. | ○ | ● |
| 3. I got wet in the pool, so I must change clothes. | 3. | ● | ○ |
| 4. We shop for groceries in the city. | 4. | ● | ○ |
| 5. The school danse will be tomorrow night. | 5. | ○ | ● |
| 6. My brother and I painted the fence white. | 6. | ● | ○ |
| 7. Would you like some ice for your juice? | 7. | ● | ○ |
| 8. The new pants were too larje for him. | 8. | ○ | ● |
| 9. Which page tells about pet care? | 9. | ● | ○ |
| 10. Make sure you have a sharp pensil. | 10. | ○ | ● |
| 11. Do you know which place has the best books? | 11. | ● | ○ |
| 12. I will buy that bike if the price is right. | 12. | ● | ○ |
| 13. How long has it been cince you have eaten? | 13. | ○ | ● |
| 14. I would like a large slice of watermelon. | 14. | ● | ○ |
| 15. The strange ship came from outer space. | 15. | ● | ○ |




81

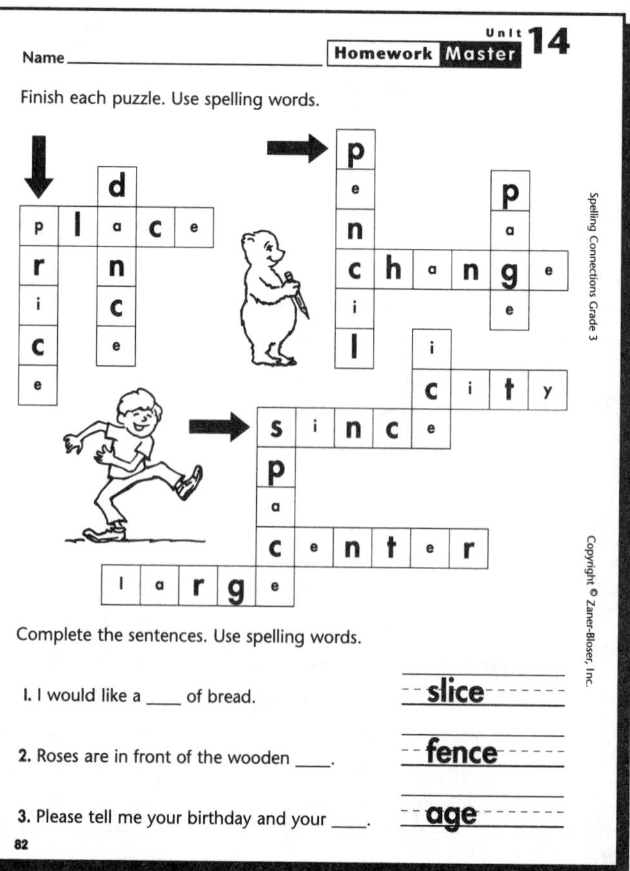

Name ____________ **Homework Master** Unit 14

Finish each puzzle. Use spelling words.

Complete the sentences. Use spelling words.

1. I would like a ____ of bread. **slice**
2. Roses are in front of the wooden ____. **fence**
3. Please tell me your birthday and your ____. **age**




82

# Answer Key

Unit 15 **Practice Master**

Name ______________________

| | | | |
|---|---|---|---|
| 1. shook | 3. splash | 5. stretch | 7. strong |
| 2. fresh | 4. speech | 6. think | 8. cloth |

**A.** Write the spelling words in a-b-c order.

1. cloth
2. fresh
3. shook
4. speech
5. splash
6. stretch
7. strong
8. think

**B.** Write the spelling word that belongs in each sentence.

1. Mom ____ the rug. — shook
2. I had to ____ about the answer. — think
3. Use this ____ to wash the windows. — cloth
4. The heavy rope was very ____. — strong




85

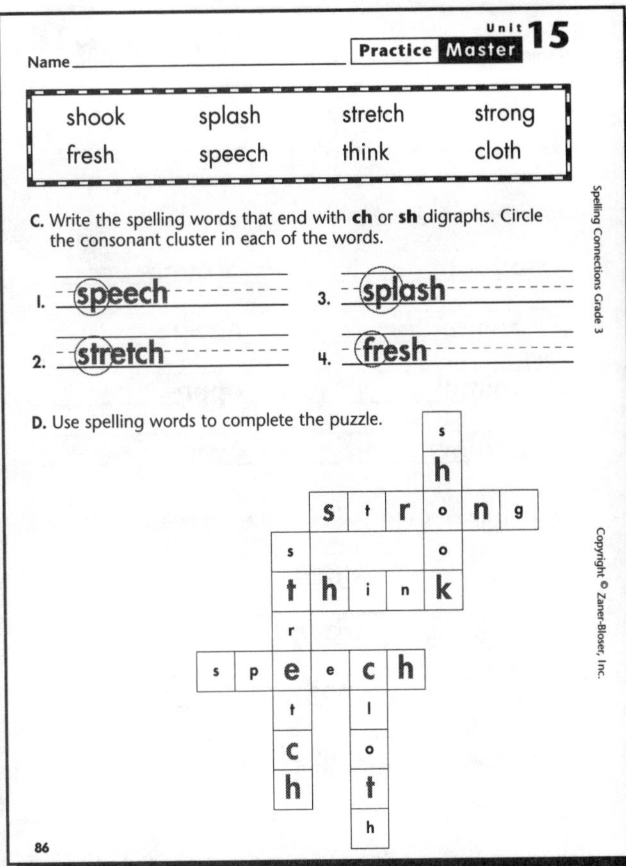

Unit 15 **Practice Master**

Name ______________________

| | | | |
|---|---|---|---|
| shook | splash | stretch | strong |
| fresh | speech | think | cloth |

**C.** Write the spelling words that end with **ch** or **sh** digraphs. Circle the consonant cluster in each of the words.

1. speech
2. stretch
3. splash
4. fresh

**D.** Use spelling words to complete the puzzle.




86

Unit 15 **Test Master**

Name ______________________

Read each sentence. Look at the underlined spelling word. Fill in a circle. Show if the word is spelled **Right** or **Wrong**.

**Sample** Let's count the stripes on the flag. — Right ● Wrong ○

| Sentence | Right | Wrong |
|---|---|---|
| 1. A rubber band can stritch very far. | ○ | ● |
| 2. He waxed his car with a clean cloth. | ● | ○ |
| 3. We saw a bright flash of light in the sky. | ● | ○ |
| 4. Nothing tastes better than fresh fruit. | ● | ○ |
| 5. A cat can scrach with its hind leg. | ○ | ● |
| 6. We shook the paint can before we opened it. | ● | ○ |
| 7. The mayor gave a speach. | ○ | ● |
| 8. The dog went into the pool with a splash. | ● | ○ |
| 9. Many pretty flowers bloom in the spring. | ● | ○ |
| 10. My dad can stich the cuff of my pants. | ○ | ● |
| 11. We built a bridge across the bruk. | ○ | ● |
| 12. My cat likes to play with a ball of string. | ● | ○ |
| 13. A steel beam is very stronge. | ○ | ● |
| 14. We can switch seats at the next stop. | ● | ○ |
| 15. Do you think that we'll be done on time? | ● | ○ |




87

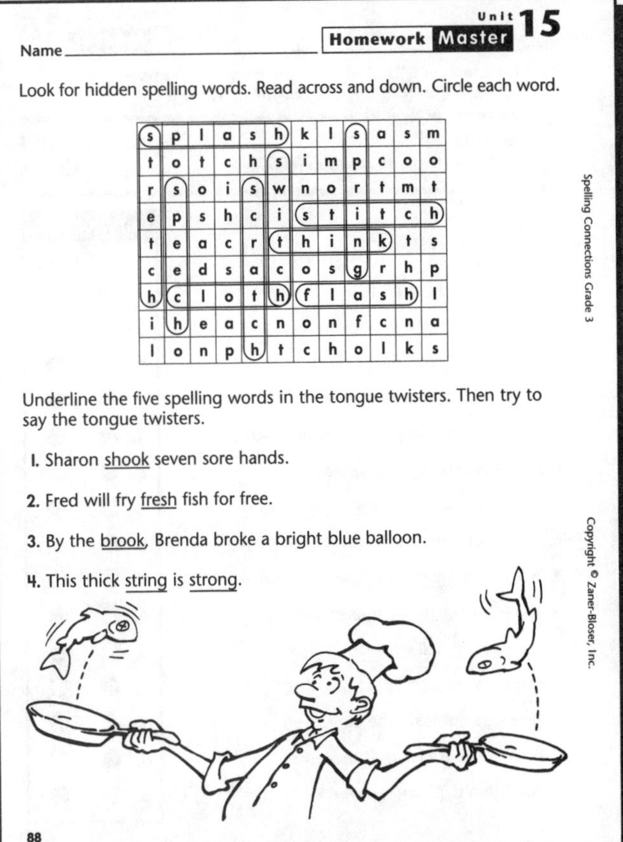

Unit 15 **Homework Master**

Name ______________________

Look for hidden spelling words. Read across and down. Circle each word.

| | | | | | | | | | | | |
|---|---|---|---|---|---|---|---|---|---|---|---|
| s | p | l | a | s | h | k | l | s | a | s | m |
| t | o | t | c | h | s | i | m | p | c | o | o |
| r | s | o | i | s | w | n | o | r | t | m | t |
| e | p | s | h | c | i | s | t | i | t | c | h |
| t | e | a | c | r | t | h | i | n | k | t | s |
| c | e | d | s | a | c | o | s | g | r | h | p |
| h | c | l | o | t | h | f | l | a | s | h | l |
| i | h | e | a | c | n | o | n | f | c | n | a |
| l | o | n | p | h | t | c | h | o | l | k | s |

Underline the five spelling words in the tongue twisters. Then try to say the tongue twisters.

1. Sharon shook seven sore hands.
2. Fred will fry fresh fish for free.
3. By the brook, Brenda broke a bright blue balloon.
4. This thick string is strong.




88

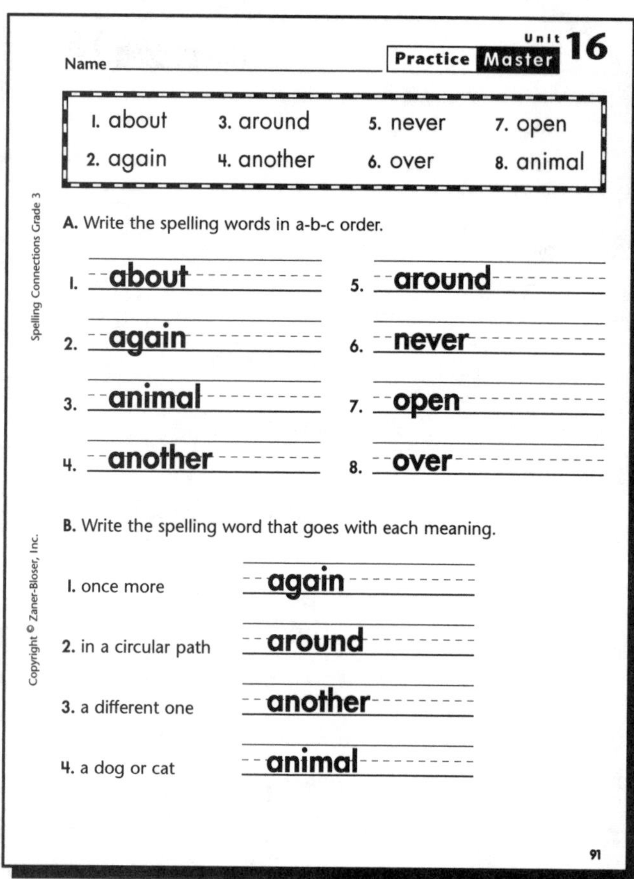

Unit 16 Practice Master

Name ____________________

| | | | |
|---|---|---|---|
| 1. about | 3. around | 5. never | 7. open |
| 2. again | 4. another | 6. over | 8. animal |

**A.** Write the spelling words in a-b-c order.

1. about
2. again
3. animal
4. another
5. around
6. never
7. open
8. over

**B.** Write the spelling word that goes with each meaning.

1. once more — again
2. in a circular path — around
3. a different one — another
4. a dog or cat — animal



91

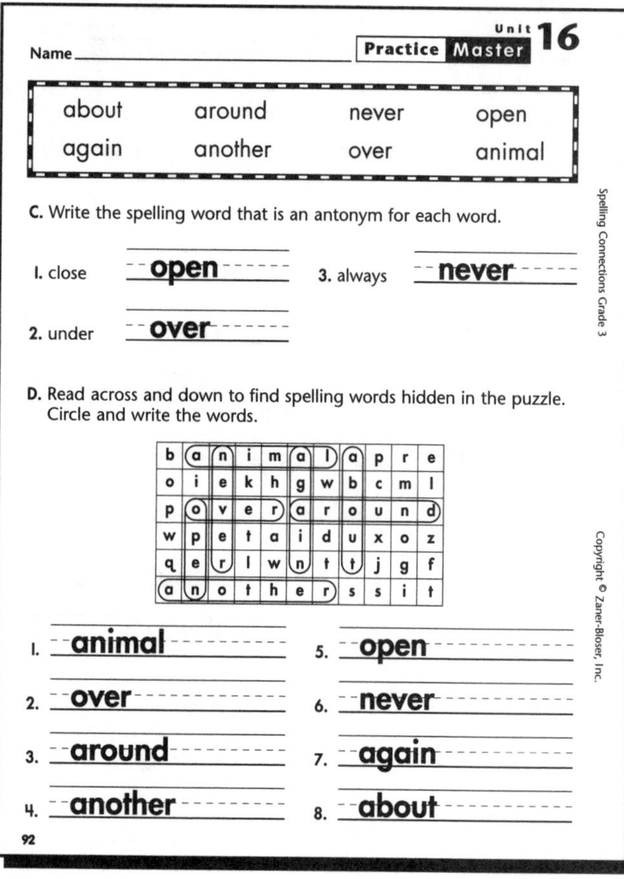

Unit 16 Practice Master

Name ____________________

| | | | |
|---|---|---|---|
| about | around | never | open |
| again | another | over | animal |

**C.** Write the spelling word that is an antonym for each word.

1. close — open
2. under — over
3. always — never

**D.** Read across and down to find spelling words hidden in the puzzle. Circle and write the words.

| | | | | | | | | | | |
|---|---|---|---|---|---|---|---|---|---|---|
| b | a | n | i | m | a | l | a | p | r | e |
| o | i | e | k | h | g | w | b | c | m | l |
| p | o | v | e | r | a | r | o | u | n | d |
| w | p | e | t | a | i | d | u | x | o | z |
| q | e | r | l | w | n | t | t | j | g | f |
| a | n | o | t | h | e | r | s | s | i | t |

1. animal
2. over
3. around
4. another
5. open
6. never
7. again
8. about



92

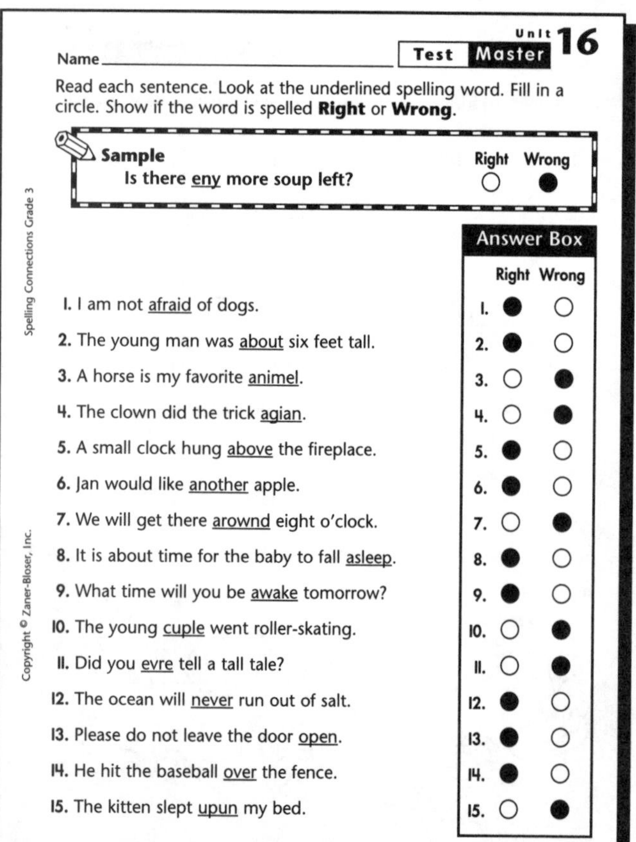

Unit 16 Test Master

Name ____________________

Read each sentence. Look at the underlined spelling word. Fill in a circle. Show if the word is spelled **Right** or **Wrong**.

**Sample**
Is there eny more soup left? — Right ○ Wrong ●

Answer Box

| Sentence | Right | Wrong |
|---|---|---|
| 1. I am not afraid of dogs. | ● | ○ |
| 2. The young man was about six feet tall. | ● | ○ |
| 3. A horse is my favorite animel. | ○ | ● |
| 4. The clown did the trick agian. | ○ | ● |
| 5. A small clock hung above the fireplace. | ● | ○ |
| 6. Jan would like another apple. | ● | ○ |
| 7. We will get there arownd eight o'clock. | ○ | ● |
| 8. It is about time for the baby to fall asleep. | ● | ○ |
| 9. What time will you be awake tomorrow? | ● | ○ |
| 10. The young cuple went roller-skating. | ○ | ● |
| 11. Did you evre tell a tall tale? | ○ | ● |
| 12. The ocean will never run out of salt. | ● | ○ |
| 13. Please do not leave the door open. | ● | ○ |
| 14. He hit the baseball over the fence. | ● | ○ |
| 15. The kitten slept upun my bed. | ○ | ● |



93

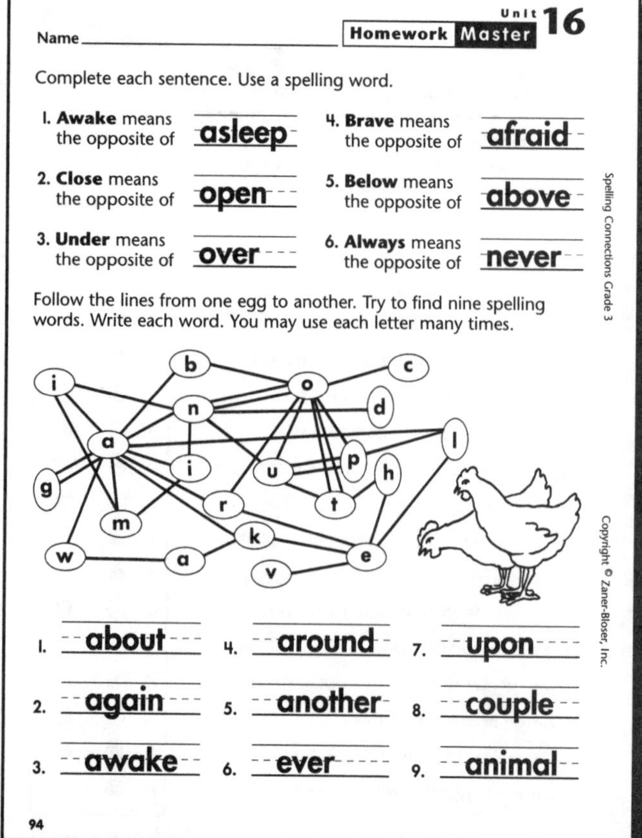

Unit 16 Homework Master

Name ____________________

Complete each sentence. Use a spelling word.

1. **Awake** means the opposite of asleep
2. **Close** means the opposite of open
3. **Under** means the opposite of over
4. **Brave** means the opposite of afraid
5. **Below** means the opposite of above
6. **Always** means the opposite of never

Follow the lines from one egg to another. Try to find nine spelling words. Write each word. You may use each letter many times.



1. about
2. again
3. awake
4. around
5. another
6. ever
7. upon
8. couple
9. animal



94

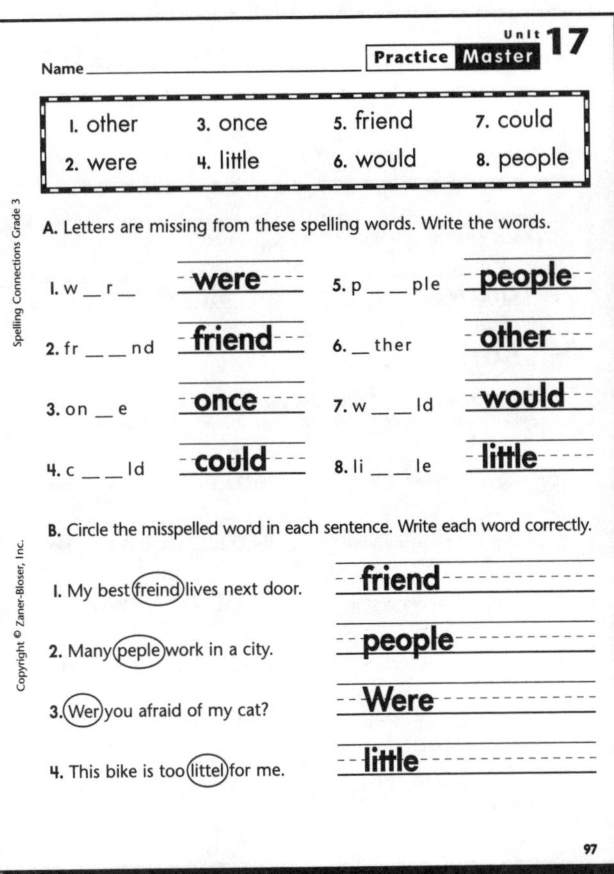

Unit 17 Practice Master

Name ____________

| | | | |
|---|---|---|---|
| 1. other | 3. once | 5. friend | 7. could |
| 2. were | 4. little | 6. would | 8. people |

A. Letters are missing from these spelling words. Write the words.

1. w _ r _ — were
2. fr _ _ nd — friend
3. on _ e — once
4. c _ _ ld — could
5. p _ _ ple — people
6. _ ther — other
7. w _ _ ld — would
8. li _ _ le — little

B. Circle the misspelled word in each sentence. Write each word correctly.

1. My best (freind) lives next door. — friend
2. Many (peple) work in a city. — people
3. (Wer) you afraid of my cat? — Were
4. This bike is too (littel) for me. — little

Spelling Connections Grade 3

Copyright © Zaner-Bloser, Inc.

97

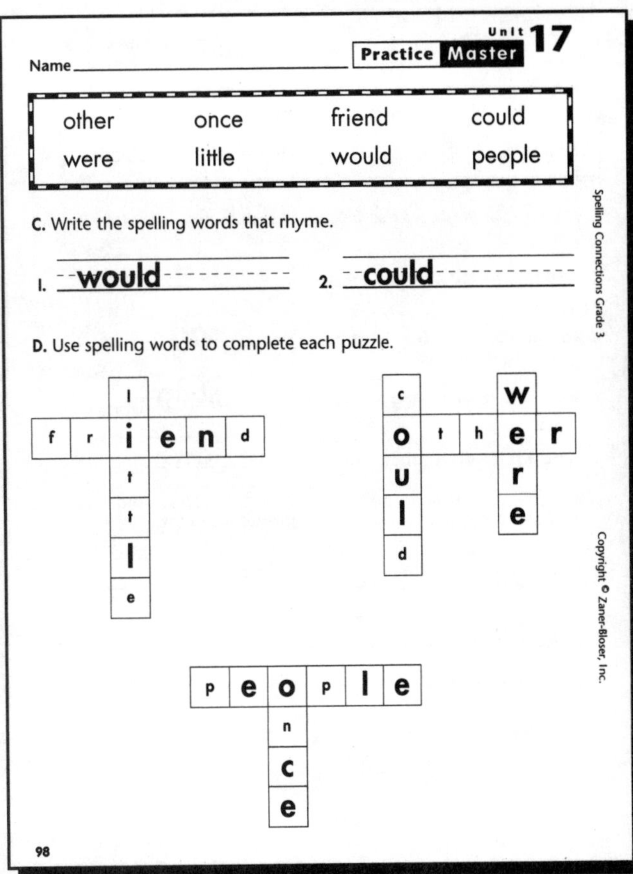

Unit 17 Practice Master

Name ____________

| | | | |
|---|---|---|---|
| other | once | friend | could |
| were | little | would | people |

C. Write the spelling words that rhyme.

1. would
2. could

D. Use spelling words to complete each puzzle.

friend / little

other / could / were

people / once

Spelling Connections Grade 3

Copyright © Zaner-Bloser, Inc.

98

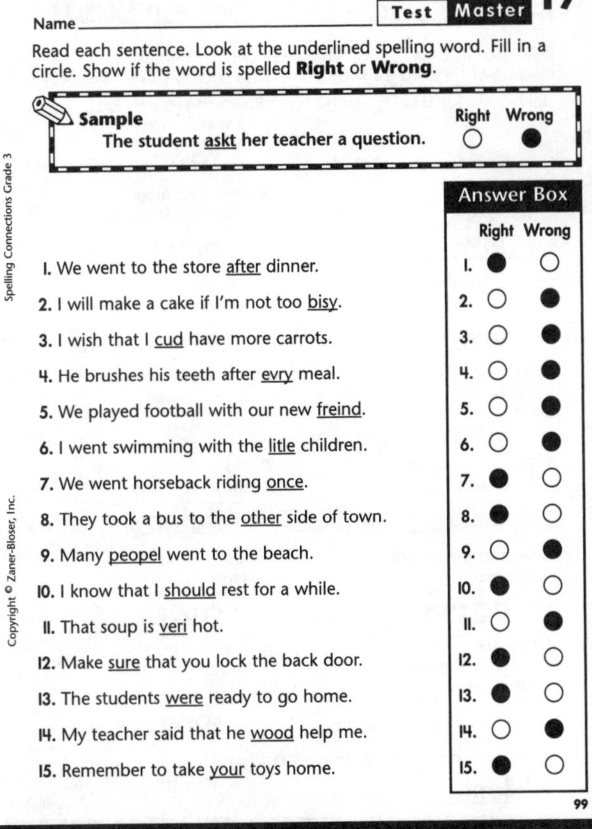

Unit 17 Test Master

Name ____________

Read each sentence. Look at the underlined spelling word. Fill in a circle. Show if the word is spelled **Right** or **Wrong**.

**Sample** The student askt her teacher a question. Right ○ Wrong ●

Answer Box

| Sentence | | Right | Wrong |
|---|---|---|---|
| 1. We went to the store after dinner. | 1. | ● | ○ |
| 2. I will make a cake if I'm not too bisy. | 2. | ○ | ● |
| 3. I wish that I cud have more carrots. | 3. | ○ | ● |
| 4. He brushes his teeth after evry meal. | 4. | ○ | ● |
| 5. We played football with our new freind. | 5. | ○ | ● |
| 6. I went swimming with the litle children. | 6. | ○ | ● |
| 7. We went horseback riding once. | 7. | ● | ○ |
| 8. They took a bus to the other side of town. | 8. | ● | ○ |
| 9. Many peopel went to the beach. | 9. | ○ | ● |
| 10. I know that I should rest for a while. | 10. | ● | ○ |
| 11. That soup is veri hot. | 11. | ○ | ● |
| 12. Make sure that you lock the back door. | 12. | ● | ○ |
| 13. The students were ready to go home. | 13. | ● | ○ |
| 14. My teacher said that he wood help me. | 14. | ○ | ● |
| 15. Remember to take your toys home. | 15. | ● | ○ |

Spelling Connections Grade 3

Copyright © Zaner-Bloser, Inc.

99

Unit 17 Homework Master

Name ____________

Circle the misspelled word in each sentence. Write each word correctly on the line.

1. We will paint (aftr) we clean the walls. — after
2. Today is a (viry) hot day. — very
3. (Evre) spring we go on a class trip. — Every
4. My best (freind) lives next door. — friend
5. Many (peple) work in a city. — people
6. (Wer) you afraid of my cat? — Were
7. Is this (yuor) desk? — your
8. (Wons) I saw a fawn in the woods. — Once
9. I (woud) like you to play with me. — would
10. This bike is too (littel) for me. — little

Find the hidden spelling words. Circle each word.

| | | | | | | | | | |
|---|---|---|---|---|---|---|---|---|---|
| c | a | s | g | o | c | h | a | n | m |
| w | h | y | i | z | o | t | h | e | r |
| a | s | k | v | b | u | s | y | a | s |
| s | o | m | e | p | l | u | t | d | e |
| s | h | o | u | l | d | r | e | a | d |
| a | t | o | h | a | v | e | n | o | f |

Spelling Connections Grade 3

Copyright © Zaner-Bloser, Inc.

100

## Answer Key

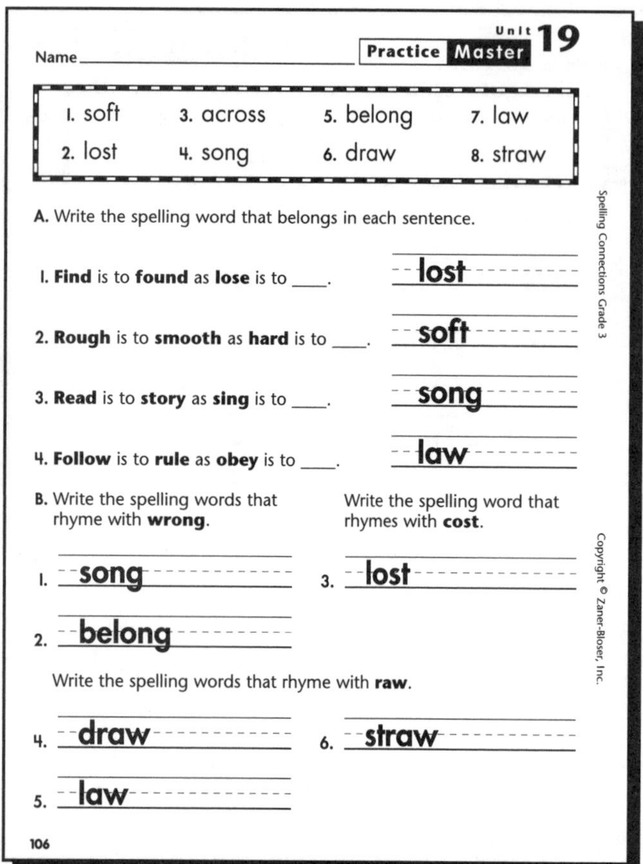

Name ______________ Practice Master Unit 19

| | | | |
|---|---|---|---|
| 1. soft | 3. across | 5. belong | 7. law |
| 2. lost | 4. song | 6. draw | 8. straw |

A. Write the spelling word that belongs in each sentence.

1. **Find** is to **found** as **lose** is to ____. lost
2. **Rough** is to **smooth** as **hard** is to ____. soft
3. **Read** is to **story** as **sing** is to ____. song
4. **Follow** is to **rule** as **obey** is to ____. law

B. Write the spelling words that rhyme with **wrong**.

1. song
2. belong

Write the spelling word that rhymes with **cost**.

3. lost

Write the spelling words that rhyme with **raw**.

4. draw
5. law
6. straw

Spelling Connections Grade 3

Copyright © Zaner-Bloser, Inc.

106

Name ______________ Practice Master Unit 19

| | | | |
|---|---|---|---|
| soft | across | belong | law |
| lost | song | draw | straw |

C. Write the spelling words that end with the vowel sound you hear in **saw**. Circle the letters that make that sound.

1. dr(aw)
2. l(aw)
3. str(aw)

D. Read each question. Unscramble the letters in dark print to make spelling words. Write the words, then answer each question. Circle **Yes** or **No**.

1. Is a cat's fur **fsto**? soft (Yes) No
2. Should you obey the **wal**? law (Yes) No
3. Do cars go **socars** bridges? across (Yes) No
4. Do little animals sometimes get **stlo**? lost (Yes) No
5. Do you know where the erasers **longbe**? belong (Yes) No
6. Can you be quiet and sing a **ongs**? song Yes (No)

Spelling Connections Grade 3

Copyright © Zaner-Bloser, Inc.

107

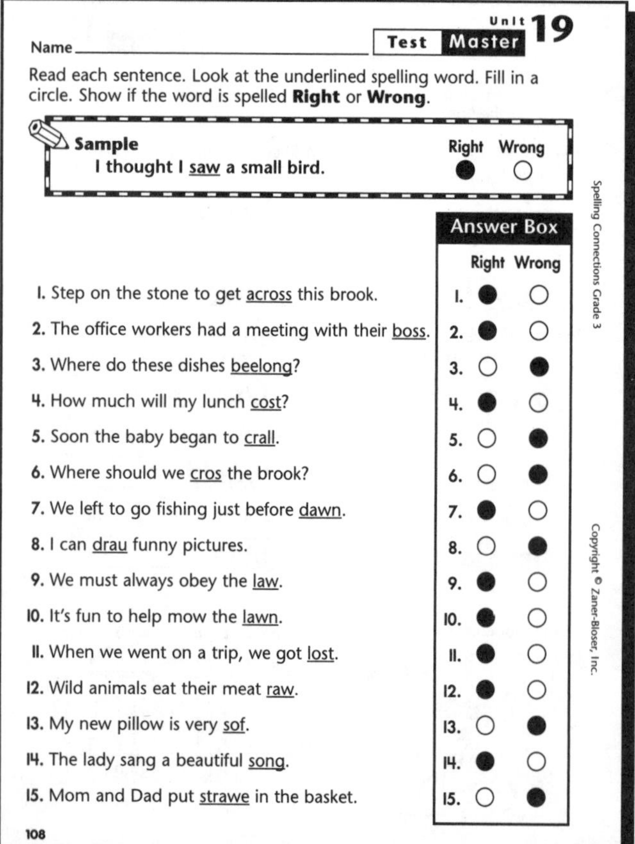

Name ______________ Test Master Unit 19

Read each sentence. Look at the underlined spelling word. Fill in a circle. Show if the word is spelled **Right** or **Wrong**.

**Sample** I thought I saw a small bird. Right ● Wrong ○

| Sentence | Right | Wrong |
|---|---|---|
| 1. Step on the stone to get across this brook. | ● | ○ |
| 2. The office workers had a meeting with their boss. | ● | ○ |
| 3. Where do these dishes beelong? | ○ | ● |
| 4. How much will my lunch cost? | ● | ○ |
| 5. Soon the baby began to crall. | ○ | ● |
| 6. Where should we cros the brook? | ○ | ● |
| 7. We left to go fishing just before dawn. | ● | ○ |
| 8. I can drau funny pictures. | ○ | ● |
| 9. We must always obey the law. | ● | ○ |
| 10. It's fun to help mow the lawn. | ● | ○ |
| 11. When we went on a trip, we got lost. | ● | ○ |
| 12. Wild animals eat their meat raw. | ● | ○ |
| 13. My new pillow is very sof. | ○ | ● |
| 14. The lady sang a beautiful song. | ● | ○ |
| 15. Mom and Dad put strawe in the basket. | ○ | ● |

Spelling Connections Grade 3

Copyright © Zaner-Bloser, Inc.

108

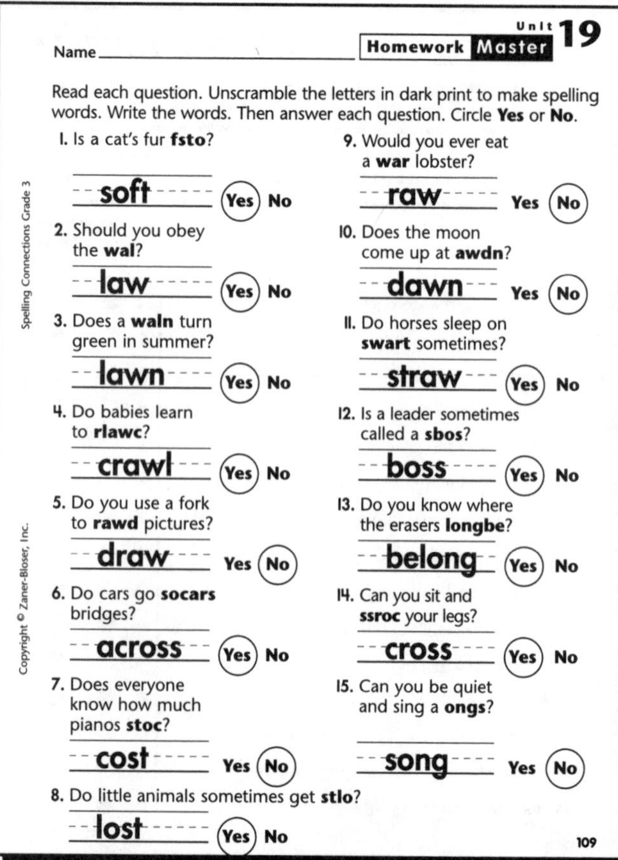

Name ______________ Homework Master Unit 19

Read each question. Unscramble the letters in dark print to make spelling words. Write the words. Then answer each question. Circle **Yes** or **No**.

1. Is a cat's fur **fsto**? soft (Yes) No
2. Should you obey the **wal**? law (Yes) No
3. Does a **waln** turn green in summer? lawn (Yes) No
4. Do babies learn to **rlawc**? crawl (Yes) No
5. Do you use a fork to **rawd** pictures? draw Yes (No)
6. Do cars go **socars** bridges? across (Yes) No
7. Does everyone know how much pianos **stoc**? cost Yes (No)
8. Do little animals sometimes get **stlo**? lost (Yes) No
9. Would you ever eat a **war** lobster? raw Yes (No)
10. Does the moon come up at **awdn**? dawn Yes (No)
11. Do horses sleep on **swart** sometimes? straw (Yes) No
12. Is a leader sometimes called a **sbos**? boss (Yes) No
13. Do you know where the erasers **longbe**? belong (Yes) No
14. Can you sit and **ssroc** your legs? cross (Yes) No
15. Can you be quiet and sing a **ongs**? song Yes (No)

Spelling Connections Grade 3

Copyright © Zaner-Bloser, Inc.

109

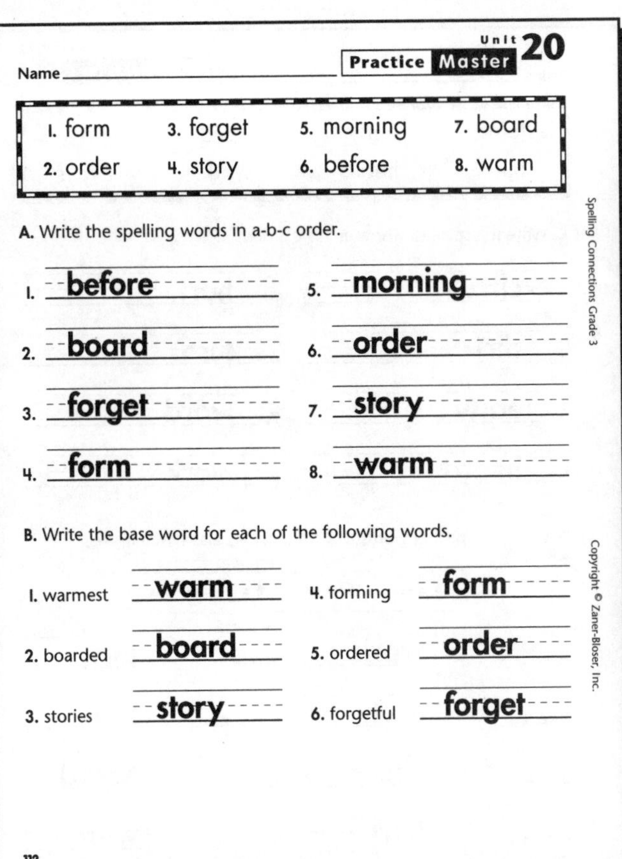

Unit **20** Practice Master

Name ____________________

| | | | |
|---|---|---|---|
| 1. form | 3. forget | 5. morning | 7. board |
| 2. order | 4. story | 6. before | 8. warm |

**A.** Write the spelling words in a-b-c order.

1. before
2. board
3. forget
4. form
5. morning
6. order
7. story
8. warm

**B.** Write the base word for each of the following words.

1. warmest — warm
2. boarded — board
3. stories — story
4. forming — form
5. ordered — order
6. forgetful — forget



112

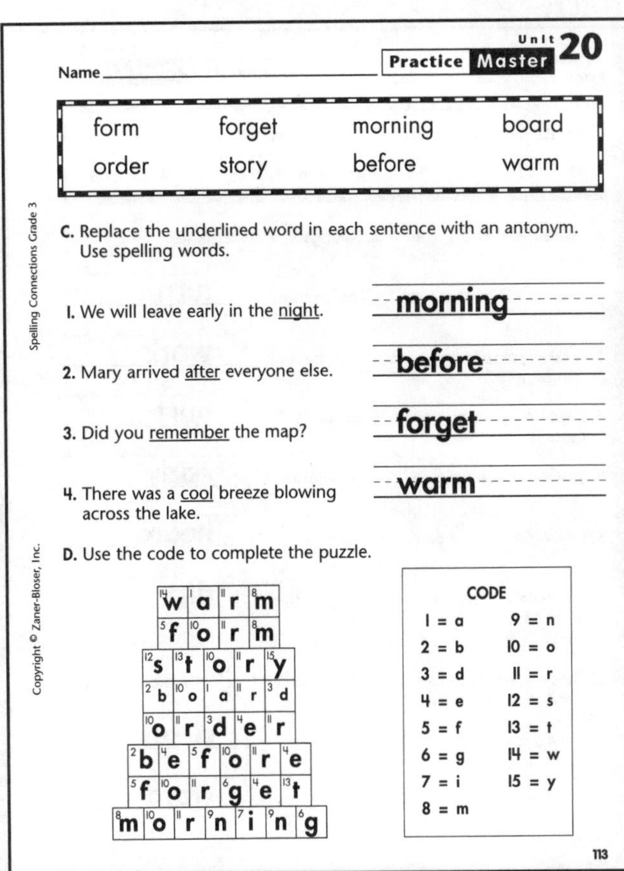

Unit **20** Practice Master

Name ____________________

| | | | |
|---|---|---|---|
| form | forget | morning | board |
| order | story | before | warm |

**C.** Replace the underlined word in each sentence with an antonym. Use spelling words.

1. We will leave early in the <u>night</u>. — morning
2. Mary arrived <u>after</u> everyone else. — before
3. Did you <u>remember</u> the map? — forget
4. There was a <u>cool</u> breeze blowing across the lake. — warm

**D.** Use the code to complete the puzzle.

warm
form
story
board
order
before
forget
morning

CODE

| | |
|---|---|
| 1 = a | 9 = n |
| 2 = b | 10 = o |
| 3 = d | 11 = r |
| 4 = e | 12 = s |
| 5 = f | 13 = t |
| 6 = g | 14 = w |
| 7 = i | 15 = y |
| 8 = m | |



113

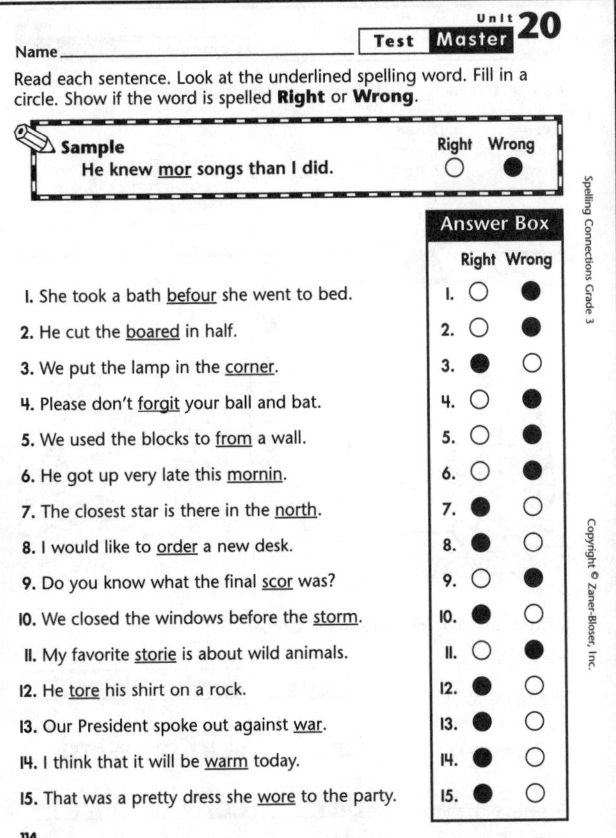

Unit **20** Test Master

Name ____________________

Read each sentence. Look at the underlined spelling word. Fill in a circle. Show if the word is spelled **Right** or **Wrong**.

**Sample** He knew <u>mor</u> songs than I did. Right ○ Wrong ●

**Answer Box**

| | Sentence | Right | Wrong |
|---|---|---|---|
| 1. | She took a bath <u>befour</u> she went to bed. | ○ | ● |
| 2. | He cut the <u>boared</u> in half. | ○ | ● |
| 3. | We put the lamp in the <u>corner</u>. | ● | ○ |
| 4. | Please don't <u>forgit</u> your ball and bat. | ○ | ● |
| 5. | We used the blocks to <u>from</u> a wall. | ○ | ● |
| 6. | He got up very late this <u>mornin</u>. | ○ | ● |
| 7. | The closest star is there in the <u>north</u>. | ● | ○ |
| 8. | I would like to <u>order</u> a new desk. | ● | ○ |
| 9. | Do you know what the final <u>scor</u> was? | ○ | ● |
| 10. | We closed the windows before the <u>storm</u>. | ● | ○ |
| 11. | My favorite <u>storie</u> is about wild animals. | ○ | ● |
| 12. | He <u>tore</u> his shirt on a rock. | ● | ○ |
| 13. | Our President spoke out against <u>war</u>. | ● | ○ |
| 14. | I think that it will be <u>warm</u> today. | ● | ○ |
| 15. | That was a pretty dress she <u>wore</u> to the party. | ● | ○ |



114

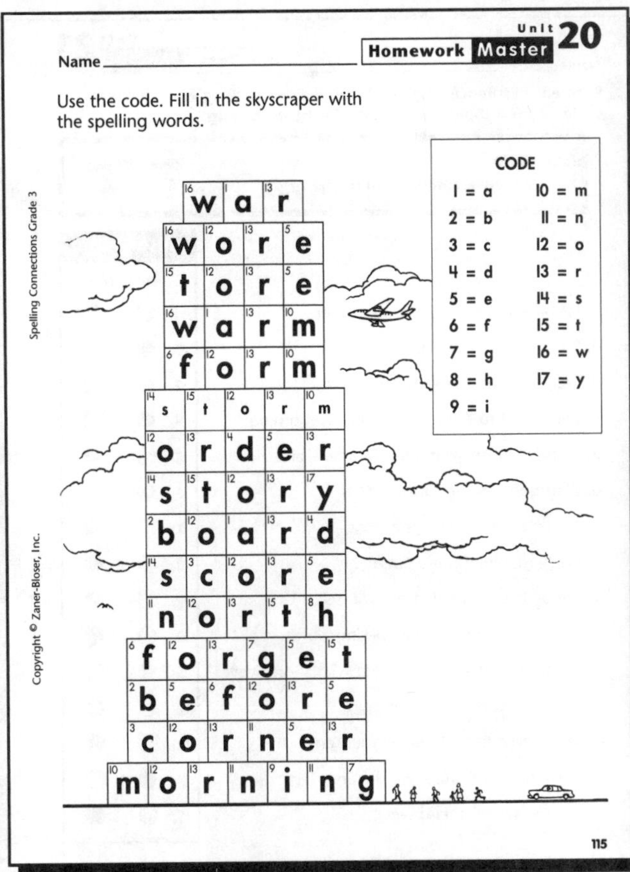

Unit **20** Homework Master

Name ____________________

Use the code. Fill in the skyscraper with the spelling words.

war
wore
tore
warm
form
storm
order
story
board
score
north
forget
before
corner
morning

CODE

| | |
|---|---|
| 1 = a | 10 = m |
| 2 = b | 11 = n |
| 3 = c | 12 = o |
| 4 = d | 13 = r |
| 5 = e | 14 = s |
| 6 = f | 15 = t |
| 7 = g | 16 = w |
| 8 = h | 17 = y |
| 9 = i | |



115

# Answer Key

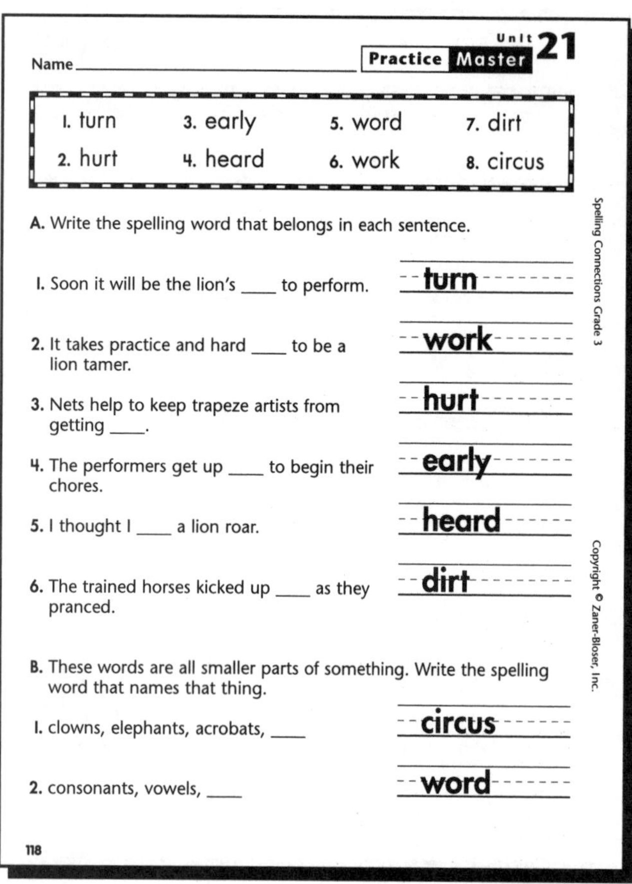

Name ____________ **Practice Master** Unit **21**

| 1. turn | 3. early | 5. word | 7. dirt |
|---|---|---|---|
| 2. hurt | 4. heard | 6. work | 8. circus |

**A.** Write the spelling word that belongs in each sentence.

1. Soon it will be the lion's ____ to perform. **turn**
2. It takes practice and hard ____ to be a lion tamer. **work**
3. Nets help to keep trapeze artists from getting ____. **hurt**
4. The performers get up ____ to begin their chores. **early**
5. I thought I ____ a lion roar. **heard**
6. The trained horses kicked up ____ as they pranced. **dirt**

**B.** These words are all smaller parts of something. Write the spelling word that names that thing.

1. clowns, elephants, acrobats, ____ **circus**
2. consonants, vowels, ____ **word**



118

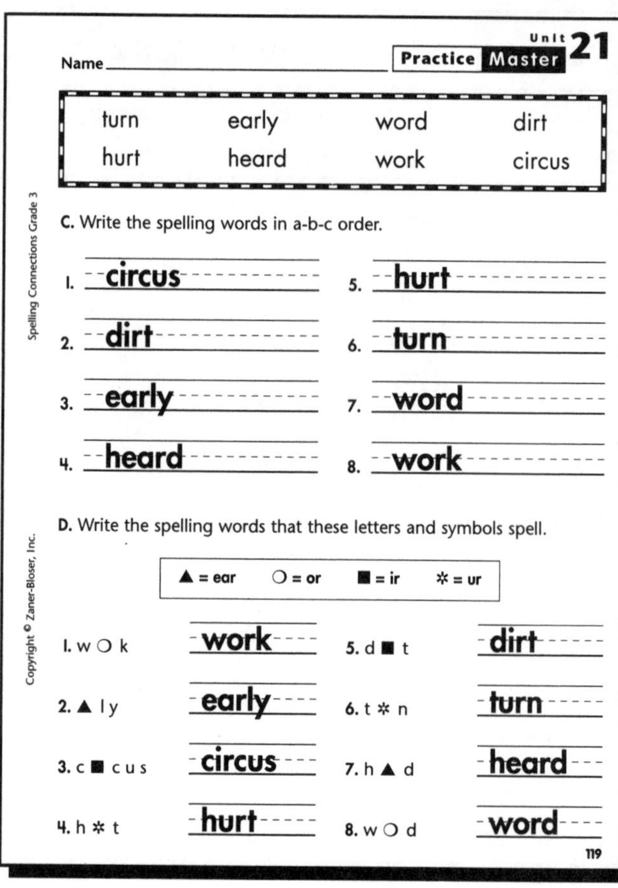

Name ____________ **Practice Master** Unit **21**

| turn | early | word | dirt |
|---|---|---|---|
| hurt | heard | work | circus |

**C.** Write the spelling words in a-b-c order.

1. **circus**
2. **dirt**
3. **early**
4. **heard**
5. **hurt**
6. **turn**
7. **word**
8. **work**

**D.** Write the spelling words that these letters and symbols spell.

▲ = ear ❍ = or ■ = ir ✲ = ur

1. w ❍ k **work**
2. ▲ l y **early**
3. c ■ c u s **circus**
4. h ✲ t **hurt**
5. d ■ t **dirt**
6. t ✲ n **turn**
7. h ▲ d **heard**
8. w ❍ d **word**



119

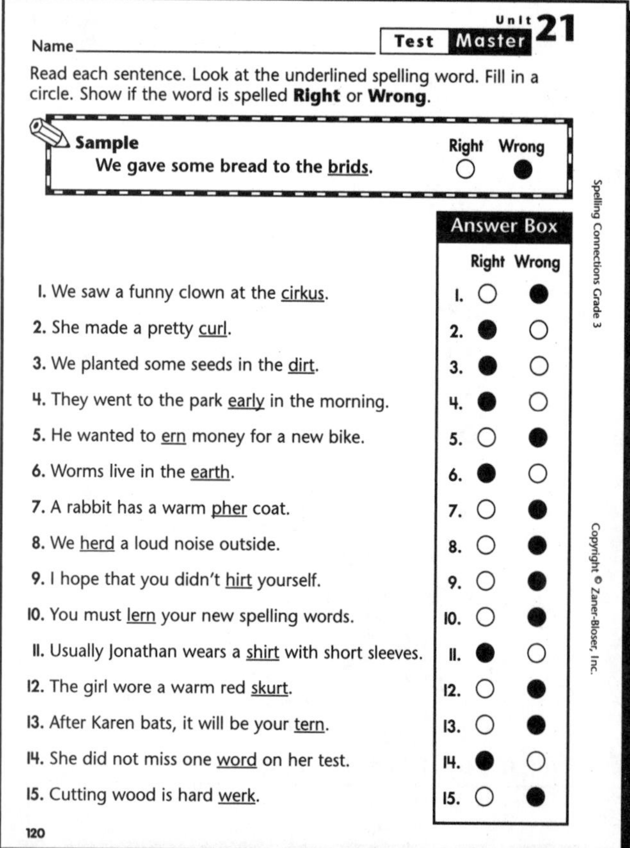

Name ____________ **Test Master** Unit **21**

Read each sentence. Look at the underlined spelling word. Fill in a circle. Show if the word is spelled **Right** or **Wrong**.

**Sample**
We gave some bread to the brids. Right ○ Wrong ●

**Answer Box**

| | Sentence | Right | Wrong |
|---|---|---|---|
| 1. | We saw a funny clown at the cirkus. | ○ | ● |
| 2. | She made a pretty curl. | ● | ○ |
| 3. | We planted some seeds in the dirt. | ● | ○ |
| 4. | They went to the park early in the morning. | ● | ○ |
| 5. | He wanted to ern money for a new bike. | ○ | ● |
| 6. | Worms live in the earth. | ● | ○ |
| 7. | A rabbit has a warm pher coat. | ○ | ● |
| 8. | We herd a loud noise outside. | ○ | ● |
| 9. | I hope that you didn't hirt yourself. | ○ | ● |
| 10. | You must lern your new spelling words. | ○ | ● |
| 11. | Usually Jonathan wears a shirt with short sleeves. | ● | ○ |
| 12. | The girl wore a warm red skurt. | ○ | ● |
| 13. | After Karen bats, it will be your tern. | ○ | ● |
| 14. | She did not miss one word on her test. | ● | ○ |
| 15. | Cutting wood is hard werk. | ○ | ● |



120

Name ____________ **Homework Master** Unit **21**

Add an **s** to each verb. Put the new words in the puzzle.

**Across**
3. curl — **curls**
5. work — **works**
6. turn — **turns**

**Down**
1. earn — **earns**
2. hurt — **hurts**
4. learn — **learns**

Write each group of words in a-b-c order.

1. heard, earth, circus — **circus earth heard**
2. fur, word, skirt — **fur skirt word**
3. early, dirt, shirt — **dirt early shirt**



121

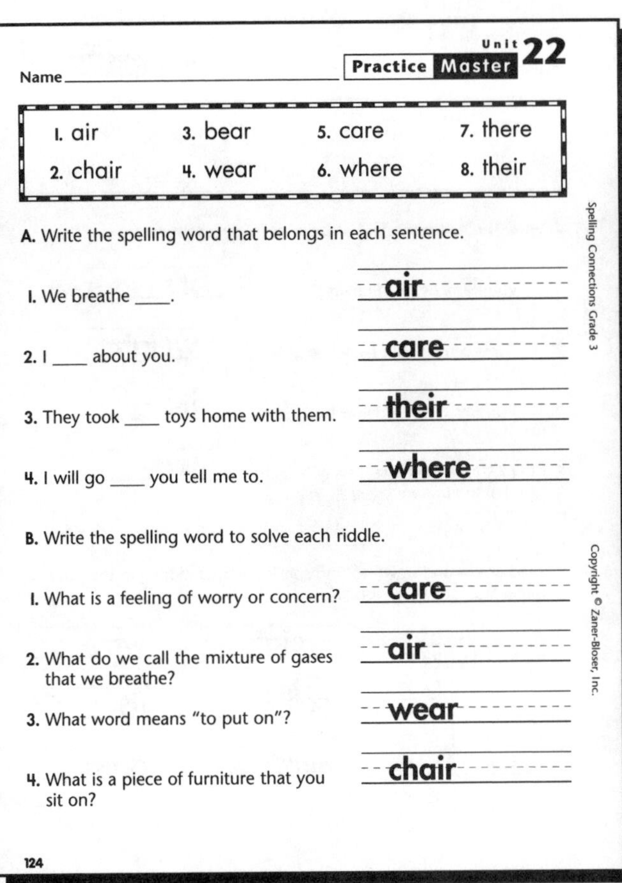

Unit 22 Practice Master

Name ____________________

| | | | |
|---|---|---|---|
| 1. air | 3. bear | 5. care | 7. there |
| 2. chair | 4. wear | 6. where | 8. their |

**A.** Write the spelling word that belongs in each sentence.

1. We breathe ____. **air**
2. I ____ about you. **care**
3. They took ____ toys home with them. **their**
4. I will go ____ you tell me to. **where**

**B.** Write the spelling word to solve each riddle.

1. What is a feeling of worry or concern? **care**
2. What do we call the mixture of gases that we breathe? **air**
3. What word means "to put on"? **wear**
4. What is a piece of furniture that you sit on? **chair**

Spelling Connections Grade 3



124

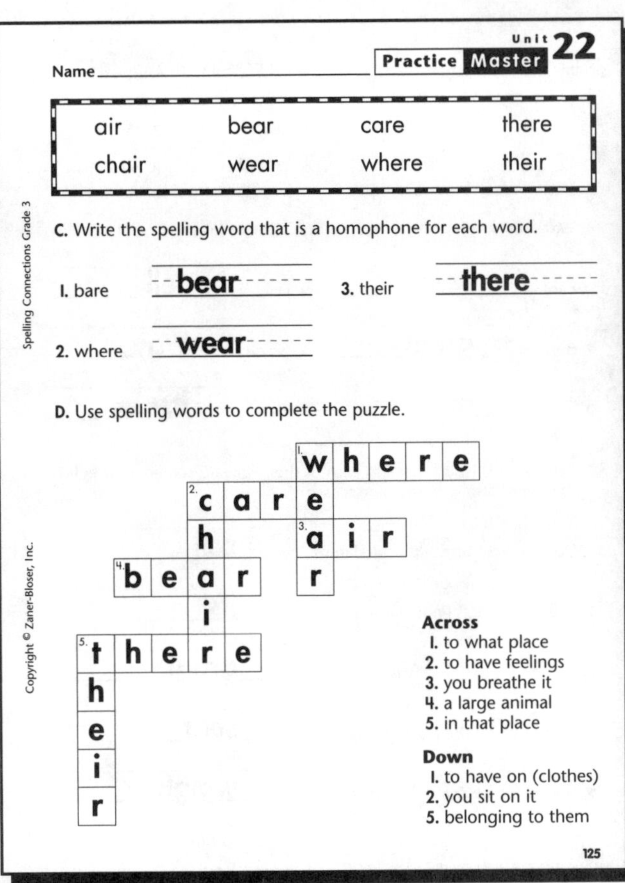

Unit 22 Practice Master

Name ____________________

| | | | |
|---|---|---|---|
| air | bear | care | there |
| chair | wear | where | their |

**C.** Write the spelling word that is a homophone for each word.

1. bare **bear**
2. where **wear**
3. their **there**

**D.** Use spelling words to complete the puzzle.

1. where
2. care
3. air
4. bear
5. there

**Across**
1. to what place
2. to have feelings
3. you breathe it
4. a large animal
5. in that place

**Down**
1. to have on (clothes)
2. you sit on it
5. belonging to them

Spelling Connections Grade 3



125

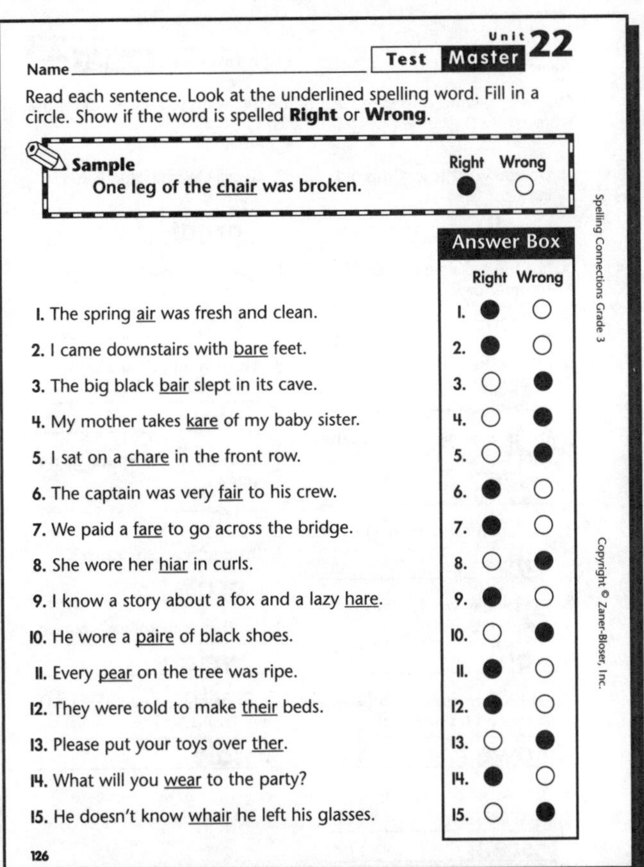

Unit 22 Test Master

Name ____________________

Read each sentence. Look at the underlined spelling word. Fill in a circle. Show if the word is spelled **Right** or **Wrong**.

**Sample**
**One leg of the chair was broken.** Right ● Wrong ○

Answer Box

| | Sentence | Right | Wrong |
|---|---|---|---|
| 1. | The spring air was fresh and clean. | ● | ○ |
| 2. | I came downstairs with bare feet. | ● | ○ |
| 3. | The big black bair slept in its cave. | ○ | ● |
| 4. | My mother takes kare of my baby sister. | ○ | ● |
| 5. | I sat on a chare in the front row. | ○ | ● |
| 6. | The captain was very fair to his crew. | ● | ○ |
| 7. | We paid a fare to go across the bridge. | ● | ○ |
| 8. | She wore her hiar in curls. | ○ | ● |
| 9. | I know a story about a fox and a lazy hare. | ● | ○ |
| 10. | He wore a paire of black shoes. | ○ | ● |
| 11. | Every pear on the tree was ripe. | ● | ○ |
| 12. | They were told to make their beds. | ● | ○ |
| 13. | Please put your toys over ther. | ○ | ● |
| 14. | What will you wear to the party? | ● | ○ |
| 15. | He doesn't know whair he left his glasses. | ○ | ● |

Spelling Connections Grade 3



126

Unit 22 Homework Master

Name ____________________

Change the letters around to make spelling words. The clues will help you. Write each spelling word.

| | | Clues | |
|---|---|---|---|
| 1. | r e a p | a fruit | **pear** |
| 2. | w a r e | to put on | **wear** |
| 3. | h e a r | like a rabbit | **hare** |
| 4. | t h r e e | at or in that place | **there** |
| 5. | f e a r | the price of a bus ride | **fare** |

Finish each rhyme by writing two spelling words.

1. Sniff the **air** at the **fair**.
2. Sit in the **chair** and comb your **hair**.
3. I do not know **where** the zoo keeps the **bear**.
4. If for shoes I wear this **pair**, will you **care**?
5. **Their** feathers are not there, so baby birds look **bare**!

Spelling Connections Grade 3



127

# Answer Key

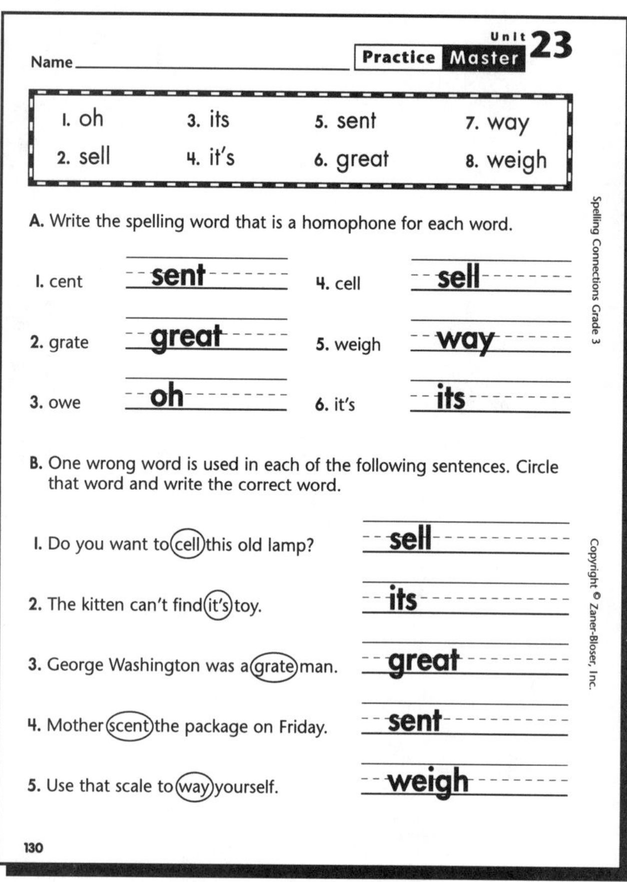

Name ______________________ **Practice Master** Unit **23**

| | | | |
|---|---|---|---|
| 1. oh | 3. its | 5. sent | 7. way |
| 2. sell | 4. it's | 6. great | 8. weigh |

**A.** Write the spelling word that is a homophone for each word.

1. cent **sent**
2. grate **great**
3. owe **oh**
4. cell **sell**
5. weigh **way**
6. it's **its**

**B.** One wrong word is used in each of the following sentences. Circle that word and write the correct word.

1. Do you want to (cell) this old lamp? **sell**
2. The kitten can't find (it's) toy. **its**
3. George Washington was a (grate) man. **great**
4. Mother (scent) the package on Friday. **sent**
5. Use that scale to (way) yourself. **weigh**

130

Spelling Connections Grade 3



---

Name ______________________ **Practice Master** Unit **23**

| | | | |
|---|---|---|---|
| oh | its | sent | way |
| sell | it's | great | weigh |

**C.** Write the homophone that belongs in each sentence.

1. Do you think (its, it's) raining? **it's**
2. How much does that (way, weigh)? **weigh**
3. That puppy seems to have hurt (its, it's) paw. **its**
4. I think this is the correct (way, weigh) to solve the puzzle. **way**

**D.** Read across and down to find spelling words hidden in the puzzle. Circle and write the words.

| | | | | | |
|---|---|---|---|---|---|
| w | e | i | g | h | d |
| a | b | t | r | c | e |
| y | f | s | e | l | l |
| a | g | h | a | i | o |
| s | e | n | t | j | r |

1. **weigh**
2. **sell**
3. **sent**
4. **way**
5. **its**
6. **great**

131

Spelling Connections Grade 3



---

Name ______________________ **Test Master** Unit **23**

Read each sentence. Look at the underlined spelling word. Fill in a circle. Show if the word is spelled **Right** or **Wrong**.

**Sample**
Our flag is read, white, and blue. Right ○ Wrong ●

**Answer Box**

| | Sentence | Right | Wrong |
|---|---|---|---|
| 1. | Each cell of the plant stores water. | ● | ○ |
| 2. | This pencil will cost only one cent. | ● | ○ |
| 3. | It's a long way to go from here. | ● | ○ |
| 4. | The kitten stayed close to its mother. | ● | ○ |
| 5. | When she heard the crash, Mom said, "Oh, no!" | ● | ○ |
| 6. | I owe my friend some baseball cards. | ● | ○ |
| 7. | The main saile was torn. | ○ | ● |
| 8. | Beth and Tom went to a garage sale. | ● | ○ |
| 9. | These roses have a nice scent. | ● | ○ |
| 10. | We went to the market to sel our cow. | ○ | ● |
| 11. | My dad sent my mother flowers. | ● | ○ |
| 12. | Carl said that the movie was great. | ● | ○ |
| 13. | Jean will grate the carrots for the salad. | ● | ○ |
| 14. | We didn't know which way to turn. | ● | ○ |
| 15. | The clerk had to wiegh the seeds on a scale. | ○ | ● |

132

Spelling Connections Grade 3



---

Name ______________________ **Homework Master** Unit **23**

One wrong word is used in each of the following sentences. Circle that word. Write the correct word on the line.

1. Do you want to (cell) this old lamp? **sell**
2. It is fun to (sale) on a hot summer day. **sail**
3. (Its) your turn to go first. **It's**
4. The police officer will lock the door to the (sell). **cell**
5. The kitten can't find (it's) toy. **its**
6. The fall day was breezy but (owe) so nice. **oh**
7. My brother does not (oh) any money on his new bike. **owe**
8. The (sent) of the roses made me sneeze. **scent**
9. George Washington was a (grate) man. **great**
10. A penny is only worth one (scent). **cent**
11. Which (weigh) should we turn at the stop sign? **way**
12. Mother (scent) the package on Friday. **sent**
13. I helped (great) the carrots. **grate**
14. Use that scale to (way) yourself. **weigh**
15. Our neighbors had a big (sail) on Saturday. **sale**

133

Spelling Connections Grade 3

# Answer Key

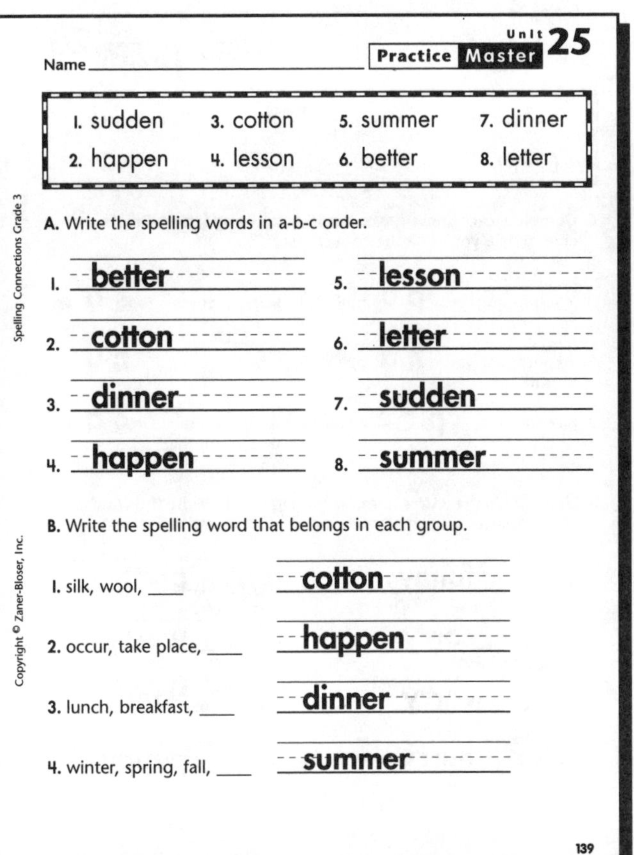

Unit 25 Practice Master

Name ____________

| 1. sudden | 3. cotton | 5. summer | 7. dinner |
|---|---|---|---|
| 2. happen | 4. lesson | 6. better | 8. letter |

**A.** Write the spelling words in a-b-c order.

1. better
2. cotton
3. dinner
4. happen
5. lesson
6. letter
7. sudden
8. summer

**B.** Write the spelling word that belongs in each group.

1. silk, wool, ____ cotton
2. occur, take place, ____ happen
3. lunch, breakfast, ____ dinner
4. winter, spring, fall, ____ summer

139

Spelling Connections Grade 3

Copyright © Zaner-Bloser, Inc.

Unit 25 Practice Master

Name ____________

| sudden | cotton | summer | dinner |
|---|---|---|---|
| happen | lesson | better | letter |

**C.** Unscramble the letters. Use them to complete the spelling words. Write the words.

1. n o l e — l e ss o n — lesson
2. r e e l — l e tt e r — letter
3. u s e n — s u dd e n — sudden
4. r e e b — b e tt e r — better

**D.** Write spelling words to complete the puzzle.

1. something to be learned — lesson
2. to take place — happen
3. good, ____, best — better
4. cloth made from a plant — cotton
5. supper — dinner
6. season between spring and fall — summer

Write the word spelled in the boxes. letter

140

Spelling Connections Grade 3

Copyright © Zaner-Bloser, Inc.

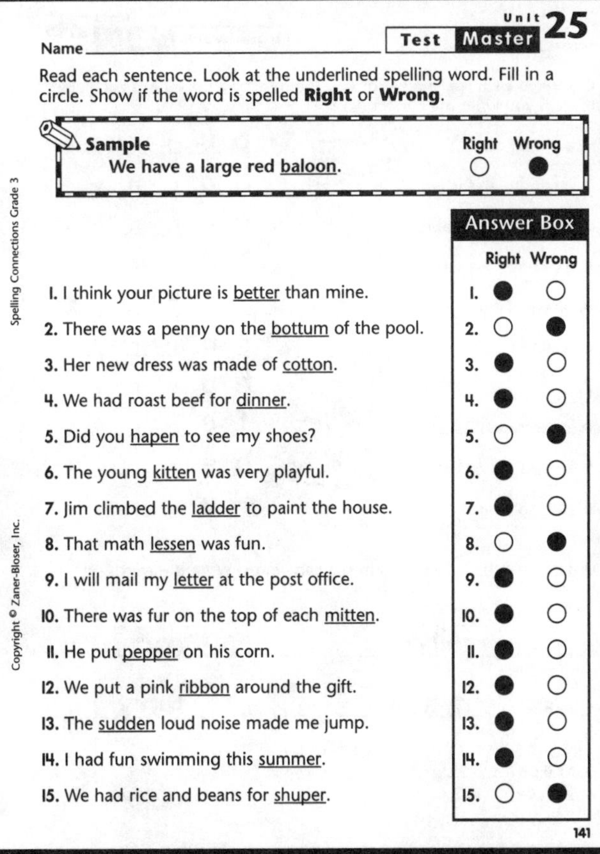

Unit 25 Test Master

Name ____________

Read each sentence. Look at the underlined spelling word. Fill in a circle. Show if the word is spelled **Right** or **Wrong**.

**Sample**
We have a large red baloon. — Right ○ Wrong ●

Answer Box

| Sentence | | Right | Wrong |
|---|---|---|---|
| 1. I think your picture is better than mine. | 1. | ● | ○ |
| 2. There was a penny on the bottum of the pool. | 2. | ○ | ● |
| 3. Her new dress was made of cotton. | 3. | ● | ○ |
| 4. We had roast beef for dinner. | 4. | ● | ○ |
| 5. Did you hapen to see my shoes? | 5. | ○ | ● |
| 6. The young kitten was very playful. | 6. | ● | ○ |
| 7. Jim climbed the ladder to paint the house. | 7. | ● | ○ |
| 8. That math lessen was fun. | 8. | ○ | ● |
| 9. I will mail my letter at the post office. | 9. | ● | ○ |
| 10. There was fur on the top of each mitten. | 10. | ● | ○ |
| 11. He put pepper on his corn. | 11. | ● | ○ |
| 12. We put a pink ribbon around the gift. | 12. | ● | ○ |
| 13. The sudden loud noise made me jump. | 13. | ● | ○ |
| 14. I had fun swimming this summer. | 14. | ● | ○ |
| 15. We had rice and beans for shuper. | 15. | ○ | ● |

141

Spelling Connections Grade 3

Copyright © Zaner-Bloser, Inc.

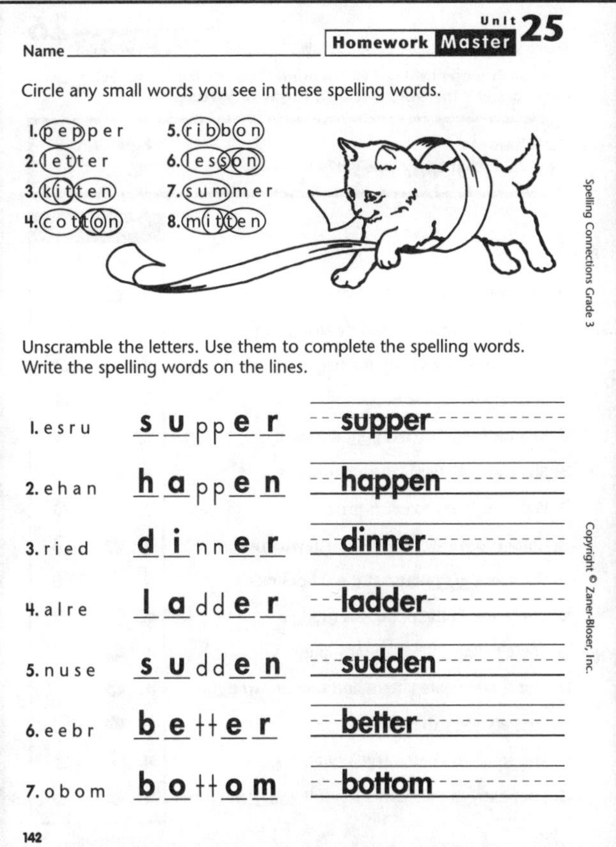

Unit 25 Homework Master

Name ____________

Circle any small words you see in these spelling words.

1. pepper
2. letter
3. kitten
4. cotton
5. ribbon
6. lesson
7. summer
8. mitten

Unscramble the letters. Use them to complete the spelling words. Write the spelling words on the lines.

1. e s r u — s u pp e r — supper
2. e h a n — h a pp e n — happen
3. r i e d — d i nn e r — dinner
4. a l r e — l a dd e r — ladder
5. n u s e — s u dd e n — sudden
6. e e b r — b e tt e r — better
7. o b o m — b o tt o m — bottom

142

Spelling Connections Grade 3

Copyright © Zaner-Bloser, Inc.

# Answer Key

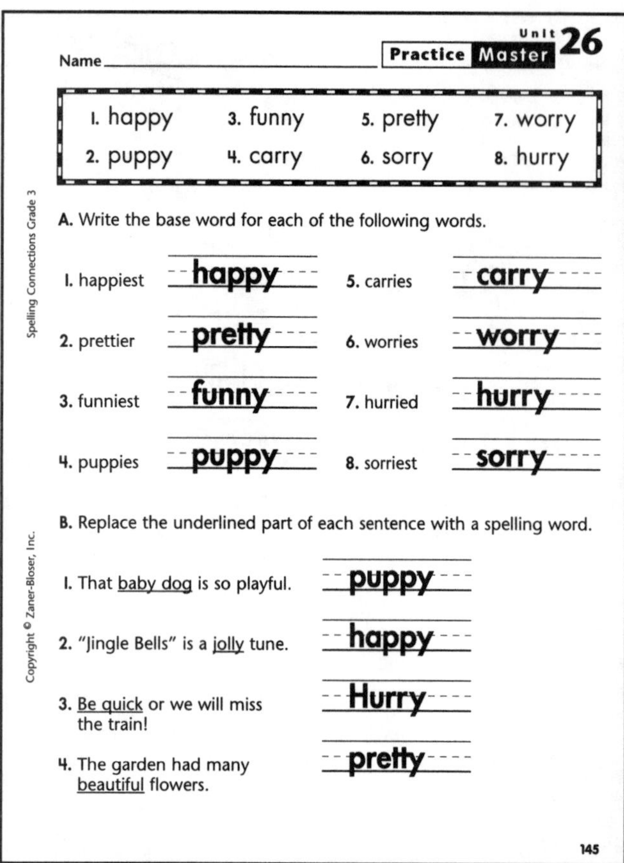

Name ____________ **Practice Master** Unit **26**

| 1. happy | 3. funny | 5. pretty | 7. worry |
|---|---|---|---|
| 2. puppy | 4. carry | 6. sorry | 8. hurry |

**A.** Write the base word for each of the following words.

1. happiest **happy**
2. prettier **pretty**
3. funniest **funny**
4. puppies **puppy**
5. carries **carry**
6. worries **worry**
7. hurried **hurry**
8. sorriest **sorry**

**B.** Replace the underlined part of each sentence with a spelling word.

1. That baby dog is so playful. **puppy**
2. "Jingle Bells" is a jolly tune. **happy**
3. Be quick or we will miss the train! **Hurry**
4. The garden had many beautiful flowers. **pretty**

Spelling Connections Grade 3



145

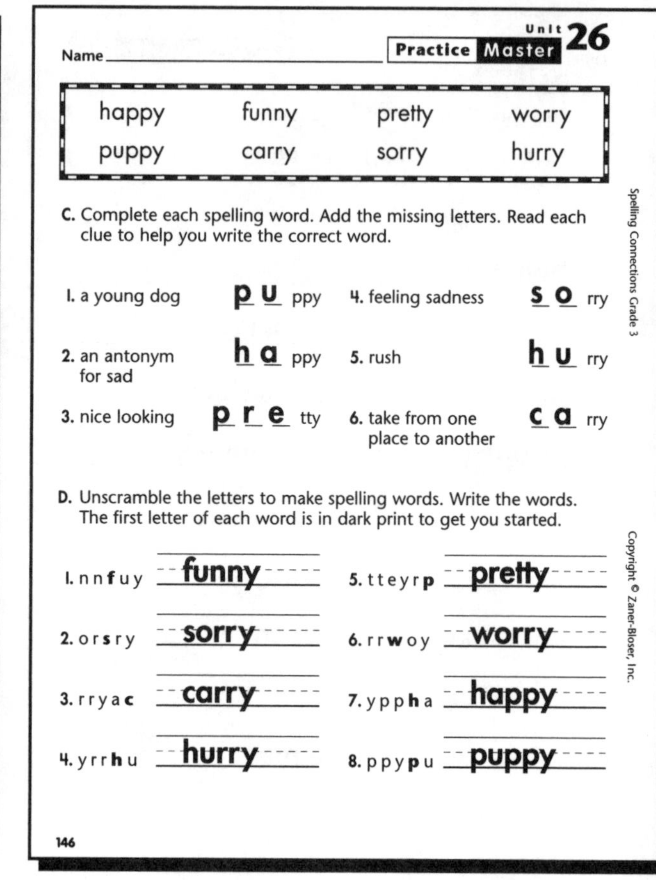

Name ____________ **Practice Master** Unit **26**

| happy | funny | pretty | worry |
|---|---|---|---|
| puppy | carry | sorry | hurry |

**C.** Complete each spelling word. Add the missing letters. Read each clue to help you write the correct word.

1. a young dog **p u** ppy
2. an antonym for sad **h a** ppy
3. nice looking **p r e** tty
4. feeling sadness **s o** rry
5. rush **h u** rry
6. take from one place to another **c a** rry

**D.** Unscramble the letters to make spelling words. Write the words. The first letter of each word is in dark print to get you started.

1. n n **f** u y **funny**
2. o r **s** r y **sorry**
3. r r y a **c** **carry**
4. y r r **h** u **hurry**
5. t t e y r **p** **pretty**
6. r r **w** o y **worry**
7. y p p **h** a **happy**
8. p p y **p** u **puppy**

Spelling Connections Grade 3



146

Name ____________ **Test Master** Unit **26**

Read each sentence. Look at the underlined spelling word. Fill in a circle. Show if the word is spelled **Right** or **Wrong**.

**Sample**
Is that berry ripe yet? Right ● Wrong ○

**Answer Box**

| | Sentence | Right | Wrong |
|---|---|---|---|
| 1. | My friend told me a funny story. | ● | ○ |
| 2. | All the lettuce was eaten by that bunny. | ● | ○ |
| 3. | I helped my dad karry the bags. | ○ | ● |
| 4. | I like chery pie the best. | ○ | ● |
| 5. | The birds like the red bury the best. | ○ | ● |
| 6. | She was very happy with her new toy. | ● | ○ |
| 7. | We must herry to catch the bus. | ○ | ● |
| 8. | Carol made jelly from those strawberries. | ● | ○ |
| 9. | We had a marry time at the school picnic. | ○ | ● |
| 10. | The water in the pond was muddie. | ○ | ● |
| 11. | The city lights were a pretty sight. | ● | ○ |
| 12. | I have two white kittens and one brown puppy. | ● | ○ |
| 13. | I'm very sorry that I'm late. | ● | ○ |
| 14. | The small zoo had a few fury animals. | ○ | ● |
| 15. | I hope my grandmother doesn't worry about me. | ● | ○ |

Spelling Connections Grade 3



147

Name ____________ **Homework Master** Unit **26**

Complete each spelling word. Add the missing letters. Read each clue to help you write the correct word.

1. a young dog **p u** p p y
2. an antonym for sad **h a** p p y
3. a synonym for rabbit **b u** n n y
4. a red fruit with a pit **c h e** r r y
5. nice-looking **p r e** t t y
6. feeling sadness **s o** r r y
7. rush **h u** r r y
8. an antonym for serious **f u** n n y
9. a small red or blue fruit **b e** r r y
10. wet, soft earth **m u** d d y

Unscramble the letters to form spelling words. Write the words on the lines.

1. y j e l l **jelly**
2. r r e m y **merry**
3. r r y o w **worry**
4. c r r y a **carry**
5. r r y u f **furry**

Spelling Connections Grade 3



148

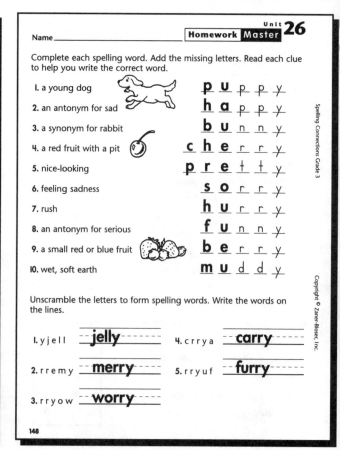

# Answer Key

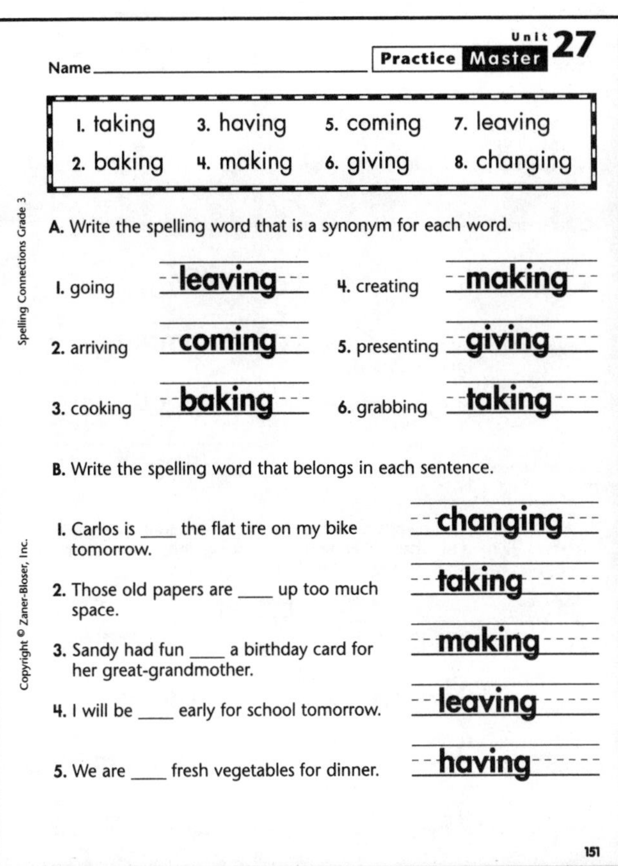

Unit 27 **Practice Master**

Name ____________________

| | | | |
|---|---|---|---|
| 1. taking | 3. having | 5. coming | 7. leaving |
| 2. baking | 4. making | 6. giving | 8. changing |

**A.** Write the spelling word that is a synonym for each word.

1. going **leaving**
2. arriving **coming**
3. cooking **baking**
4. creating **making**
5. presenting **giving**
6. grabbing **taking**

**B.** Write the spelling word that belongs in each sentence.

1. Carlos is ____ the flat tire on my bike tomorrow. **changing**
2. Those old papers are ____ up too much space. **taking**
3. Sandy had fun ____ a birthday card for her great-grandmother. **making**
4. I will be ____ early for school tomorrow. **leaving**
5. We are ____ fresh vegetables for dinner. **having**

151



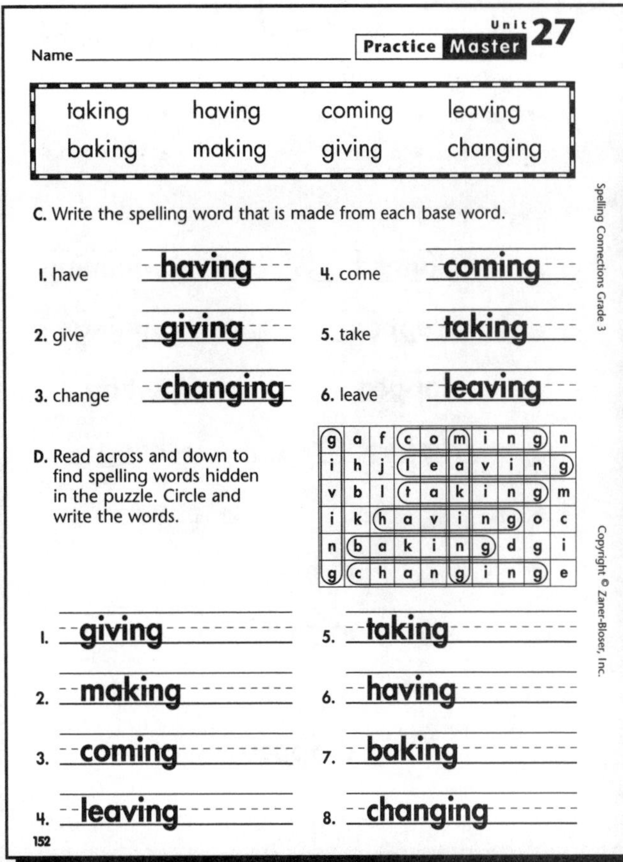

Unit 27 **Practice Master**

Name ____________________

| | | | |
|---|---|---|---|
| taking | having | coming | leaving |
| baking | making | giving | changing |

**C.** Write the spelling word that is made from each base word.

1. have **having**
2. give **giving**
3. change **changing**
4. come **coming**
5. take **taking**
6. leave **leaving**

**D.** Read across and down to find spelling words hidden in the puzzle. Circle and write the words.

| | | | | | | | | | |
|---|---|---|---|---|---|---|---|---|---|
| g | a | f | c | o | m | i | n | g | n |
| i | h | j | l | e | a | v | i | n | g |
| v | b | l | t | a | k | i | n | g | m |
| i | k | h | a | v | i | n | g | o | c |
| n | b | a | k | i | n | g | d | g | i |
| g | c | h | a | n | g | i | n | g | e |

1. **giving**
2. **making**
3. **coming**
4. **leaving**
5. **taking**
6. **having**
7. **baking**
8. **changing**

152



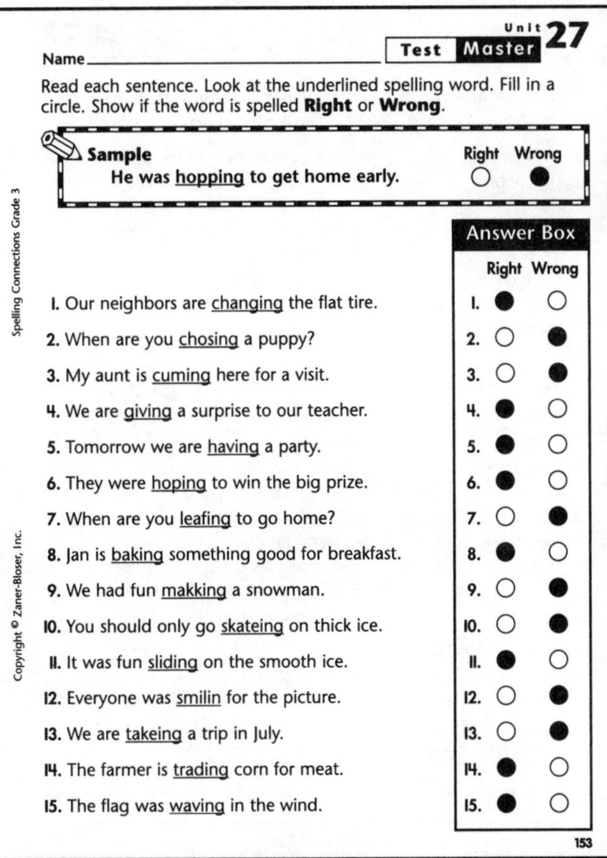

Unit 27 **Test Master**

Name ____________________

Read each sentence. Look at the underlined spelling word. Fill in a circle. Show if the word is spelled **Right** or **Wrong**.

**Sample**
He was hopping to get home early. Right ○ Wrong ●

**Answer Box**

| Sentence | | Right | Wrong |
|---|---|---|---|
| 1. Our neighbors are changing the flat tire. | 1. | ● | ○ |
| 2. When are you chosing a puppy? | 2. | ○ | ● |
| 3. My aunt is cuming here for a visit. | 3. | ○ | ● |
| 4. We are giving a surprise to our teacher. | 4. | ● | ○ |
| 5. Tomorrow we are having a party. | 5. | ● | ○ |
| 6. They were hoping to win the big prize. | 6. | ● | ○ |
| 7. When are you leafing to go home? | 7. | ○ | ● |
| 8. Jan is baking something good for breakfast. | 8. | ● | ○ |
| 9. We had fun makking a snowman. | 9. | ○ | ● |
| 10. You should only go skateing on thick ice. | 10. | ○ | ● |
| 11. It was fun sliding on the smooth ice. | 11. | ● | ○ |
| 12. Everyone was smilin for the picture. | 12. | ○ | ● |
| 13. We are takeing a trip in July. | 13. | ○ | ● |
| 14. The farmer is trading corn for meat. | 14. | ● | ○ |
| 15. The flag was waving in the wind. | 15. | ● | ○ |

153



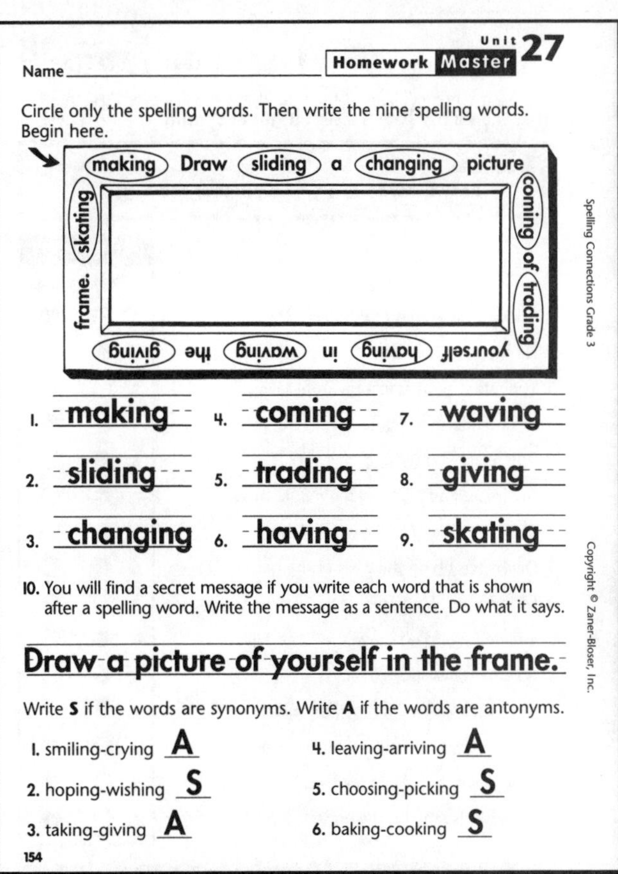

Unit 27 **Homework Master**

Name ____________________

Circle only the spelling words. Then write the nine spelling words. Begin here.



1. **making**
2. **sliding**
3. **changing**
4. **coming**
5. **trading**
6. **having**
7. **waving**
8. **giving**
9. **skating**

10. You will find a secret message if you write each word that is shown after a spelling word. Write the message as a sentence. Do what it says.

**Draw a picture of yourself in the frame.**

Write **S** if the words are synonyms. Write **A** if the words are antonyms.

1. smiling-crying **A**
2. hoping-wishing **S**
3. taking-giving **A**
4. leaving-arriving **A**
5. choosing-picking **S**
6. baking-cooking **S**

154

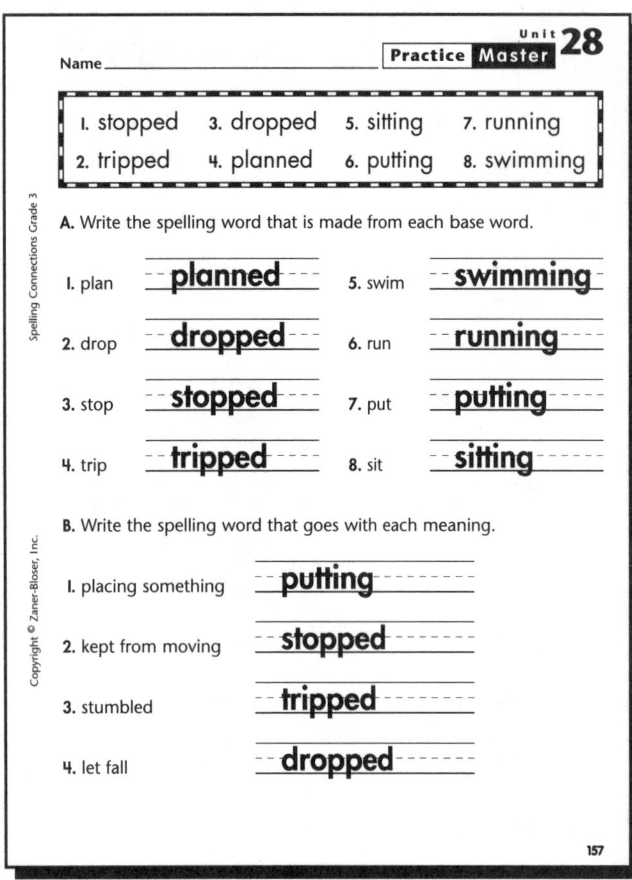

Name ____________ **Practice Master** Unit 28

| 1. stopped | 3. dropped | 5. sitting | 7. running |
|---|---|---|---|
| 2. tripped | 4. planned | 6. putting | 8. swimming |

**A.** Write the spelling word that is made from each base word.

1. plan **planned**
2. drop **dropped**
3. stop **stopped**
4. trip **tripped**
5. swim **swimming**
6. run **running**
7. put **putting**
8. sit **sitting**

**B.** Write the spelling word that goes with each meaning.

1. placing something **putting**
2. kept from moving **stopped**
3. stumbled **tripped**
4. let fall **dropped**



157

Name ____________ **Practice Master** Unit 28

| stopped | dropped | sitting | running |
|---|---|---|---|
| tripped | planned | putting | swimming |

**C.** Write the spelling word that does not belong in each group.

1. walking, jogging, running, sitting **sitting**
2. swimming, putting, setting, placing **swimming**
3. hopped, jumped, tripped, bounced **tripped**
4. skated, walked, dropped, jogged **dropped**

**D.** Add the ending shown to each base word to make four spelling words. Remember that the ending consonant of these base words doubles when **-ed** or **-ing** is added. Write the words.

Add -ed

1. stop **stopped**
2. plan **planned**
3. trip **tripped**
4. drop **dropped**

Add -ing

1. swim **swimming**
2. sit **sitting**
3. run **running**
4. put **putting**



158

Name ____________ **Test Master** Unit 28

Read each sentence. Look at the underlined spelling word. Fill in a circle. Show if the word is spelled **Right** or **Wrong**.

**Sample** The students are sitting quietly at their desks. Right ● Wrong ○

**Answer Box**

| Sentence | Right | Wrong |
|---|---|---|
| 1. My dog likes diging for bones. | ○ | ● |
| 2. He dropped the bone into the hole | ● | ○ |
| 3. The rabbit hopt across my front lawn. | ○ | ● |
| 4. After dinner we plannd to take a ride. | ○ | ● |
| 5. Where are you putting my coat? | ● | ○ |
| 6. My friend and I rubbed the magic lamp. | ● | ○ |
| 7. I will be running in the two-mile race. | ● | ○ |
| 8. Dad is scrubbing the walls of the garage. | ● | ○ |
| 9. Mr. and Mrs. Smith were siting on the park bench. | ○ | ● |
| 10. We went sledding down the steep hill. | ● | ○ |
| 11. A leopard has spotted fur. | ● | ○ |
| 12. After six hours we stopped for dinner. | ● | ○ |
| 13. We went swimmin in my friend's pool. | ○ | ● |
| 14. I tript over the rake in my yard. | ○ | ● |
| 15. My sister is rapping the present. | ○ | ● |



159

Name ____________ **Homework Master** Unit 28

Match each subject with a predicate to make a correct sentence. Draw lines to show the matches you make.

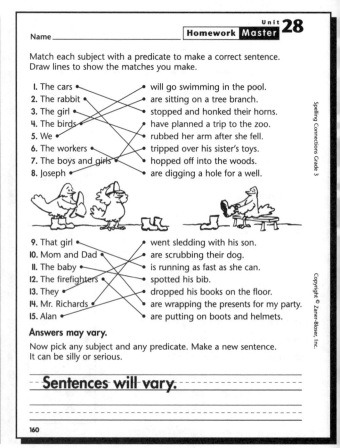

1. The cars — will go swimming in the pool.
2. The rabbit — are sitting on a tree branch.
3. The girl — stopped and honked their horns.
4. The birds — have planned a trip to the zoo.
5. We — rubbed her arm after she fell.
6. The workers — tripped over his sister's toys.
7. The boys and girls — hopped off into the woods.
8. Joseph — are digging a hole for a well.

9. That girl — went sledding with his son.
10. Mom and Dad — are scrubbing their dog.
11. The baby — is running as fast as she can.
12. The firefighters — spotted his bib.
13. They — dropped his books on the floor.
14. Mr. Richards — are wrapping the presents for my party.
15. Alan — are putting on boots and helmets.

**Answers may vary.**

Now pick any subject and any predicate. Make a new sentence. It can be silly or serious.

**Sentences will vary.**



160

# Answer Key

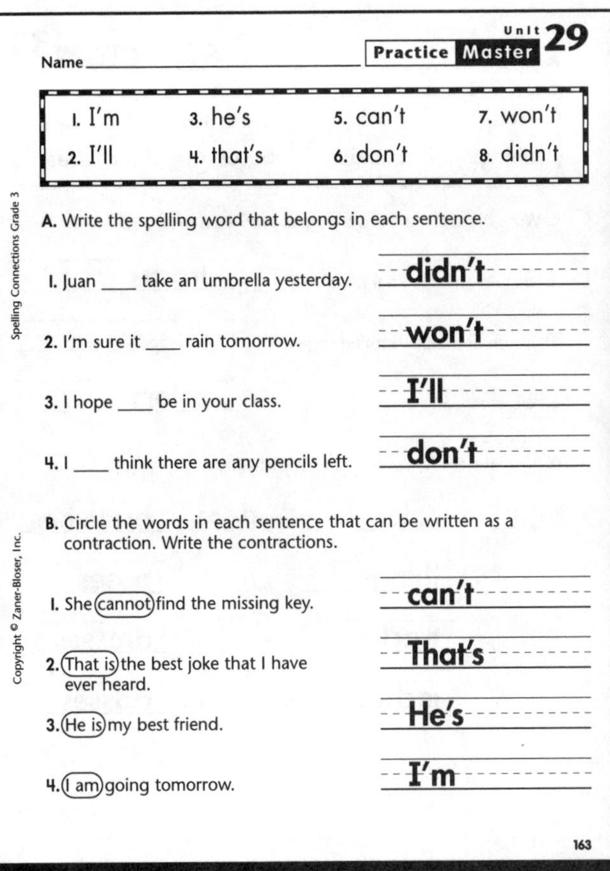

Name ____________ Unit 29 **Practice Master**

| | | | |
|---|---|---|---|
| 1. I'm | 3. he's | 5. can't | 7. won't |
| 2. I'll | 4. that's | 6. don't | 8. didn't |

**A.** Write the spelling word that belongs in each sentence.

1. Juan ____ take an umbrella yesterday. **didn't**
2. I'm sure it ____ rain tomorrow. **won't**
3. I hope ____ be in your class. **I'll**
4. I ____ think there are any pencils left. **don't**

**B.** Circle the words in each sentence that can be written as a contraction. Write the contractions.

1. She (cannot) find the missing key. **can't**
2. (That is) the best joke that I have ever heard. **That's**
3. (He is) my best friend. **He's**
4. (I am) going tomorrow. **I'm**



163

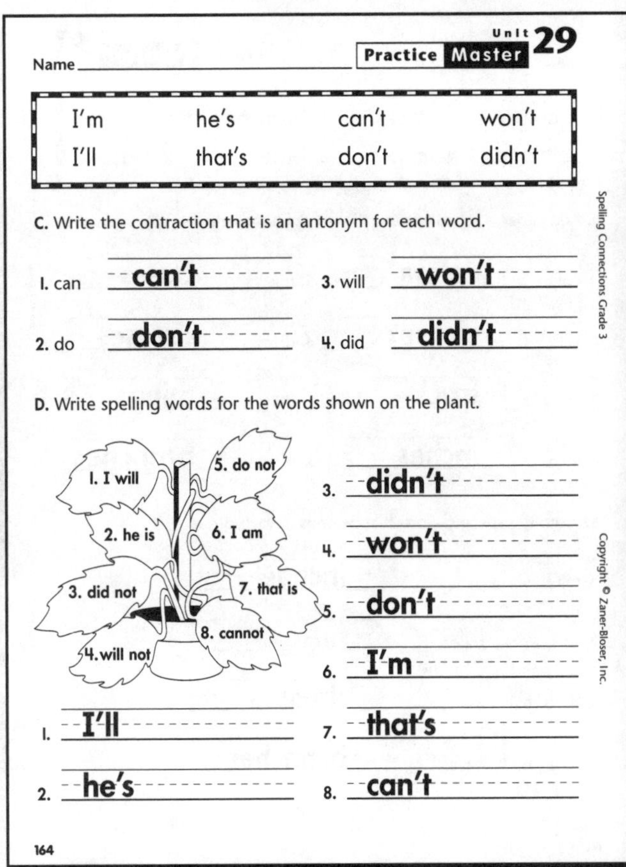

Name ____________ Unit 29 **Practice Master**

| | | | |
|---|---|---|---|
| I'm | he's | can't | won't |
| I'll | that's | don't | didn't |

**C.** Write the contraction that is an antonym for each word.

1. can **can't**
2. do **don't**
3. will **won't**
4. did **didn't**

**D.** Write spelling words for the words shown on the plant.



1. **I'll**
2. **he's**
3. **didn't**
4. **won't**
5. **don't**
6. **I'm**
7. **that's**
8. **can't**



164

Name ____________ Unit 29 **Test Master**

Read each sentence. Look at the underlined spelling word. Fill in a circle. Show if the word is spelled **Right** or **Wrong**.

**Sample**
My brother cann't lift as much as I can. Right ○ Wrong ●

**Answer Box**

| Sentence | | Right | Wrong |
|---|---|---|---|
| 1. They din't like the last act of the play. | 1. | ○ | ● |
| 2. We can't ride our bikes on that bumpy road. | 2. | ● | ○ |
| 3. I am sure he deosn't mind if I sit here. | 3. | ○ | ● |
| 4. We do'nt want to go swimming today. | 4. | ○ | ● |
| 5. Mike is very good, but he's not the best player. | 5. | ● | ○ |
| 6. Here's the ticket for the ride. | 6. | ● | ○ |
| 7. I'll draw another picture of a farm. | 7. | ● | ○ |
| 8. I do not know if I'm the winner. | 8. | ● | ○ |
| 9. I know that Mary is'nt coming with us. | 9. | ○ | ● |
| 10. Judy likes baseball, and she's a good batter. | 10. | ● | ○ |
| 11. That's the best game I ever played. | 11. | ● | ○ |
| 12. Do you know there's a parade next Saturday? | 12. | ● | ○ |
| 13. What's the score of the football game? | 13. | ● | ○ |
| 14. Do you know whoo's playing tonight? | 14. | ○ | ● |
| 15. If we hurry we won't miss the bus. | 15. | ● | ○ |



165

Name ____________ Unit 29 **Homework Master**

Write the numerals for the two words that make the contraction shown below. The first one is done as an example.

| | | |
|---|---|---|
| 1. I | 5. there | 9. here |
| 2. does | 6. do | 10. will |
| 3. what | 7. am | 11. not |
| 4. who | 8. is | 12. he |

I'm **1 7** there's **5 8** he's **12 8** don't **6 11**
what's **3 8** who's **4 8** doesn't **2 11** isn't **8 11**

Circle the words in each sentence that can be written as a contraction. Write the contraction on the line.

1. I (will not) be able to play football. **won't**
2. I (did not) know her name. **didn't**
3. She (cannot) find the missing key. **can't**
4. (What is) the answer to this problem? **What's**
5. (That is) the best joke (I have) ever heard. **That's, I've**
6. (She is) my best friend. **She's**
7. (I will) ask for help with this problem. **I'll**
8. (Here is) the lost cap. **Here's**



166

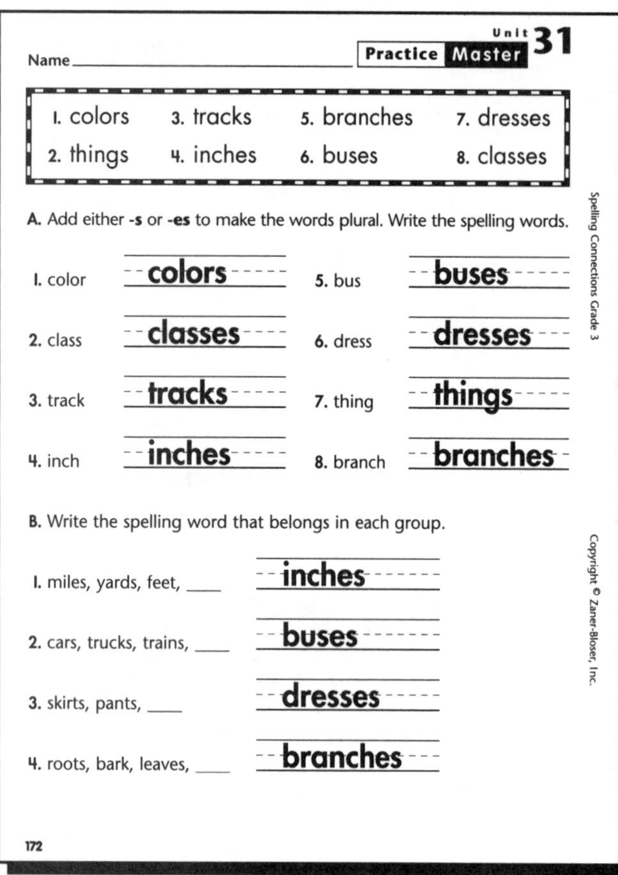

Name ____________________ Unit 31 **Practice Master**

| | | | |
|---|---|---|---|
| 1. colors | 3. tracks | 5. branches | 7. dresses |
| 2. things | 4. inches | 6. buses | 8. classes |

**A.** Add either **-s** or **-es** to make the words plural. Write the spelling words.

1. color — colors
2. class — classes
3. track — tracks
4. inch — inches
5. bus — buses
6. dress — dresses
7. thing — things
8. branch — branches

**B.** Write the spelling word that belongs in each group.

1. miles, yards, feet, ____ — inches
2. cars, trucks, trains, ____ — buses
3. skirts, pants, ____ — dresses
4. roots, bark, leaves, ____ — branches





172

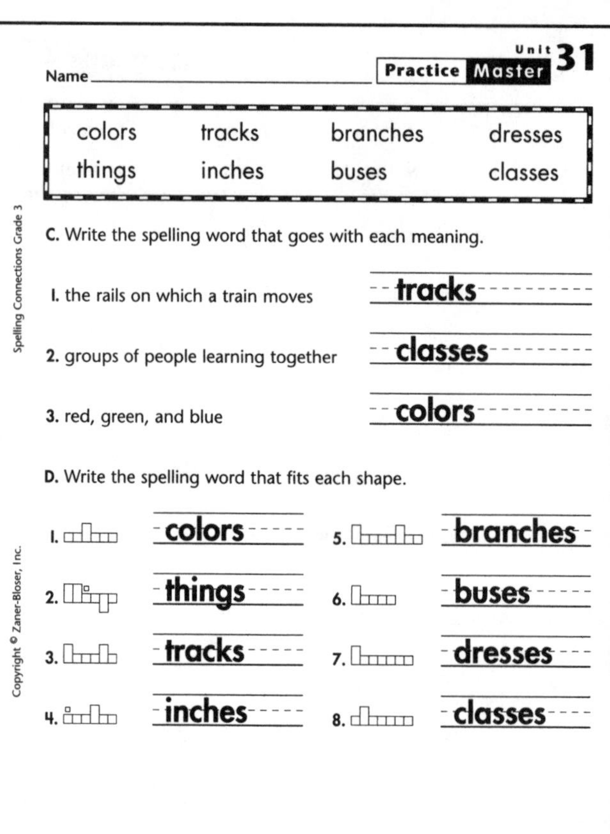

Name ____________________ Unit 31 **Practice Master**

| | | | |
|---|---|---|---|
| colors | tracks | branches | dresses |
| things | inches | buses | classes |

**C.** Write the spelling word that goes with each meaning.

1. the rails on which a train moves — tracks
2. groups of people learning together — classes
3. red, green, and blue — colors

**D.** Write the spelling word that fits each shape.

1. colors
2. things
3. tracks
4. inches
5. branches
6. buses
7. dresses
8. classes





173

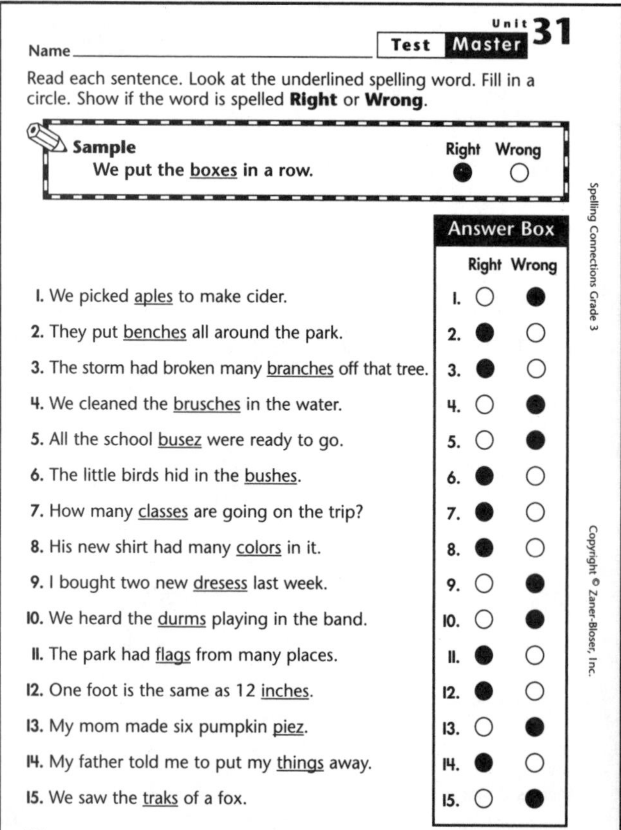

Name ____________________ Unit 31 **Test Master**

Read each sentence. Look at the underlined spelling word. Fill in a circle. Show if the word is spelled **Right** or **Wrong**.

**Sample** We put the boxes in a row. Right ● Wrong ○

**Answer Box**

| Sentence | | Right | Wrong |
|---|---|---|---|
| 1. We picked aples to make cider. | 1. | ○ | ● |
| 2. They put benches all around the park. | 2. | ● | ○ |
| 3. The storm had broken many branches off that tree. | 3. | ● | ○ |
| 4. We cleaned the brusches in the water. | 4. | ○ | ● |
| 5. All the school busez were ready to go. | 5. | ○ | ● |
| 6. The little birds hid in the bushes. | 6. | ● | ○ |
| 7. How many classes are going on the trip? | 7. | ● | ○ |
| 8. His new shirt had many colors in it. | 8. | ● | ○ |
| 9. I bought two new dresess last week. | 9. | ○ | ● |
| 10. We heard the durms playing in the band. | 10. | ○ | ● |
| 11. The park had flags from many places. | 11. | ● | ○ |
| 12. One foot is the same as 12 inches. | 12. | ● | ○ |
| 13. My mom made six pumpkin piez. | 13. | ○ | ● |
| 14. My father told me to put my things away. | 14. | ● | ○ |
| 15. We saw the traks of a fox. | 15. | ○ | ● |





174

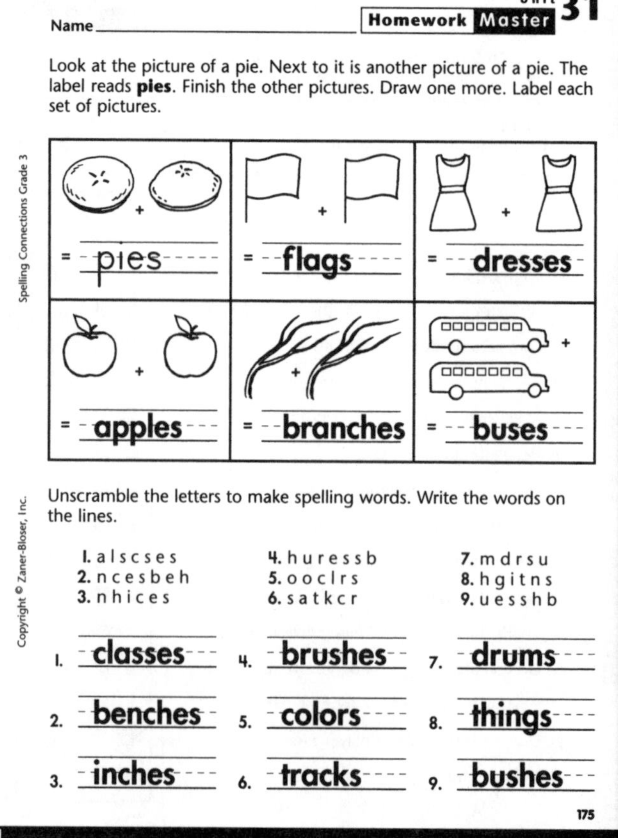

Name ____________________ Unit 31 **Homework Master**

Look at the picture of a pie. Next to it is another picture of a pie. The label reads **pies**. Finish the other pictures. Draw one more. Label each set of pictures.

| | | |
|---|---|---|
| = pies | = flags | = dresses |
| = apples | = branches | = buses |

Unscramble the letters to make spelling words. Write the words on the lines.

| | | |
|---|---|---|
| 1. a l s c s e s | 4. h u r e s s b | 7. m d r s u |
| 2. n c e s b e h | 5. o o c l r s | 8. h g i t n s |
| 3. n h i c e s | 6. s a t k c r | 9. u e s s h b |

| | | |
|---|---|---|
| 1. classes | 4. brushes | 7. drums |
| 2. benches | 5. colors | 8. things |
| 3. inches | 6. tracks | 9. bushes |





175

# Answer Key

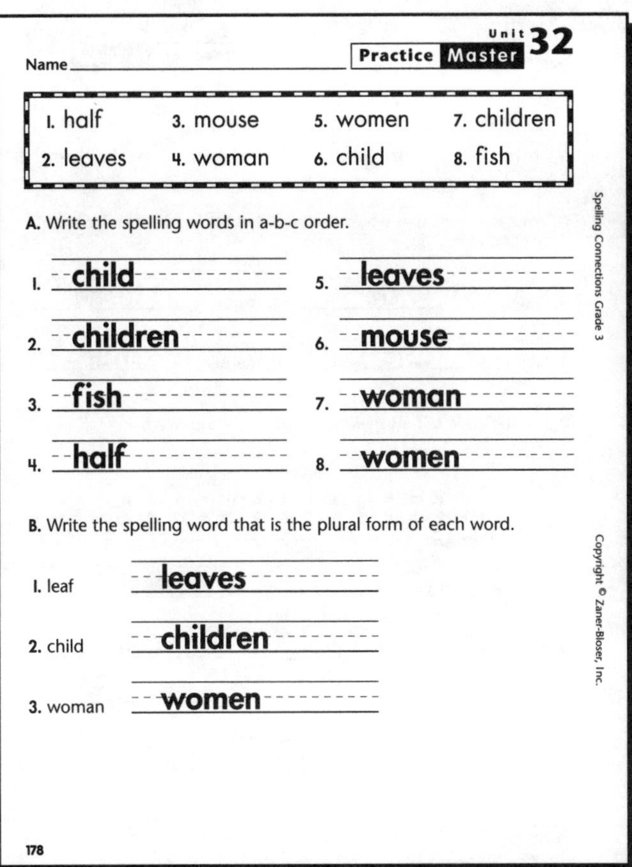
Unit 32 Practice Master

Name

1. half 3. mouse 5. women 7. children
2. leaves 4. woman 6. child 8. fish

**A.** Write the spelling words in a-b-c order.

1. child
2. children
3. fish
4. half
5. leaves
6. mouse
7. woman
8. women

**B.** Write the spelling word that is the plural form of each word.

1. leaf — leaves
2. child — children
3. woman — women

Spelling Connections Grade 3



178

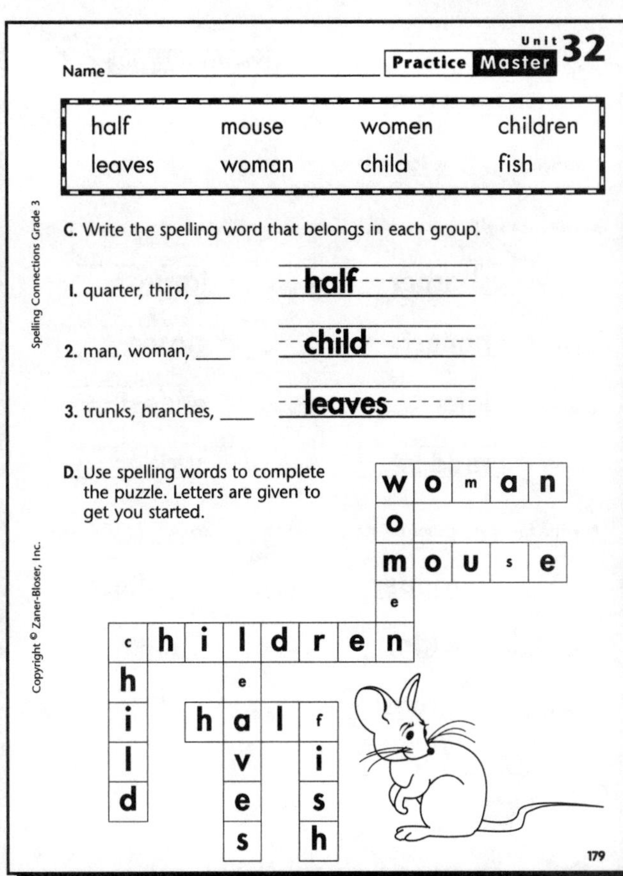
Unit 32 Practice Master

Name

half mouse women children
leaves woman child fish

**C.** Write the spelling word that belongs in each group.

1. quarter, third, ____ — half
2. man, woman, ____ — child
3. trunks, branches, ____ — leaves

**D.** Use spelling words to complete the puzzle. Letters are given to get you started.



Spelling Connections Grade 3



179

Unit 32 **Test Master**

Name

Read each sentence. Look at the underlined spelling word. Fill in a circle. Show if the word is spelled **Right** or **Wrong**.

**Sample**
We saw a herd of dear in the field. Right ○ Wrong ●

**Answer Box**

| Sentence | | Right | Wrong |
|---|---|---|---|
| 1. The young caf played near its mother. | 1. | ○ | ● |
| 2. All the calves are in the field. | 2. | ● | ○ |
| 3. This pretty picture was drawn by that child. | 3. | ● | ○ |
| 4. The third-grade class has 20 childern. | 4. | ○ | ● |
| 5. There are many fish in that pond. | 5. | ● | ○ |
| 6. The flock of geese landed on our pond. | 6. | ● | ○ |
| 7. One goos came right up to us for bits of bread. | 7. | ○ | ● |
| 8. I gave my friend haf of my apple. | 8. | ○ | ● |
| 9. We cut the cake into two haves. | 9. | ○ | ● |
| 10. The leaf has a strange shape. | 10. | ● | ○ |
| 11. In fall the leafes change to pretty colors. | 11. | ○ | ● |
| 12. The cat chased the mice into the barn. | 12. | ● | ○ |
| 13. One mouse stayed behind the boxes. | 13. | ● | ○ |
| 14. A woman with a broom chased the cat away. | 14. | ● | ○ |
| 15. She then went back and told the other women. | 15. | ● | ○ |

Spelling Connections Grade 3



180

Unit 32 **Homework Master**

Name

Write the missing spelling word to complete each sentence.

1. **Boy** is to **man** as **girl** is to ____. — woman
2. **Deer** is to **fawn** as **cow** is to ____. — calf
3. **Roar** is to **lion** as **squeak** is to ____. — mouse
4. **Job** is to a **worker** as **school** is to a ____. — child
5. **Animal** is to **tiger** as **bird** is to ____. — goose
6. **Arm** is to **hand** as **branch** is to ____. — leaf
7. **Sky** is to **bird** as **water** is to ____. — fish

Use spelling words to complete each puzzle. Letters are given in each puzzle to get you started.

women
children
calves
leaves
geese
half
calves

One spelling word has not been written yet. Write it on the line. — mice

Spelling Connections Grade 3



181

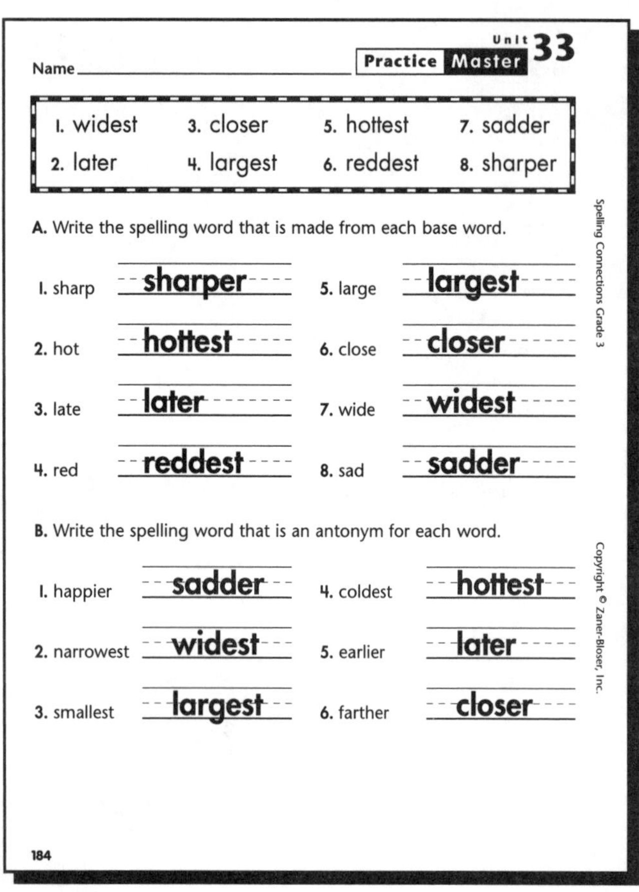

Name ____________ **Practice Master** Unit 33

| | | | |
|---|---|---|---|
| 1. widest | 3. closer | 5. hottest | 7. sadder |
| 2. later | 4. largest | 6. reddest | 8. sharper |

**A.** Write the spelling word that is made from each base word.

| | | | |
|---|---|---|---|
| 1. sharp | sharper | 5. large | largest |
| 2. hot | hottest | 6. close | closer |
| 3. late | later | 7. wide | widest |
| 4. red | reddest | 8. sad | sadder |

**B.** Write the spelling word that is an antonym for each word.

| | | | |
|---|---|---|---|
| 1. happier | sadder | 4. coldest | hottest |
| 2. narrowest | widest | 5. earlier | later |
| 3. smallest | largest | 6. farther | closer |

Spelling Connections Grade 3



184

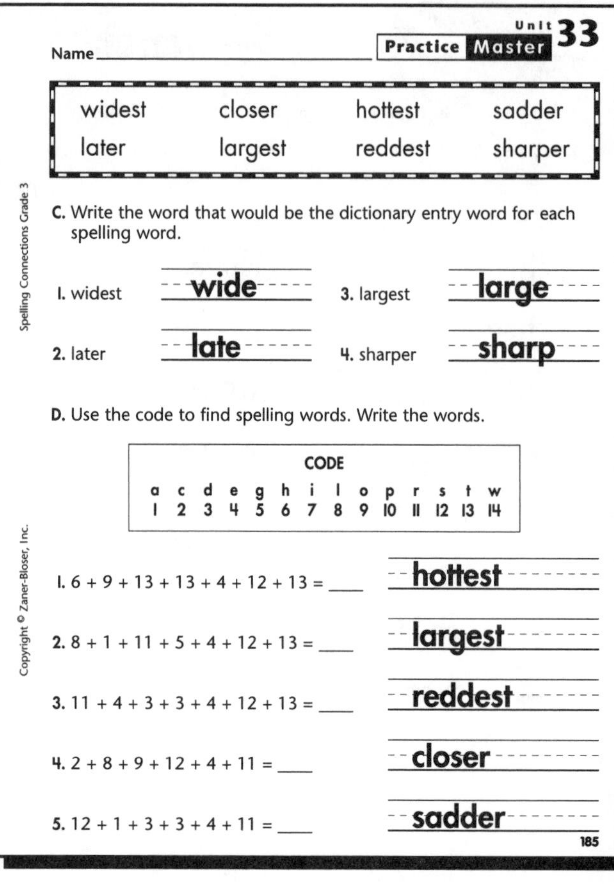

Name ____________ **Practice Master** Unit 33

| | | | |
|---|---|---|---|
| widest | closer | hottest | sadder |
| later | largest | reddest | sharper |

**C.** Write the word that would be the dictionary entry word for each spelling word.

| | | | |
|---|---|---|---|
| 1. widest | wide | 3. largest | large |
| 2. later | late | 4. sharper | sharp |

**D.** Use the code to find spelling words. Write the words.

CODE

| a | c | d | e | g | h | i | l | o | p | r | s | t | w |
|---|---|---|---|---|---|---|---|---|---|---|---|---|---|
| 1 | 2 | 3 | 4 | 5 | 6 | 7 | 8 | 9 | 10 | 11 | 12 | 13 | 14 |

1. 6 + 9 + 13 + 13 + 4 + 12 + 13 = ____ hottest
2. 8 + 1 + 11 + 5 + 4 + 12 + 13 = ____ largest
3. 11 + 4 + 3 + 3 + 4 + 12 + 13 = ____ reddest
4. 2 + 8 + 9 + 12 + 4 + 11 = ____ closer
5. 12 + 1 + 3 + 3 + 4 + 11 = ____ sadder

Spelling Connections Grade 3



185

Name ____________ **Test Master** Unit 33

Read each sentence. Look at the underlined spelling word. Fill in a circle. Show if the word is spelled **Right** or **Wrong**.

**Sample**
That clown has a sadder face than this one. Right ● Wrong ○

**Answer Box**

| Sentence | | Right | Wrong |
|---|---|---|---|
| 1. You are closer to the door than I am. | 1. | ● | ○ |
| 2. That was the closess we ever came to winning. | 2. | ○ | ● |
| 3. Your paint is reder than mine. | 3. | ○ | ● |
| 4. That clay is the reddest of all. | 4. | ● | ○ |
| 5. That stove is hottre than your fire. | 5. | ○ | ● |
| 6. An oil fire is the hotest kind. | 6. | ○ | ● |
| 7. My balloon is larjer than yours. | 7. | ○ | ● |
| 8. My friend has the largest balloon of all. | 8. | ● | ○ |
| 9. I will help you with your homework later. | 9. | ● | ○ |
| 10. That is the latest my dad ever had to work. | 10. | ● | ○ |
| 11. I'm sader today than I was yesterday. | 11. | ○ | ● |
| 12. My teacher told us the sattest tale I've ever heard. | 12. | ○ | ● |
| 13. To write better, you need a sharper pencil. | 13. | ● | ○ |
| 14. The river is whider than that brook. | 14. | ○ | ● |
| 15. That is the widest pool I've ever seen. | 15. | ● | ○ |

Spelling Connections Grade 3



186

Name ____________ **Homework Master** Unit 33

Write the antonym for each word. Then write spelling words to show the **-er** and **-est** form of the words.

| | Antonym | -er form | -est form |
|---|---|---|---|
| 1. far | close | closer | closest |
| 2. narrow | wide | wider | widest |
| 3. early | late | later | latest |
| 4. small | large | larger | largest |
| 5. happy | sad | sadder | saddest |
| 6. cold | hot | hotter | hottest |

Draw a picture of something that is red. Next to it, draw a picture of something that is even redder. Then draw the reddest thing you have ever seen. Label each picture! **Pictures will vary.**

7. red
8. redder
9. reddest

10. What is the matter with the point of this pencil? Write your answer in a sentence.

The point should be sharper.

Spelling Connections Grade 3



187

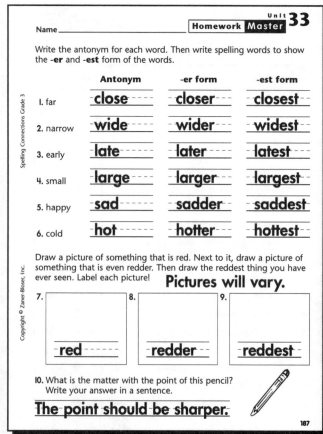

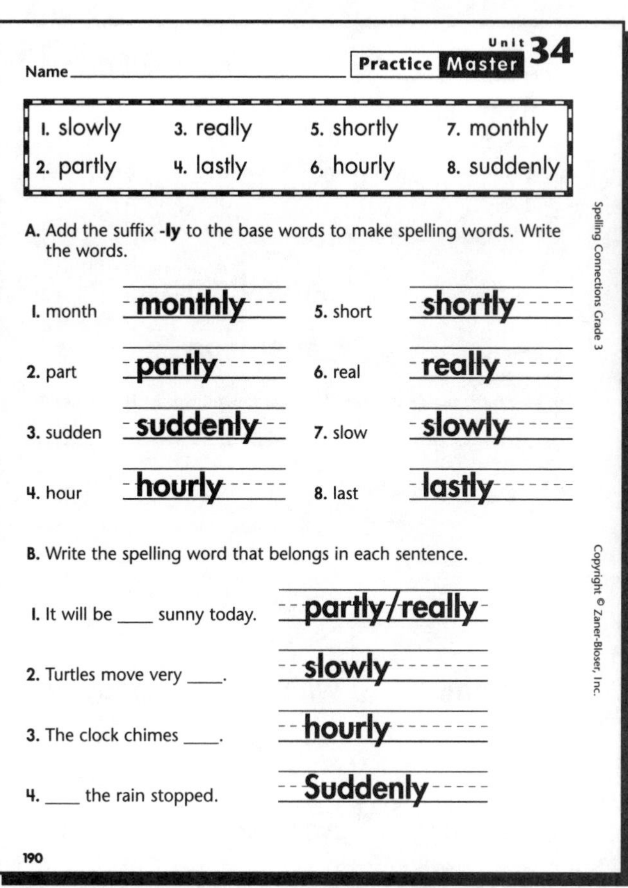

Unit 34 **Practice Master**

Name________________________

| | | | |
|---|---|---|---|
| 1. slowly | 3. really | 5. shortly | 7. monthly |
| 2. partly | 4. lastly | 6. hourly | 8. suddenly |

**A.** Add the suffix **-ly** to the base words to make spelling words. Write the words.

1. month **monthly**
2. part **partly**
3. sudden **suddenly**
4. hour **hourly**
5. short **shortly**
6. real **really**
7. slow **slowly**
8. last **lastly**

**B.** Write the spelling word that belongs in each sentence.

1. It will be ____ sunny today. **partly/really**
2. Turtles move very ____. **slowly**
3. The clock chimes ____. **hourly**
4. ____ the rain stopped. **Suddenly**

Spelling Connections Grade 3



190

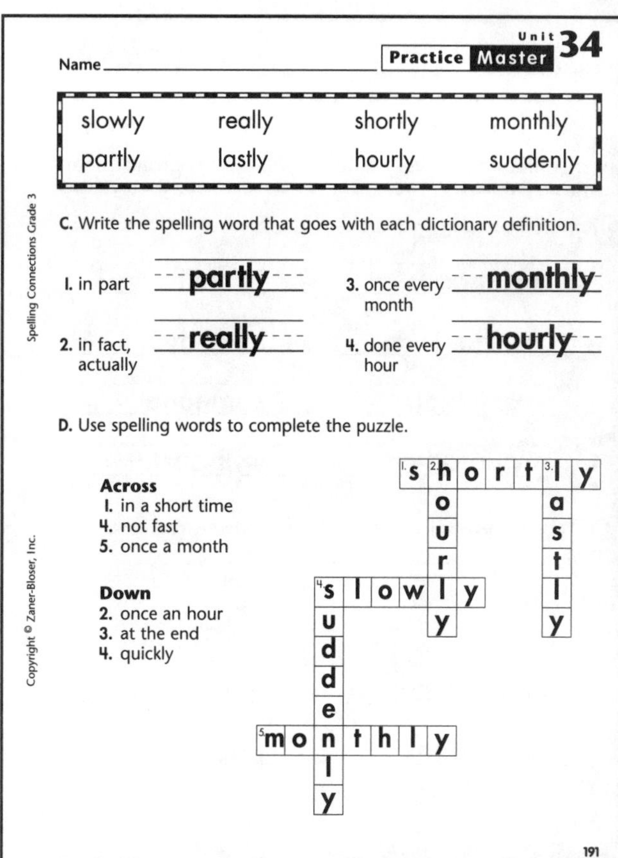

Unit 34 **Practice Master**

Name________________________

| | | | |
|---|---|---|---|
| slowly | really | shortly | monthly |
| partly | lastly | hourly | suddenly |

**C.** Write the spelling word that goes with each dictionary definition.

1. in part **partly**
2. in fact, actually **really**
3. once every month **monthly**
4. done every hour **hourly**

**D.** Use spelling words to complete the puzzle.

**Across**
1. in a short time
4. not fast
5. once a month

**Down**
2. once an hour
3. at the end
4. quickly

Spelling Connections Grade 3



191

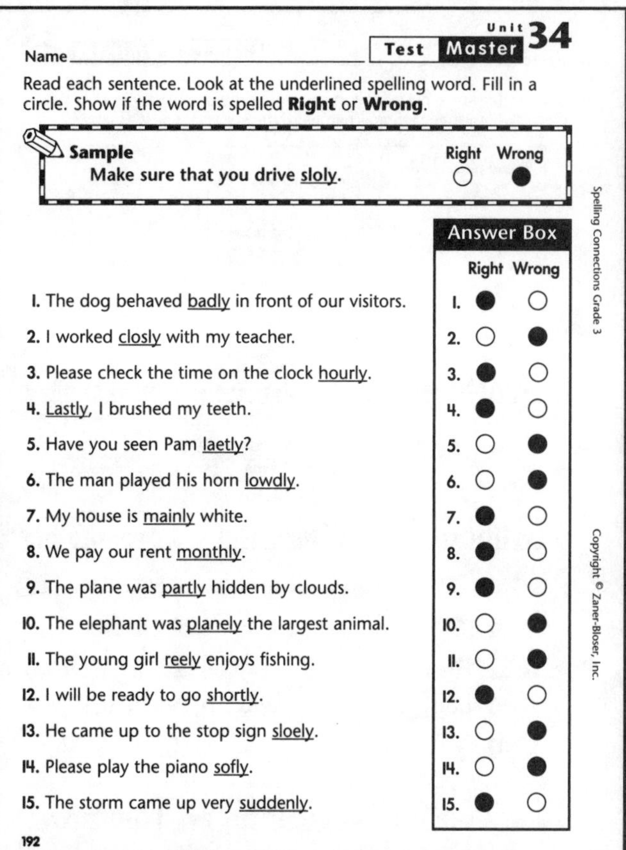

Unit 34 **Test Master**

Name________________________

Read each sentence. Look at the underlined spelling word. Fill in a circle. Show if the word is spelled **Right** or **Wrong**.

**Sample**
Make sure that you drive sloly. Right ○ Wrong ●

**Answer Box**

| Sentence | | Right | Wrong |
|---|---|---|---|
| 1. The dog behaved badly in front of our visitors. | 1. | ● | ○ |
| 2. I worked closly with my teacher. | 2. | ○ | ● |
| 3. Please check the time on the clock hourly. | 3. | ● | ○ |
| 4. Lastly, I brushed my teeth. | 4. | ● | ○ |
| 5. Have you seen Pam laetly? | 5. | ○ | ● |
| 6. The man played his horn lowdly. | 6. | ○ | ● |
| 7. My house is mainly white. | 7. | ● | ○ |
| 8. We pay our rent monthly. | 8. | ● | ○ |
| 9. The plane was partly hidden by clouds. | 9. | ● | ○ |
| 10. The elephant was planely the largest animal. | 10. | ○ | ● |
| 11. The young girl reely enjoys fishing. | 11. | ○ | ● |
| 12. I will be ready to go shortly. | 12. | ● | ○ |
| 13. He came up to the stop sign sloely. | 13. | ○ | ● |
| 14. Please play the piano sofly. | 14. | ○ | ● |
| 15. The storm came up very suddenly. | 15. | ● | ○ |

Spelling Connections Grade 3



192

Unit 34 **Homework Master**

Name________________________

Choose spelling words to complete the sentences. Write the words on the lines.

loudly monthly shortly really softly
closely badly partly slowly

1. A turtle moves ____.
2. The people will cheer ____.
3. I will tiptoe ____.
4. The gas bill comes ____.
5. You should listen ____.
6. Never treat a pet ____.
7. I am just ____ finished.
8. I know I will finish ____.
9. This plant ____ needs water.

1. **slowly**
2. **loudly**
3. **softly**
4. **monthly**
5. **closely**
6. **badly**
7. **partly**
8. **shortly**
9. **really**

Read each clue. Then use spelling words to complete the puzzle.

**Across**
3. a little while ago
5. mostly

**Down**
1. once an hour
2. quickly
3. at the end
4. clearly

Spelling Connections Grade 3



193

Unit 35 Practice Master

Name

1. nobody 3. anything 5. herself 7. afternoon
2. someone 4. everything 6. without 8. grandfather

**A.** Write the spelling words in a-b-c order.

1. afternoon
2. anything
3. everything
4. grandfather
5. herself
6. nobody
7. someone
8. without

**B.** Put words together to make compound words from the spelling list.

| out | noon | no | with |
|---|---|---|---|
| father | grand | after | body |

1. grandfather
2. afternoon
3. without
4. nobody

Spelling Connections Grade 3

Copyright © Zaner-Bloser, Inc.

196

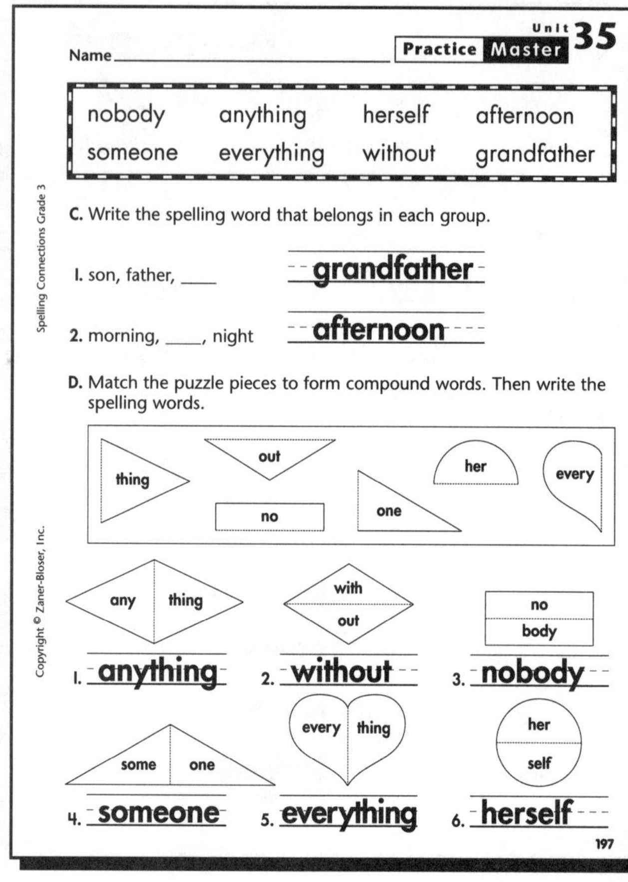

Unit 35 Practice Master

Name

nobody anything herself afternoon
someone everything without grandfather

**C.** Write the spelling word that belongs in each group.

1. son, father, ____ grandfather
2. morning, ____, night afternoon

**D.** Match the puzzle pieces to form compound words. Then write the spelling words.



1. anything
2. without
3. nobody
4. someone
5. everything
6. herself

Spelling Connections Grade 3

Copyright © Zaner-Bloser, Inc.

197

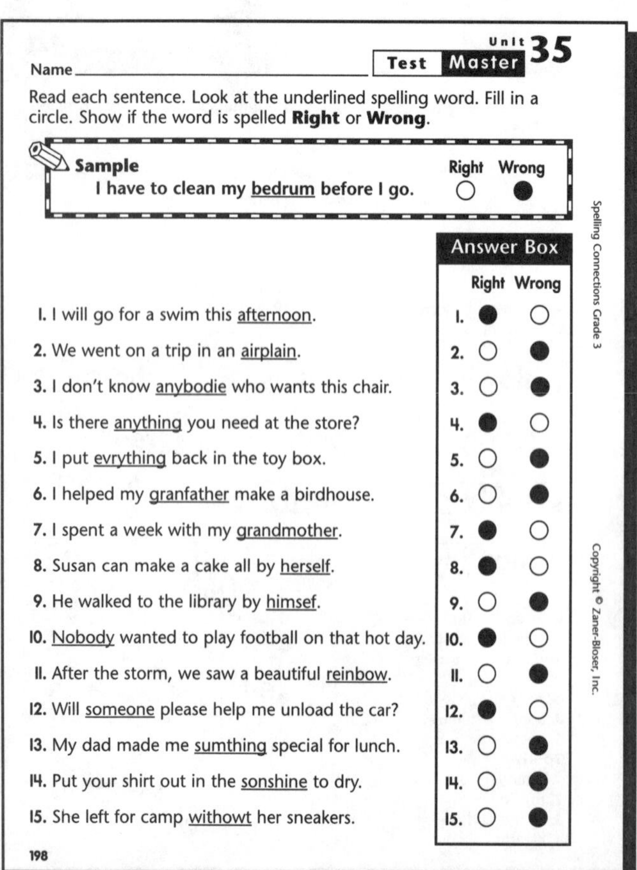

Unit 35 Test Master

Name

Read each sentence. Look at the underlined spelling word. Fill in a circle. Show if the word is spelled **Right** or **Wrong**.

**Sample** I have to clean my bedrum before I go. Right ○ Wrong ●

| | Answer Box | Right | Wrong |
|---|---|---|---|
| 1. I will go for a swim this afternoon. | 1. | ● | ○ |
| 2. We went on a trip in an airplain. | 2. | ○ | ● |
| 3. I don't know anybodie who wants this chair. | 3. | ○ | ● |
| 4. Is there anything you need at the store? | 4. | ● | ○ |
| 5. I put evrything back in the toy box. | 5. | ○ | ● |
| 6. I helped my granfather make a birdhouse. | 6. | ○ | ● |
| 7. I spent a week with my grandmother. | 7. | ● | ○ |
| 8. Susan can make a cake all by herself. | 8. | ● | ○ |
| 9. He walked to the library by himsef. | 9. | ○ | ● |
| 10. Nobody wanted to play football on that hot day. | 10. | ● | ○ |
| 11. After the storm, we saw a beautiful reinbow. | 11. | ○ | ● |
| 12. Will someone please help me unload the car? | 12. | ● | ○ |
| 13. My dad made me sumthing special for lunch. | 13. | ○ | ● |
| 14. Put your shirt out in the sonshine to dry. | 14. | ○ | ● |
| 15. She left for camp withowt her sneakers. | 15. | ○ | ● |

Spelling Connections Grade 3

Copyright © Zaner-Bloser, Inc.

198

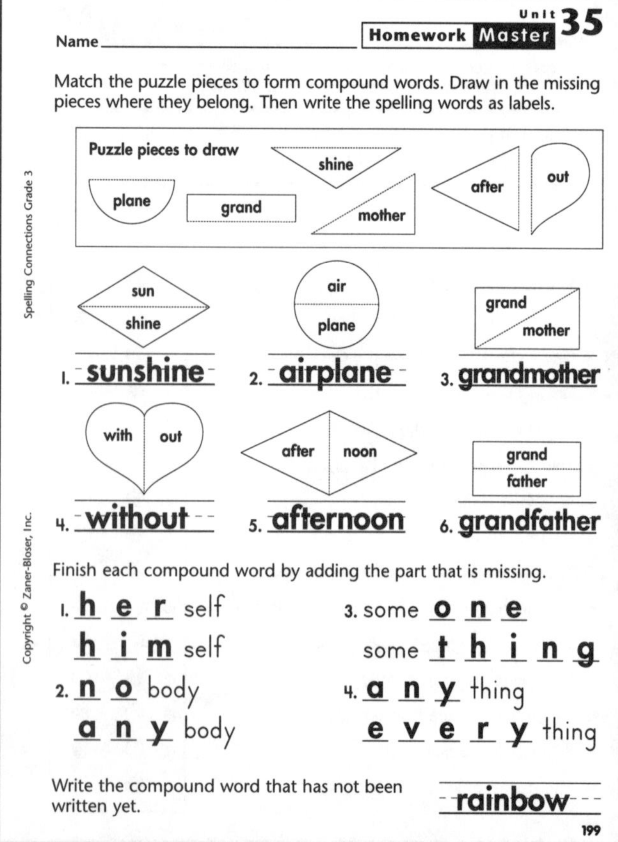

Unit 35 Homework Master

Name

Match the puzzle pieces to form compound words. Draw in the missing pieces where they belong. Then write the spelling words as labels.



1. sunshine
2. airplane
3. grandmother
4. without
5. afternoon
6. grandfather

Finish each compound word by adding the part that is missing.

1. h e r self
   h i m self
2. n o body
   a n y body
3. some o n e
   some t h i n g
4. a n y thing
   e v e r y thing

Write the compound word that has not been written yet. rainbow

Spelling Connections Grade 3

Copyright © Zaner-Bloser, Inc.

199

# Answer Key

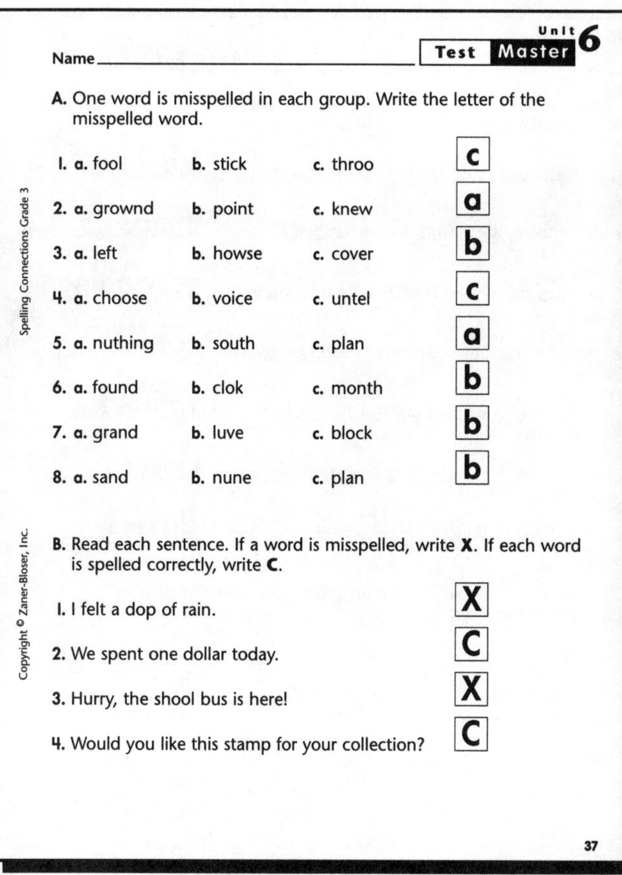

Unit 6 **Test Master**

Name ____________________

**A.** One word is misspelled in each group. Write the letter of the misspelled word.

| | | | |
|---|---|---|---|
| 1. a. fool | b. stick | c. throo | c |
| 2. a. grownd | b. point | c. knew | a |
| 3. a. left | b. howse | c. cover | b |
| 4. a. choose | b. voice | c. untel | c |
| 5. a. nuthing | b. south | c. plan | a |
| 6. a. found | b. clok | c. month | b |
| 7. a. grand | b. luve | c. block | b |
| 8. a. sand | b. nune | c. plan | b |

**B.** Read each sentence. If a word is misspelled, write **X**. If each word is spelled correctly, write **C**.

1. I felt a dop of rain. **X**
2. We spent one dollar today. **C**
3. Hurry, the shool bus is here! **X**
4. Would you like this stamp for your collection? **C**





Unit 12 **Test Master**

Name ____________________

**A.** Look at these spelling words. Write **C** for each word that is spelled correctly. Write **NC** for each word that is not spelled correctly.

| | | | | | |
|---|---|---|---|---|---|
| 1. chain | C | 6. laid | C | 11. stat | NC |
| 2. flot | NC | 7. snow | C | 12. ryte | NC |
| 3. allways | NC | 8. brite | NC | 13. techer | NC |
| 4. real | C | 9. broke | C | 14. window | C |
| 5. smile | C | 10. allmost | NC | 15. close | C |

**B.** Write the letter of the correct spelling that matches the dictionary respelling.

1. /mīld/ **a**
   a. mild
   b. milde
   c. miled
2. /strēt/ **c**
   a. steet
   b. stret
   c. street
3. /kīnd/ **b**
   a. cind
   b. kind
   c. kinde
4. /hwēlz/ **b**
   a. weels
   b. wheels
   c. weals
5. /mā′bē/ **a**
   a. maybe
   b. mabe
   c. maby





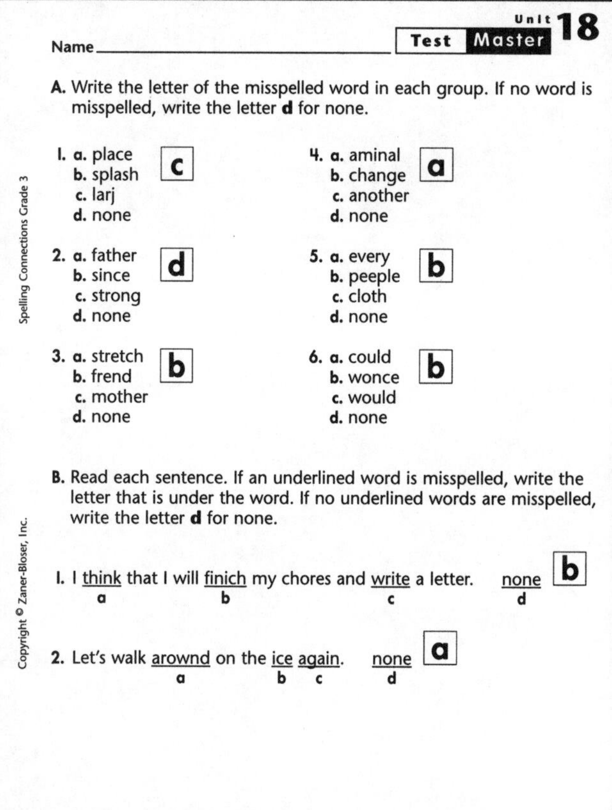

Unit 18 **Test Master**

Name ____________________

**A.** Write the letter of the misspelled word in each group. If no word is misspelled, write the letter **d** for none.

1. **c** — a. place b. splash c. larj d. none
2. **d** — a. father b. since c. strong d. none
3. **b** — a. stretch b. frend c. mother d. none
4. **a** — a. aminal b. change c. another d. none
5. **b** — a. every b. peeple c. cloth d. none
6. **b** — a. could b. wonce c. would d. none

**B.** Read each sentence. If an underlined word is misspelled, write the letter that is under the word. If no underlined words are misspelled, write the letter **d** for none.

1. I <u>think</u> (a) that I will <u>finich</u> (b) my chores and <u>write</u> (c) a letter. <u>none</u> (d) **b**
2. Let's walk <u>arownd</u> (a) on the <u>ice</u> (b) <u>again</u> (c). <u>none</u> (d) **a**





Unit 24 **Test Master**

Name ____________________

**A.** Read each of these phrases. Write the letter of the phrase that contains a misspelled word.

1. **a** — a. Befor I leave b. A warm day c. An early bus
2. **a** — a. That sercus clown b. Before the dawn c. As we work
3. **c** — a. Weigh the peanuts b. Heard a noise c. Belawng to me
4. **a** — a. Chose ther books b. Will not forget c. Tore his shirt
5. **b** — a. The scent of roses b. Acros the bridge c. Pay the fare
6. **c** — a. Knows it's mine b. In the morning c. A greate game

**B.** Write the letter of the word that is spelled correctly and fits the sentence.

1. She ____ me a letter. **c** — a. cent b. scent c. sent
2. ____ does this road lead? **c** — a. War b. Whar c. Where
3. Make a bed of ____. **c** — a. straugh b. staw c. straw
4. When will we be ____? **a** — a. there b. thare c. their
5. Shall I ____ a coat? **b** — a. ware b. wear c. where
6. Please ____ me a map. **b** — a. drau b. draw c. drawe

# Answer Key

Unit 30 Test Master

Name ____________________

**A.** Look at these spelling words. Write **C** for each word that is spelled correctly. If the word is misspelled, write the word correctly below.

| | | | | | |
|---|---|---|---|---|---|
| 1. summer | C | 6. lettre | | 11. cano't | |
| 2. didn't | C | 7. pretty | C | 12. swimming | C |
| 3. hapy | | 8. leaveing | | 13. happen | C |
| 4. funny | C | 9. sudden | C | 14. droped | |
| 5. thats | | 10. running | C | 15. baking | C |

**happy, that's, letter, leaving, can't,**

**dropped**

**B.** Find the spelling word in each sentence. If the word is misspelled, write **NC** (not correct). If the word is spelled correctly, write **C**.

1. She is haveing lunch with Beth. NC
2. I won't be late. C
3. Our bus stopped at the crosswalk. C
4. I'm sorey that I bumped into you. NC
5. Are you comeing with me? NC

Spelling Connections Grade 3





Unit 36 Test Master

Name ____________________

**A.** Look at the two underlined spelling words in each sentence. Decide which word is misspelled. Write it correctly.

1. Nobody was around to help me rake leves. **leaves**
2. I must do three tings before the hourly bell rings. **things**
3. Evrythng seemed small next to the largest statue. **everything**
4. Red is thought of as one of the hotest colors. **hottest**
5. The puppy seemed sadder whithout her owner. **without**
6. Please trim the branches that are kloser to the ground. **closer**
7. The clases will visit the factory this afternoon. **classes**

**B.** One word in each list is misspelled. Write the letter of each misspelled word.

1. a. woman b. shortly c. haf d. without — **c**
2. a. colors b. childran c. monthly d. hottest — **b**
3. a. reely b. hourly c. monthly d. sadder — **a**

Spelling Connections Grade 3